Reading Across the Disciplines
College Reading and Beyond

Kathleen T. McWhorter

Custom Edition for Bowling Green Community College at Western Kentucky University

Taken from:

Reading Across the Disciplines: College Reading and Beyond, Fourth Edition
by Kathleen T. McWhorter

Psychology, Second Edition
by Saundra K. Ciccarelli and J. Noland White

Essential Environment: The Science Behind the Stories, Second Edition
by Jay Withgott and Scott Brennan

Learning Solutions

New York   Boston   San Francisco
London   Toronto   Sydney   Tokyo   Singapore   Madrid
Mexico City   Munich   Paris   Cape Town   Hong Kong   Montreal

Cover Art: *Euphrosinum* and *Passiflora, both by Kathryn Fanelli*

Taken from:

Reading Across the Disciplines, Fourth Edition
by Kathleen T. McWhorter
Copyright © 2009 by Pearson Education, Inc.
Published by Longman
New York, New York 10036

Psychology, Second Edition
by Saundra K. Ciccarelli and J. Noland White
Copyright © 2009, 2006 by Pearson Education, Inc.
Published by Prentice Hall
Upper Saddle River, New Jersey 07458

Essential Environment: The Science Behind the Stories, Second Edition
by Jay Withgott and Scott Brennan
Copyright © 2007 by Pearson Education, Inc.
Published by Prentice Hall

Pearson Learning Solutions, 501 Boylston Street, Suite 900, Boston, MA 02116
A Pearson Education Company
www.pearsoned.com

Printed in the United States of America

7 8 9 10 V092 14 13 12 11

2009240727

LB/SB

ISBN 10: 0-558-54717-6
ISBN 13: 978-0-558-54717-2

Copyright Acknowledgments

Taken from *Psychology*, Second Edition, by Saundra K. Ciccarelli and J. Noland White

Taken from *Essential Environment: The Science Behind the Stories*, Second Edition, by Jay Withgott and Scott Brennan

Taken from *Reading Across the Disciplines: College Reading and Beyond,* Fourth Edition
by Kathleen T. McWhorter

Preface

Reading Across the Disciplines, Fourth Edition, is designed to improve college students' reading and thinking skills through brief skill instruction and extensive guided practice with academic discipline–based readings. The text is structured around 12 academic disciplines. The 36 readings—all of which aim to motivate students—are selected from college textbooks as well as from books, periodicals and popular magazines, newspapers, and Internet sources. The objective is to show the relevance of college studies to events and issues in everyday life through the use of engaging readings.

PURPOSE

The primary purposes of the text are to teach essential college reading skills and to guide their application in each of 12 academic disciplines. The text develops basic vocabulary and comprehension skills, as well as inferential and critical-reading and -thinking skills. In addition to developing overall reading skills, the text also introduces students to content-specific reading skills. Each chapter in Part Two, "Readings for Academic Disciplines," begins with a tip list for applying reading and thinking skills to text with the unique characteristics of the discipline. Questions and activities that precede and follow each reading demonstrate the application of vocabulary, comprehension, and critical-reading and -thinking skills to the particular discipline.

Another important goal of the text is to demonstrate to students the relevance and utility of college courses to their daily lives. The book attempts to answer the long-standing question frequently asked by students, "Why do I have to take a course in history, biology, etc.?" The book presents readings that show students how academic disciplines embrace and investigate topics of interest and concern to everyday human experience.

CONTENT OVERVIEW

The book is organized into two parts:

- **Part One, "A Handbook for Reading and Thinking in College,"** presents a brief skill introduction. Written in handbook format (1a, 1b, etc.), this part introduces students to essential vocabulary, comprehension, critical-reading, and reading-rate skills.
- **Part Two, "Readings for Academic Disciplines,"** has 2 chapters, each containing readings representative of a different academic discipline. Each chapter has three reading selections. The readings in each chapter are chosen from textbooks, books, periodicals, newspapers, and Internet sources that contain material relevant to the discipline. The readings in each chapter vary in length as well as difficulty. Within each chapter, readings are arranged from least to most difficult, providing students with the opportunity to strengthen their skills, experience success, and build positive attitudes toward reading. Each reading is accompanied by an extensive apparatus that guides student learning.

FEATURES

Reading Across the Disciplines guides students in learning reading and thinking skills essential for college success.

Students Approach Reading as Thinking

Reading is approached as a thinking process—a process of interacting with textual material and sorting, evaluating, and reacting to its organization and content. The apparatus preceding and following each reading focuses, guides, and shapes the students' thought processes.

Students Develop Active Reading Skills

Students learn to approach reading as a process that requires involvement and response. In doing so, they are able to master the skills that are essential to college reading. The reading apparatus provides a model for active reading.

Students Learn Essential Reading Skills

Vocabulary, comprehension, and critical-reading skills are presented concisely in Part One, "A Handbook for Reading and Thinking in College," and are accompanied by several exercises.

Students Learn Discipline-Specific Reading Skills

The high-interest readings in Part Two are grouped according to academic discipline. Each chapter begins with a brief list of tips for reading and learning within the particular discipline. Students are encouraged to apply these techniques as they read the selections within the chapter.

Students Learn as They Work

Unlike many books, which simply test students after they have read a selection, this text teaches students as they work. Some of the apparatus provides new material on vocabulary, methods of organizing information, transitions, and reading/study strategies.

Students Understand the Importance of Academic Disciplines to Their Daily Lives

Through the high-interest topics selected, students will come to understand the relevance of various academic disciplines to their daily lives, careers, and workplace.

Students Learn Visually

Increasingly, college students are becoming visual learners, and visual literacy is critical to success in today's world. To promote visual learning, this text is four-color and contains numerous photographs, graphics, graphic organizers (maps), charts, and diagrams.

Students Appreciate Consistent Format

Because students often need structure and organization, this text uses a consistent format for each reading selection. Students always know what to expect and what is expected of them.

Students Can Build Success by Progressing from Less to More Difficult Readings

The readings within each chapter are organized conceptually from less to more difficult. Instructors may choose a starting level that is appropriate for their classes. By starting with a relatively easy reading, students can build confidence and success before approaching more challenging readings.

Students Refer to Part One, "A Handbook for Reading and Thinking in College," to Get Help Answering Questions

The activities following each reading are parallel to the topics in Part One of the book, which presents a brief skill overview in a handbook format. For example, if students have difficulty answering inferential questions, they may refer to the section in Part One that explains how to make inferences. The handbook also includes a section on reading and evaluating electronic sources.

Format of the Apparatus

The apparatus for each reading selection follows a consistent format. The sections vary in the number of questions and the specific skills reviewed. Each reading selection has the following parts:

- **Headnote.** A headnote introduces the reading, identifies its source, provokes the students' interest, and most important, establishes a framework or purpose for reading.
- **Previewing the Reading.** Students are directed to preview the reading using the guidelines provided in Part One and to answer several questions based on their preview.
- **Making Connections.** This brief section encourages students to draw connections between the topic of the reading and their own knowledge and experience.
- **Reading Tip.** The reading tip is intended to help students approach and work through the reading. A different reading tip is offered for each reading. For example, a reading tip might suggest how to highlight to strengthen comprehension or how to write annotations to enhance critical thinking.
- **Reading Selection/Vocabulary Annotation.** Most reading selections contain difficult vocabulary words that are essential to the meaning of the selection. Often these are words that students are unlikely to know and cannot figure out from context. These words are highlighted, and their meanings are given as marginal annotations. Preferable to a list of words preceding the reading, this format allows students to check meanings on an as-needed basis, within the context of the selection. Annotations are also used occasionally to provide necessary background information that students may need to grasp concepts in a reading.
- **Understanding the Thesis and Other Main Ideas.** This section helps students figure out the thesis of the reading and identify the main idea of selected paragraphs.
- **Identifying Details.** This section focuses on recognizing the relationship between main ideas and details, as well as distinguishing primary from secondary details. The format of questions within this section varies to expose students to a variety of thinking strategies.
- **Recognizing Methods of Organization and Transitions.** This part of the apparatus guides students in identifying the overall organizational pattern of the selection and in identifying transitional words and phrases within the reading. Prompts are provided that serve as teaching tips or review strategies.
- **Reviewing and Organizing Ideas.** Since many students are proficient at literal recall of information but have difficulty seeing relationships and organizing information into usable formats for study and review, this section emphasizes important review and organizational skills such as paraphrasing, mapping, outlining, and summarizing.
- **Figuring Out Inferred Meanings.** The ability to think inferentially is expected of college students. This section guides students in making inferences based on information presented in the reading selection.
- **Thinking Critically.** This section covers essential critical-thinking skills including distinguishing fact from opinion, identifying the author's purpose, recognizing bias, evaluating the source, identifying tone, making judgments, and evaluating supporting evidence.
- **Building Vocabulary.** The first part of this section focuses on vocabulary in context, while the second is concerned with word parts. Using words from the reading selection, exercises are structured to encourage students to expand their vocabulary and strengthen their word-analysis skills. A brief review of the meanings of prefixes, roots, and suffixes used in the exercise is provided for ease of reference and to create a meaningful learning situation. The third vocabulary section focuses on a wide range of interesting features of language, drawing upon unusual or striking usage within the reading. Topics such as figurative language, idioms, and connotative meanings are included.
- **Selecting a Learning/Study Strategy.** College students are responsible for learning and studying what they read; many use the same study method for all disciplines and all types of material. This section helps students to choose appropriate study methods and to adapt their study methods to suit particular academic disciplines.

- **Exploring Ideas Through Discussion and Writing.** Questions provided in this section are intended to stimulate thought, provoke discussion, and serve as a springboard to writing about the reading.
- **Beyond the Classroom to the Web.** These activities draw on the skills students have learned by directing them to the Internet, where they are asked to read particular articles. These activities also demonstrate the relevance of the academic discipline beyond the classroom and provide guidance in using Web sources.

FEATURES OF THE FOURTH EDITION

The goal of this revision was to give greater emphasis to the skills beginning college students need to succeed in a variety of academic disciplines. The revision also recognizes and addresses new technology that has entered the learning environment, including e-books, online study groups, and course management systems. Readings have also been replaced with new selections on current and relevant topics.

NEW Ten Success Strategies for Learning and Studying Academic Disciplines

This new introduction to the book provides students with basic skills they need to succeed in the numerous academic disciplines they will study and addresses the new technology available to enhance communication and learning. Students learn to

- Develop new skills appropriate for each discipline.
- Acquire the right tools to enhance learning.
- Learn the technical and specialized language of each discipline.
- Communicate with classmates (e-mail, online study groups, IM, etc.).
- Communicate with professors.
- Develop new means of acquiring information.
- Use new information sources (databases, discipline-specific learning aids, and so on).
- Record and organize information using a computer.
- Approach online courses.
- Develop academic integrity (avoid plagiarism, cyberplagiarism, etc.).

NEW Introduction to Part Two, "Readings for Academic Disciplines"

This section acquaints students with the structure of the apparatus following each reading and demonstrates its utility as they work within a new academic discipline.

NEW Reading Selections

Eight new reading selections have been added. Seven are on the topics of video games, online dating, cultural differences in nonverbal communication, issue-oriented and street art, product placement in the media, DNA fingerprinting, and stem cell research. A new poem by Gladys Cardiff explores traditions passed through generations.

NEW Readings in Part One

Two new readings, one on commercial jingles, another on snitching, have been added to Part One to provide skill application and practice.

EXPANDED Coverage of Evaluating Online Sources

Chapter 9 has been revised to drop information that has become common knowledge and to add information and exercises on evaluating Web sites, including new material on objectivity, authority, and usability.

NEW Linkage to MyReadingLab

MyReadingLab

Icons throughout Part One link content to coverage on the MyReadingLab site, the extensive online reading skills resource, where students can obtain further practice in the skills indicated.

BOOK-SPECIFIC ANCILLARIES

- **Annotated Instructor's Edition.** The Annotated Instructor's Edition is identical to the student text, but it includes answers printed directly on the pages where questions and exercises appear. ISBN 0-205-66278-1
- **Test Bank.** This supplement contains numerous tests for each chapter, formatted for easy distribution and scoring. It includes content review quizzes and skill-based mastery tests for Part One and a discipline-based test and two discipline-based mastery tests for Part Two. ISBN 0-205-66276-5
- **Instructor's Manual.** The manual includes teaching suggestions for each section of Part One. For each reading in Part Two, the manual provides numerous suggestions for introducing the reading and offers a variety of follow-up activities designed to review and reinforce skills. ISBN 0-205-66277-3
- **Expanding Your Vocabulary.** Instructors may choose to shrink-wrap *Reading Across the Disciplines* with a copy of *Expanding Your Vocabulary*. This book, written by Kathleen McWhorter, works well as a supplemental text providing additional instruction and practice in vocabulary. Students can work through the book independently, or units may be incorporated into weekly lesson plans. Topics covered include methods of vocabulary learning, contextual aids, word parts, connotative meanings, idioms, euphemisms, and many more interesting and fun topics. The book concludes with vocabulary lists and exercises representative of ten academic disciplines. To preview this book, contact your Longman sales consultant for an examination copy.

ACKNOWLEDGMENTS

I wish to express my gratitude to my reviewers for their excellent ideas, suggestions, and advice on the preparation and revision of this text:

Maria Spelleri, Manatee Community College; Sylvia D. Ybarra, San Antonio College; Valerie Hicks, Community College Beaver County; Lynette D. Shaw-Smith, Springfield College Illinois/Benedictine University; Kathleen S. Britton, Florence-Darlington Technical College; Kimberly S. Hall, Harrisburg Area Community College; Debra Herrera, Cisco Junior College; Michael Vensel, Miami Dade College; and Anne Hepfer, Seattle University.

I also wish to thank Gill Cook, my development editor, for her creative vision of the project, her helpful suggestions, and her assistance in preparing and organizing the manuscript. I am particularly indebted to Kate Edwards, acquisitions editor, for her enthusiastic support, valuable advice, and expert guidance of the revision.

KATHLEEN T. MCWHORTER

PART ONE

A Handbook for Reading and Thinking in College

1 Active Reading and Thinking Strategies

What does it take to do well in biology? In psychology? In history? In business? In answer to these questions, college students are likely to say:

- "Knowing how to study."
- "You have to like the course."
- "Hard work!"
- "Background in the subject area."
- "A good teacher!"

Students seldom mention reading as an essential skill. In a sense, reading is a hidden factor in college success. When you think of college, you think of attending classes and labs, completing assignments, studying for and taking exams, and writing papers. A closer look at these activities, however, reveals that reading is an important part of each.

Reading stays "behind the scenes" because instructors rarely evaluate it directly. Grades are based on production: how well you express your ideas in papers or how well you do on exams. Yet reading is the primary means by which you acquire your ideas and gather information.

Throughout this handbook you will learn numerous ways to use reading as a tool for college success.

1a ACTIVE READING: THE KEY TO ACADEMIC SUCCESS

MyReadingLab

To practice active reading skills, go to

➤ Study Plan
➤ Reading Skills
➤ Active Reading Strategies

Reading involves much more than moving your eyes across lines of print, more than recognizing words, and more than reading sentences. Reading is thinking. It is an active process of identifying important ideas and comparing, evaluating, and applying them.

Have you ever gone to a ball game and watched the fans? Most do not sit and watch passively. Instead, they direct the plays, criticize the calls, encourage the players, and reprimand the coach. They care enough to get actively involved in the game. Just like interested fans, active readers get involved. They question, challenge, and criticize, as well as understand. Table 1.1 on this page contrasts the active strategies of successful readers with the passive ones of less successful readers. Not all strategies will work for everyone. Experiment to discover those that work particularly well for you.

TABLE 1.1 ACTIVE VERSUS PASSIVE READING

ACTIVE READERS . . .	PASSIVE READERS . . .
Tailor their reading to suit each assignment.	Read all assignments the same way.
Analyze the purpose of an assignment.	Read an assignment because it was assigned.
Adjust their speed to suit their purpose.	Read everything at the same speed.

(continued on next page)

(continued from preceding page)

ACTIVE READERS . . .	PASSIVE READERS . . .
Question ideas in the assignment.	Accept whatever is in print as true.
Compare and connect textbook material with lecture content.	Study lecture notes and the textbook separately.
Skim headings to find out what an assignment is about before beginning to read.	Check the length of an assignment and then begin reading.
Make sure they understand what they are reading as they go along.	Read until the assignment is completed.
Read with pencil in hand, highlighting, jotting notes, and marking key vocabulary.	Read.
Develop personalized strategies that are particularly effective.	Follow routine, standard methods. Read all assignments the same way.

▶ NOW PRACTICE . . . ACTIVE READING

Consider each of the following reading assignments. Discuss ways to get actively involved in each assignment.

1. Reading two poems by Maya Angelou for an American literature class.

   _____

   _____

2. Reading the procedures for your next biology lab.

   _____

   _____

3. Reading an article in *Newsweek* magazine assigned by your political science instructor in preparation for a class discussion.

   _____

   _____

1b   PREVIEWING

Previewing is a means of familiarizing yourself with the content and organization of an assignment *before* you read it. Think of previewing as getting a "sneak preview" of what a chapter or reading will be about. You can then read the material more easily and more rapidly.

How to Preview Reading Assignments

Use the following steps to become familiar with the content and organization of a chapter, essay, or article.

1. **Read the title.** The title indicates the topic of the article or chapter; the subtitle suggests the specific focus of, or approach to, the topic.

2. **Check the author and the source of an article and essay.** This information may provide clues about the article's content or focus.

3. **Read the introduction or the first paragraph.** The introduction or first paragraph serves as a lead-in, establishing the overall subject and suggesting how it will be developed.

4. **Read each boldface (dark print) heading.** Headings label the contents of each section and announce the major topic covered. If there are no headings, read the first sentence of each paragraph. The first sentence of the paragraph is often the topic sentence, which states the main idea of the paragraph. By reading first sentences, you will encounter most of the key ideas in the article.

5. **Read the first sentence under each major heading.** The first sentence often states the central thought of the section. If the first sentence seems introductory, read the last sentence; often this sentence states or restates the central thought.

6. **Note any typographical aids.** Colored print, boldface font, and italics are used to emphasize important terminology and definitions, distinguishing them from the rest of a passage. Material that is numbered 1, 2, 3; lettered a, b, c; or presented in list form is also of special importance.

7. **Note any graphic aids.** Graphs, charts, photographs, and tables often suggest what is important. Be sure to read the captions of photographs and the legends on graphs, charts, or tables.

8. **Read the last paragraph or summary.** This provides a condensed view of the article or chapter, often outlining the key points.

9. **Read quickly any end-of-article or end-of-chapter material.** This might include references, study questions, discussion questions, chapter outlines, or vocabulary lists. If there are study questions, read them through quickly because they tell you what is important to remember in the chapter. If a vocabulary list is included, rapidly skim through it to identify the terms you will be learning as you read.

A section of an interpersonal communication textbook chapter discussing the breakup of a relationship is reprinted here to illustrate how previewing is done. The portions to focus on when previewing are shaded. Read only those portions. After you have finished, test how well your previewing worked by answering the questions that follow, titled, "What Did You Learn from Previewing?"

Ending a Relationship

1   Some relationships, of course, do end. Sometimes there is simply not enough to hold the couple together. Sometimes there are problems that cannot be resolved. Sometimes the costs are too high and the rewards too few, or the relationship is recognized as destructive and escape is the only alternative. As a relationship ends, you're confronted with two general issues: (1) how to end the relationship, and (2) how to deal with the inevitable problems that relationship endings cause.

The Strategies of Disengagement

2   When you wish to exit a relationship you need some way of explaining this—to yourself as well as to your partner. You develop a strategy for getting out of a relationship that you no longer find satisfying or profitable. The table identifies five major disengagement strategies (Cody 1982). As you read down the table, note that the strategies depend on your goal. For example, you're more likely to remain friends if you use de-escalation than if you use justification or avoidance (Banks, Altendorf, Greene, and Cody 1987). You may find it interesting to identify the disengagement strategies you have heard of or used yourself and see how they fit in with these five types.

Dealing With a Breakup

3   Regardless of the specific reason, relationship breakups are difficult to deal with; invariably they cause stress. You're likely to experience high levels of distress over the breakup of a relationship in which you were satisfied, were close to your partner, had dated your partner for a long time, and felt it would not be easy to replace the relationship with another one (Simpson 1987, Frazier and Cook 1993).

4   Given both the inevitability that some relationships will break up and the importance of such breakups, here are some suggestions to ease the difficulty that is sure to be experienced. These suggestions apply to the termination of any type of relationship—between friends or lovers, through death, separation, or breakup.

Break the Loneliness-Depression Cycle

5   The two most common feelings following the end of a relationship are loneliness and depression. These feelings are significant; treat them seriously. Realize that depression often leads to serious illness. In most cases, fortunately, loneliness and depression are temporary. Depression, for example, usually does not last longer than three or four days. Similarly, the loneliness that follows a breakup is generally linked to this specific situation and will fade when the situation changes. When depression does last, is especially deep, or disturbs your normal functioning, it's time for professional help.

Take Time Out

6   Resist the temptation to jump into a new relationship while the old one is still warm or before a new one can be assessed with some objectivity. At the same time, resist swearing off all relationships. Neither extreme works well.

7   Take time out for yourself. Renew your relationship with yourself. If you were in a long-term relationship, you probably saw yourself as part of a team, as part of a couple. Now get to know yourself as a unique individual, standing alone at present but fully capable of entering a meaningful relationship in the near future.

Bolster Self-Esteem

8   When relationships fail, self-esteem often declines. This seems especially true for those who did not initiate the breakup (Collins and Clark 1989). You may feel guilty for having caused the breakup or inadequate for not holding on to the relationship. You may feel unwanted and unloved. Your task is to regain the positive self-image needed to function effectively.

9   Recognize, too, that having been in a relationship that failed—even if you view yourself as the main cause of the breakup—does not mean that you are a failure. Neither does it mean that you cannot succeed in a new and different relationship. It does mean that something went wrong with this one

FIVE DISENGAGEMENT STRATEGIES

Think back to relationships that you have tried to dissolve or that your partner tried to dissolve. Did you or your partner use any of the strategies listed here? These strategies are taken from research by Michael Cody (1982).

STRATEGY	FUNCTION	EXAMPLES
Positive tone	To maintain a positive relationship; to express positive feelings for the other person	I really care for you a great deal but I'm not ready for such an intense relationship.
Negative identity management	To blame the other person for the breakup; to absolve oneself of the blame for the breakup	I can't stand your jealousy, your constant suspicions, your checking up on me. I need my freedom.
Justification	To give reasons for the breakup	I'm going away to college for four years; there's no point in not dating others.
Behavioral de-escalation	To reduce the intensity of the relationship	Avoidance; cut down on phone calls; reduce time spent together, especially time alone.
De-escalation	To reduce the exclusivity and hence the intensity of the relationship	I'm just not ready for so exclusive a relationship. I think we should see other people.

relationship. Ideally, it was a failure from which you have learned something important about yourself and about your relationship behavior.

Remove or Avoid Uncomfortable Symbols

10   After any breakup, there are a variety of reminders—photographs, gifts, and letters, for example. Resist the temptation to throw these out. Instead, remove them. Give them to a friend to hold or put them in a closet where you'll not see them. If possible, avoid places you frequented together. These symbols will bring back uncomfortable memories. After you have achieved some emotional distance, you can go back and enjoy these as reminders of a once pleasant relationship. Support for this suggestion comes from research showing that the more vivid your memory of a broken love affair—a memory greatly aided by these relationship symbols—the greater your depression is likely to be (Harvey, Flanary, and Morgan 1986).

Seek Support

11   Many people feel they should bear their burdens alone. Men, in particular, have been taught that this is the only "manly" way to handle things. But seeking the support of others is one of the best antidotes to the unhappiness caused when a relationship ends. Tell your friends and family of your situation—in only general terms, if you prefer—and make it clear that you want support. Seek out people who are positive and nurturing. Avoid negative individuals who will paint the world in even darker tones. Make the distinction between seeking support and seeking advice. If you feel you need advice, seek out a professional.

Avoid Repeating Negative Patterns

12   Many people repeat their mistakes. They enter second and third relationships with the same blinders, faulty preconceptions, and unrealistic expectations with which they entered earlier ones. Instead, use the knowledge gained from your failed relationship to prevent repeating the same patterns.

13   At the same time, don't become a prophet of doom. Don't see in every relationship vestiges of the old. Don't jump at the first conflict and say, "Here it goes all over again." Treat the new relationship as the unique relationship it is. Don't evaluate it through past experiences. Use past relationships and experiences as guides, not filters.

—From De Vito, Joseph A. *The Interpersonal Communication Book*, 9e. Published by Allyn and Bacon, Boston, MA. Copyright © 2001 by Pearson Education. Reprinted by permission of the publisher.

➤ WHAT DID YOU LEARN FROM PREVIEWING?

Without referring to the passage, answer each of the following true/false questions.

_____ 1. To end a relationship you need to find a way to explain the breakup to yourself and to your partner.

_____ 2. The breakup of a relationship almost always causes stress.

_____ 3. The two most common feelings following the end of a relationship are anger and fear of desertion.

_____ 4. After a breakup occurs, it is important to keep letters and photographs as reminders of the relationship at its best.

_____ 5. One mistake people often make after a breakup is to enter into a new relationship too soon.

You probably were able to answer all (or most) of the questions correctly. Previewing, then, does provide you with a great deal of information. If you were to return to the passage from the textbook and read the entire section, you would find it easier to do than if you hadn't previewed it.

Why Previewing Is Effective

Previewing is effective for several reasons:

- **Previewing helps you to make decisions about how you will approach the material.** On the basis of what you discover about the assignment's organization and content, you can select the reading and study strategies that will be most effective.
- **Previewing puts your mind in gear and helps you start thinking about the subject.**
- **Previewing also gives you a mental outline of the chapter's content.** It enables you to see how ideas are connected, and since you know where the author is headed, your reading will be easier than if you had not previewed. Previewing, however, is never a substitute for careful, thorough reading.

NOW PRACTICE . . . PREVIEWING

Assume you are taking a psychology course. Your instructor has assigned the following article from Wiretap, an online news and culture magazine. Preview the article using the procedure described in this section. When you have finished, answer the questions that follow.

Deadly Silence: Stop Snitching's Fatal Legacy
By Ayah Young

1   In 2004, a DVD called *Stop Snitching* began to circulate in Baltimore, Maryland. The homemade film featured self-proclaimed drug dealers who issued violent threats against people who reported any information about their crimes to the police. An immediate underground success, this film brought snitching to the forefront of hip-hop culture and soon after its release, t-shirts with an image of a stop sign bearing the phrase "Stop Snitching" began to appear on the streets. The message was assimilated into hip-hop lyrics, and in October of 2005, stop snitching was brought to a national audience by an article about the t-shirts in the *New York Times*.

Snitching's Many Meanings

2   So what exactly is snitching? Dr. Rick Frei, an applied psychology professor at the Community College of Philadelphia has been working with a team of student researchers to determine just that. In an effort known as the Snitching Project, Frei and his students developed a questionnaire that they administered to nearly 1500 community college students. The resulting data illustrated that a wide variety of definitions exist. While 82.6 percent of students polled identified that ratting someone else out to get out of a crime would be considered snitching, other activities—tattling on a brother or sister, reporting a classmate cheating on an exam, helping the police set someone up, picking a suspect out of a police lineup, or answering questions from police at the scene of the crime—could also be considered snitching.

3   Cooperating witnesses often fear retaliation from those they've informed upon, and frequently the fear of physical harm or death is so intense that it causes witnesses to remain silent. Without witnesses to speak out, more crimes go unsolved. So when the "Stop Snitching" campaign became national, its reception by police and the general public was less than favorable. People were quick to blame the t-shirts, and hip-hop, as the cause of the problem.

4   In a 60 *Minutes* special called "Stop Snitching" that aired on April 22, 2007, social activist and author Geoffrey Canada placed blame for unsolved crimes in urban communities directly on

hip-hop, stating emphatically, "Rappers are preaching anarchy." He went on to articulate, "The message is, go out and do things that will destroy you, that will get you locked up in jail, that will ruin your relationships, that will estrange you from your kids, that's what this music is preaching." He believes that some hip-hop music is the driving force behind violence in the streets.

5   Geoffrey Canada's hostility toward this music stems from a personal experience. Israel Ramirez, a student whom he mentored and loved like a son, was shot and killed while providing security on the set of a Busta Rhymes music video. With a possible dozen witnesses to the crime, and no one willing to speak with the police, it's easy to see how Canada would readily place the blame of this unsolved crime on hip-hop itself.

6   In another famous instance from the same show, rapper Cam'ron controversially outlined his "code of ethics" to host Anderson Cooper. "If I knew a serial killer was living next door to me, I wouldn't call and tell anybody on him." This clip outraged average Americans and sensationalized the correlation between hip-hop and the credo of street silence.

7   The music industry has long been blamed for violent behavior. When the infamous shootings occurred at Columbine High School in 1999, the media was quick to implicate Marilyn Manson's music as a cause for Klebold and Harris' killing spree.

8   But does music shape society? Or is music merely a reflection of preexisting ideals within society? As a part of the Snitching Project's study, participants were asked about their music listening habits. The report stated, "While over one-third of all students said that they listened to music that explicitly said snitching was bad, only 5.5 percent of students said that the music that they listened to influenced their opinion of snitching." In a discussion with Dr. Frei he explained, "It may be that people are not really influenced by the music that they listen to. Or it might be that people seek out music that confirms their own personal worldview. While the 'Stop Snitching' campaign has probably influenced some people, I think most people didn't trust the police long before Cam'ron ever recorded a song."

Informant Woes

9   In an era where each is out to get their own, the problem of snitches working with the police is very different. The same message, lacking the community context, makes for an entirely different reality. Individuals, who may be trying to save themselves jail time, can make a deal with the police in exchange for information regarding another wanted party. When that person gets locked up, the snitch gains enemies, further perpetuating violence on the streets.

10   Police work with snitches and informants has a checkered history. Tafari explains how in his work, he has frequently encountered kids brought in on charges who don't know their rights. They are offered a deal and are willing to say just about anything to get off the hook. "The really bad part is that these deals they cut with people might not even be [based on] the truth."

11   This issue of false information has serious real-life implications. In a study conducted by the Northwestern University School of Law Center on wrongful convictions, they found that of 111 capital cases studied since 1973, 45 percent of wrongful convictions were a result of snitches. That's an overwhelming percentage of people who were given death sentences as a result of bad information.

Snitching Solutions?

12   So what is to be done? We can't just ban "Stop Snitching" messages from the culture and hope that the problem goes away. Ethan Brown, the author of Snitch: Informants, Cooperators, and the Corruption of Justice, suggests that we restore faith in the legal system by refocusing our federal sentencing policies, including placing limits on the number of times that an individual can provide assistance in an investigation in exchange for a reduced sentence, and requiring that information provided by cooperators be corroborated with evidence. These suggestions, if put into practice, could have an extremely positive effect on the quality of "justice" in America.

13   But while these measures may help to reduce crime and unjust sentencing, they are a band-aid solution for the issue's root cause. Beyond our current judicial system lies the reality that high levels of crime in this country often stem from a history of institutionalized racism and classism that denies some populations opportunities for fair work opportunities and safer environments. This lack of resources and development has had a disastrous effect on America's low-income urban communities. As Abel Habtegeorgies bluntly stated, "If our urban areas weren't so neglected and if greater investment in communities like parks and recreation programs, job training programs, and jobs existed, you wouldn't have people resorting to illegal opportunities."

14   With continual cuts to vital resources like education, it is not likely that we will see the government step in to enhance these kinds of services anytime soon. The task of revitalizing these communities has fallen on the shoulders of concerned citizens and grassroots organizations like the Ella Baker Center, Elementz, Youth Uprising, and H.O.M.E.Y, who are engaging youth and community members in constructive dialogue and offering them inspiration, training and empowerment. And there are people like Dr. Frei who are working to understand social attitudes about snitching and building classroom curriculum to address the issue.

15   While the work these people and organizations do is vital to the future of our cities, it is important to remember that to create radical change in our society requires everyone's participation, consciousness and diligence. So the next time you see a "Stop Snitching" shirt or read about uncooperative witnesses, ask yourself: "What is my community or city doing to empower itself, form stronger familial bonds and improve not just my safety, but everyone's?" If you don't have a good answer, it's time to get to work, and clean our collective dirty laundry.

—Reprinted from WiretapMag.org

1. What is the overall subject of this article?

_____

2. How did the topic of this reading become popular?

_____

_____

3. Why are some people afraid to snitch?

_____

4. Who or what is being blamed for unsolved crimes in urban areas?

_____

5. What solution does the author offer to the problem of "stop snitching"?

_____

6. On a scale of 1 to 5 (1 = easy, 5 = very difficult), how difficult do you expect the article to be?

_____

1c   ACTIVATING BACKGROUND KNOWLEDGE

After previewing your assignment, you should take a moment to think about what you already know about the topic. Whatever the topic, you probably know *something* about it: This is your background knowledge. For example, a student was about to read an article titled "Growing Urban Problems" for a sociology class. His first thought was that he knew very little about urban problems because he lived in a rural area. But when he thought of a recent trip to a nearby city, he remembered seeing the homeless people and crowded conditions. This recollection helped him remember reading about drug problems, drive-by shootings, and muggings.

Activating your background knowledge aids your reading in three ways. First, it makes reading easier because you have already thought about the topic. Second, the material is easier to remember because you can connect the new information with what you already know. Third, topics become more interesting if you can link them to your own experiences. Here are some techniques to help you activate your background knowledge.

- **Ask questions, and try to answer them.** If a chapter in your biology textbook titled "Human Diseases" contains headings such as "Infectious diseases," "Sexually transmitted diseases," "Cancer," and "Vascular diseases," you might ask and try to answer such questions as the following: What kinds of infectious diseases have I seen? What caused them? What do I know about preventing cancer and other diseases?

- **Draw on your own experience.** If a chapter in your business textbook is titled "Advertising: Its Purpose and Design," you might think of several ads you have seen and analyze the purpose of each and how it was constructed.
- **Brainstorm.** Write down everything that comes to mind about the topic. Suppose you're about to read a chapter in your sociology textbook on domestic violence. You might list types of violence—child abuse, rape, and so on. You might write questions such as "What causes child abuse?" and "How can it be prevented?" Alternatively, you might list incidents of domestic violence you have heard or read about. Any of these approaches will help to make the topic interesting.

> **NOW PRACTICE . . . ACTIVATING BACKGROUND KNOWLEDGE**

Use one of the three strategies listed above to discover what you already know about snitching.

1d CHECKING YOUR COMPREHENSION

What happens when you read material you can understand easily? Does it seem that everything "clicks"? Do ideas seem to fit together and make sense? Is that "click" noticeably absent at other times?

Table 1.2 lists and compares common signals to assist you in checking your comprehension. Not all the signals appear at the same time, and not all the signals work for everyone. But becoming aware of these positive and negative signals will help you gain more control over your reading.

TABLE 1.2 COMPREHENSION SIGNALS

POSITIVE SIGNALS	NEGATIVE SIGNALS
You feel comfortable and have some knowledge about the topic.	The topic is unfamiliar, yet the author assumes you understand it.
You recognize most words or can figure them out from context.	Many words are unfamiliar.
You can express the main ideas in your own words.	You must reread the main ideas and use the author's language to explain them.
You understand why the material was assigned.	You do not know why the material was assigned and cannot explain why it is important.
You read at a regular, comfortable pace.	You often slow down or reread.
You are able to make connections between ideas.	You are unable to detect relationships; the organization is not apparent.
You are able to see where the author is leading.	You feel as if you are struggling to stay with the author and are unable to predict what will follow.
You understand what is important.	Nothing (or everything) seems important.

> **NOW PRACTICE . . . CHECKING YOUR COMPREHENSION**

Read the article titled "Deadly Silence: Stop Snitching's Fatal Legacy" that appears on page 8. Be alert for positive and negative comprehension signals as you read. After reading the article, answer the following questions.

1. On a scale of 1 to 5 (1 = very poor, 5 = excellent), how would you rate your overall comprehension? _____

2. What positive signals did you sense? List them below.

_____

_____

_____

3. What negative signals did you experience, if any? List them below.

_____

_____

_____

4. In which sections was your comprehension strongest? List the paragraph numbers. _____

5. Did you feel at any time that you had lost, or were about to lose, comprehension? If so, go back to that part now. What made it difficult to read?

_____

_____

1e   STRENGTHENING YOUR COMPREHENSION

Here are some suggestions to follow when you realize you need to strengthen your comprehension.

1. **Analyze the time and place in which you are reading.** If you've been reading or studying for several hours, mental fatigue may be the source of the problem. If you are reading in a place with distractions or interruptions, you might not be able to understand what you're reading.
2. **Rephrase each paragraph in your own words.** You might need to approach complicated material sentence by sentence, expressing each in your own words.
3. **Read aloud sentences or sections that are particularly difficult.** Reading out loud sometimes makes complicated material easier to understand.
4. **Reread difficult or complicated sections.** In fact, at times several readings are appropriate and necessary.
5. **Slow down your reading rate.** On occasion, simply reading more slowly and carefully will provide you with the needed boost in comprehension.
6. **Write questions next to headings.** Refer to your questions frequently and jot down or underline answers.
7. **Write a brief outline of major points.** This will help you see the overall organization and progression of ideas.
8. **Highlight key ideas.** After you've read a section, go back and think about and underline what is important. Underlining forces you to sort out what is important, and this sorting process builds comprehension and recall. (Refer to 7a for suggestions on how to highlight effectively.)
9. **Write notes in the margins.** Explain or rephrase difficult or complicated ideas or sections.
10. **Determine whether you lack background knowledge.** Comprehension is difficult, or at times impossible, if you lack essential information that the writer assumes you have. Suppose you are reading a section of a political science text in which the author describes implications of the balance of

> ➤ NOW PRACTICE . . . USING CONTRAST CLUES 2

Read the following paragraph and use contrast clues to help you determine the meaning of each boldfaced word. Consult a dictionary, if necessary.

The Whigs chose General William Henry Harrison to run against President Martin Van Buren in 1840, using a **specious** but effective argument: General Harrison is a plain man of the people who lives in a log cabin. Contrast him with the suave Van Buren, **luxuriating** amid "the Regal Splendor of the President's Palace." Harrison drinks ordinary hard cider with his hog meat and grits, while Van Buren **eschews** plain food in favor of expensive foreign wines and fancy French cuisine. The general's furniture is **unpretentious** and sturdy; the president dines off gold plates and treads on carpets that cost the people $5 a yard. In a country where all are equal, the people will reject an **aristocrat** like Van Buren and put their trust in General Harrison, a simple, brave, honest, public-spirited common man. (In fact, Harrison came from a distinguished family, was well educated and financially comfortable, and certainly did not live in a log cabin.)

—adapted from Carnes and Garraty, *The American Nation,* p. 267

1. specious _____

2. luxuriating _____

3. eschews _____

4. unpretentious _____

5. aristocrat _____

Logic of the Passage Clues

Many times you can figure out the meaning of an unknown word by using logic and reasoning skills. For instance, look at the following sentence:

Bob is quite **versatile;** he is a good student, a top athlete, an excellent car mechanic, and a gourmet cook.

You can see that Bob is successful at many different types of activities, and you could reason that *versatile* means "capable of doing many things competently."

Examples

When the customer tried to pay with Mexican **pesos,** the clerk explained that the store accepted only U.S. dollars.

Logic tells you that customers pay with money; *pesos,* then, are a type of Mexican currency.

We had to leave the car and walk up because the **incline** was too steep to drive.

Something that is too steep must be slanted or have a slope; *incline* means a slope.

Since Reginald was nervous, he brought his rabbit's foot **talisman** with him to the exam.

A rabbit's foot is often thought to be a good luck charm; *talisman* means a good luck charm.

> NOW PRACTICE . . . USING LOGIC OF THE PASSAGE CLUES 1

Read each sentence and write a definition or synonym for each boldfaced word. Use information provided in the context to help you determine word meaning.

1. The foreign students quickly **assimilated** many aspects of American culture.

   _____

2. The legal aid clinic was **subsidized** by city and county funds.

   _____

3. When the bank robber reached his **haven,** he breathed a sigh of relief and began to count his money.

   _____

4. The teenager was **intimidated** by the presence of a police officer walking the beat and decided not to spray-paint the school wall.

   _____

5. If the plan did not work, the colonel had a **contingency** plan ready.

   _____

> NOW PRACTICE . . . USING LOGIC OF THE PASSAGE CLUES 2

Read the following paragraphs and use the logic of the passage clues to help you choose and circle the correct meaning of each boldfaced word or phrase.

The map of the geography of languages is not **static.** The use of some languages is expanding because the speakers of those languages are **diffusing** around the world, are gaining greater power and influence in world affairs, or are winning new **adherents** to their ideas.

For international **discourse,** English is the world's leading **lingua franca,** partly because of its widespread use in science and business. Many multinational corporations have designated English their corporate language, whatever the languages of their home countries might be.

—adapted from Bergman and Renwick, *Introduction to Geography,* p. 263

1. static
   a. difficult
   b. unchanging
   c. unfit
   d. unlikely

2. diffusing
   a. spreading
   b. revealing
   c. being eliminated
   d. causing confusion

3. adherents
   a. opponents
   b. meanings
   c. supporters
   d. power

4. discourse
   a. communication
   b. problems
   c. currency exchange
   d. society

5. lingua franca
   a. international currency
   b. form of negotiation
   c. language held in common
      by many countries
   d. corporate policy

CONTEXT CLUES

CONTEXT CLUE	HOW TO FIND MEANING	EXAMPLE
Definition	1. Look for words that announce that meanings are to follow (*is, refers to, means*).	Broad, flat noodles that are served with sauce or butter are called **fettucine.**
	2. Look for parentheses, dashes, or commas that set apart synonyms or brief definitions.	Psychologists often wonder whether **stereotypes**—the assumptions we make about what people are like—might be self-fulfilling.
Example	Figure out what the examples have in common. (Peas and beans both are vegetables and both grow in pods.)	Most **condiments,** such as pepper, mustard, and cat-sup, are used to improve the flavor of foods.
Contrast	Look for a word or phrase that is the opposite in meaning of a word you don't know.	Before their classes in manners, the children were disorderly; after "graduation" they acted with much **decorum.**
Logic of the Passage	Use the rest of the sentence to help you. Pretend the word is a blank line and fill in the blank with a word that makes sense.	On hot, humid afternoons, I often feel **languid.**

2b   LEARNING PREFIXES, ROOTS, AND SUFFIXES

Suppose that you came across the following sentence in a human anatomy textbook:

> Trichromatic plates are used frequently in the text to illustrate the position of body organs.

If you did not know the meaning of *trichromatic,* how could you determine it? There are no clues in the sentence context. One solution is to look up the word in a dictionary. An easier and faster way is to break the word into parts and analyze the meaning of each part. Many words in the English language are made up of word parts called **prefixes, roots,** and **suffixes.** These word parts have specific meanings that, when added together, can help you determine the meaning of the word as a whole.

The word *trichromatic* can be divided into three parts: its prefix, root, and suffix.

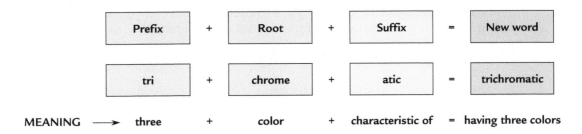

You can see from this analysis that *trichromatic* means "having three colors."

Here are two other examples of words that you can figure out by using prefixes, roots, and suffixes:

The parents thought the child was **unteachable.**

un- = not

teach = help someone learn

-able = able to do something

unteachable = not able to be taught

The student was a **nonconformist.**

non- = not

conform = go along with others

-ist = one who does something

nonconformist = someone who does not go along with others

The first step in using the prefix-root-suffix method is to become familiar with the most commonly used word parts. The prefixes and roots listed in Tables 2.1 and 2.2 (pages 23–25) will give you a good start in determining the meanings of thousands of words without looking them up in the dictionary. Before you begin to use word parts to figure out new words, there are a few things you need to know:

1. **In most cases, a word is built upon at least one root.**
2. **Words can have more than one prefix, root, or suffix.**
   a. Words can be made up of two or more roots (*geo/logy*).
   b. Some words have two prefixes (*in/sub/ordination*).
   c. Some words have two suffixes (*beauti/ful/ly*).
3. **Words do not always have a prefix and a suffix.**
   a. Some words have neither a prefix nor a suffix (*read*).
   b. Others have a suffix but no prefix (*read/ing*).
   c. Others have a prefix but no suffix (*pre/read*).
4. **The spelling of roots may change as they are combined with suffixes.** Some common variations are included in Table 2.2.
5. **Different prefixes, roots, or suffixes may have the same meaning.** For example, the prefixes *bi-*, *di*, and *duo-* all mean "two."
6. **Sometimes you may identify a group of letters as a prefix or root but find that it does not carry the meaning of that prefix or root.** For example, the letters *mis* in the word *missile* are part of the root and are not the prefix *mis-*, which means "wrong; bad."

Prefixes

Prefixes appear at the beginnings of many English words. They alter the meaning of the root to which they are connected. For example, if you add the prefix *re-* to the word *read*, the word *reread* is formed, meaning "to read again." If *pre-* is added to the word *reading*, the word *prereading* is formed, meaning "before reading." If the prefix *post-* is added, the word *postreading* is formed, meaning "after reading." Table 2.1 lists 62 common prefixes grouped according to meaning.

► NOW PRACTICE . . . USING PREFIXES 1

Read each of the following sentences. Use your knowledge of prefixes to fill in the blank and complete the word.

1. A person who speaks two languages is _____ lingual.

2. A letter or number written beneath a line of print is called a _____ script.

3. The new sweater had a snag, and I returned it to the store because it was _____ perfect.

4. The flood damage was permanent and _____ reversible.

5. I was not given the correct date and time; I was _____ informed.

6. People who speak several different languages are _____ lingual.

7. A musical _____ lude was played between the events in the ceremony.

8. I decided the magazine was uninteresting, so I _____ continued my subscription.

9. Merchandise that does not pass factory inspection is considered _____ standard and is sold at a discount.

10. The tuition refund policy approved this week will apply to last year's tuition as well; the policy will be _____ active to January 1 of last year.

TABLE 2.1 COMMON PREFIXES

PREFIX	MEANING	SAMPLE WORD
Prefixes referring to amount or number		
mono-/uni-	one	monocle/unicycle
bi-/di-/du-	two	bimonthly/divorce/duet
tri-	three	triangle
quad-	four	quadrant
quint-/pent-	five	quintet/pentagon
dec-/deci-	ten	decimal
centi-	hundred	centigrade
homo-	same	homogenized
mega-	large	megaphone
milli-	thousand	milligram
micro-	small	microscope
multi-/poly-	many	multipurpose/polygon
nano-	extremely small	nanoplankton
semi-	half	semicircle
equi	equal	equidistant
Prefixes meaning "not" (negative)		
a-	not	asymmetrical
anti-	against	antiwar
contra-/counter-	against, opposite	contradict
dis-	apart, away, not	disagree
in-/il-/ir-/im-	not	incorrect/illogical/irreversible/impossible
mal-	poorly, wrongly	malnourished

(continued on next page)

(continued from preceding page)

PREFIX	MEANING	SAMPLE WORD
Prefixes meaning "not" (negative)		
mis-	wrongly	misunderstand
non-	not	nonfiction
un-	not	unpopular
pseudo-	false	pseudoscientific
Prefixes giving direction, location, or placement		
ab-	away	absent
ad-	toward	adhesive
ante-/pre-	before	antecedent/premarital
circum-/peri-	around	circumference/perimeter
com-/col-/con-	with, together	compile/collide/convene
de-	away, from	depart
dia-	through	diameter
ex-/extra-	from, out of, former	ex-wife/extramarital
hyper-	over, excessive	hyperactive
hypo-	below, beneath	hypodermic
inter-	between	interpersonal
intro-/intra-/in-	within, into, in	introduction
post-	after	posttest
pre-	before	preview
re-	back, again	review
retro-	backward	retrospect
sub-	under, below	submarine
super-	above, extra	supercharge
tele-	far	telescope
trans-	cross, over	transcontinental

▶ NOW PRACTICE . . . USING PREFIXES 2

Read the following paragraph and choose the correct prefix from the box below to fill in the blank next to each boldfaced word part. One prefix will not be used.

multi	uni	pseudo
tri	bi	sub

    Neurons, or nerve cells, can be classified structurally according to the number of axons and dendrites that project from the cell body. (1) _____ **polar** neurons have a single projection from the cell body and are rare in humans. (2) _____ **polar** neurons have two projections, an axon and a dendrite, extending from the cell body. Other sensory neurons are (3) _____ **unipolar** neurons, a (4) _____ **class** of bipolar neurons. Although only one projection seems to extend from the cell body of this type of neuron, there are actually two projections that extend in opposite directions. (5) _____ **polar** neurons, the most common neurons, have multiple projections from the cell body; one projection is an axon, all the others are dendrites.

                —adapted from Germann and Stanfield, *Principles of Human Physiology*, p. 174

TABLE 2.2 COMMON ROOTS

COMMON ROOT	MEANING	SAMPLE WORD
anthropo	human being	anthropology
archaeo	ancient or past	archeology
aster/astro	star	astronaut
aud/audit	hear	audible
bene	good, well	benefit
bio	life	biology
cap	take, seize	captive
cardi	heart	cardiology
chron(o)	time	chronology
corp	body	corpse
cred	believe	incredible
dict/dic	tell, say	predict
duc/duct	lead	introduce
fact/fac	make, do	factory
geo	earth	geophysics
graph	write	telegraph
gyneco	woman	gynecology
log/logo/logy	study, thought	psychology
mit/miss	send	permit/dismiss
mort/mor	die, death	immortal
neuro	nerve	neurology
path	feeling	sympathy
phono	sound, voice	telephone
photo	light	photosensitive
port	carry	transport
pulmo	lungs	pulmonary
scop	seeing	microscope
scrib/script	write	inscription
sen/sent	feel	insensitive
spec/spic/spect	look, see	retrospect
tend/tent/tens	stretch or strain	tension
terr/terre	land, earth	territory
theo	god	theology
ven/vent	come	convention
vert/vers	turn	invert
vis/vid	see	invisible/video
voc	call	vocation

Roots

Roots carry the basic or core meaning of a word. Hundreds of root words are used to build words in the English language. Thirty-seven of the most common and most useful are listed in Table 2.2. Knowledge of the meanings of these roots will enable you to unlock the meanings of many words. For example, if you know that the root *dic/dict* means "tell or say," then you have a clue to the meanings of such words as *dictate* (to speak for someone to write down), *diction* (wording or manner of speaking), or *dictionary* (book that "tells" what words mean).

➤ NOW PRACTICE . . . USING ROOTS 1

Use the list of common roots in Table 2.2 to determine the meanings of the following words. Write a brief definition or synonym for each, checking a dictionary if necessary.

1. photocopy

   _____

2. visibility

   _____

3. credentials

   _____

4. speculate

   _____

5. terrain

   _____

6. audition

   _____

7. astrophysics

   _____

8. chronicle

   _____

9. autograph

   _____

➤ NOW PRACTICE . . . USING ROOTS 2

Read the following paragraph and choose the correct root from the box below to fill in the blank next to each boldfaced word part. One root will not be used.

graph	scope	mit
astro	photo	logy

You might think that the easiest way to discover extrasolar planets, or planets around other stars, would be simply to (1) _____ **graph** them through a powerful (2) **tele** _____.

Unfortunately, current observational (3) **techno** _____ cannot produce such images. The primary problem arises from the fact that any light that an orbiting planet might (4) **trans** _____ would be overwhelmed by light from the star it orbits. For example, a Sun-like star would be a *billion times* brighter than the reflected light from an Earth-like planet. Because even the best telescopes blur the light from stars at least a little, finding the small blip of planetary light amid the glare of scattered starlight would be very difficult. For now, (5) _____ **nomers** must rely on techniques that observe the star itself to find indirect evidence of planets.

—adapted from Bennett, Donahue, Schneider, and Voit,
The Cosmic Perspective, p. 218

Suffixes

Suffixes are word endings that often change the tense and/or part of speech of a word. For example, adding the suffix *-y* to the noun *cloud* forms the adjective *cloudy*. Accompanying the change in part of speech is a shift in meaning (*cloudy* means "resembling clouds; overcast with clouds; dimmed or dulled as if by clouds").

Often, several different words can be formed from a single root word by adding different suffixes.

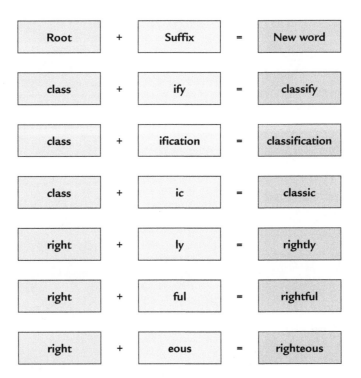

If you know the meaning of the root word and the ways in which different suffixes affect the meaning of the root word, you will be able to figure out a word's meaning when a suffix is added. A list of common suffixes and their meanings appears in Table 2.3.

You can expand your vocabulary by learning the variations in meaning that occur when suffixes are added to words you already know. When you find a word that you do not know, look for the root. Then, using the sentence the word is in, figure out what the word means with the suffix added. Occasionally you may find that the spelling of the root word has been changed. For instance, a final *e* may be dropped, a final consonant may be doubled, or a final *y* may be changed to *i*. Consider the possibility of such changes when trying to identify the root word.

TABLE 2.3 COMMON SUFFIXES

SUFFIX	SAMPLE WORD
Suffixes that refer to a state, condition, or quality	
-able	touchable
-ance	assistance
-ation	confrontation
-ence	reference
-ible	tangible
-ic	chronic
-ion	discussion
-ish	girlish
-ity	superiority
-ive	permissive
-less	hopeless
-ment	amazement
-ness	kindness
-ous	jealous
-ty	loyalty
-y	creamy
Suffixes that mean "one who"	
-an/-ian	Italian
-ant	participant
-ee	referee
-eer	engineer
-ent	resident
-er	teacher
-ist	activist
-or	advisor
Suffixes that mean "pertaining to or referring to"	
-ac	cardiac
-al	autumnal
-ary	secondary
-hood	brotherhood
-ship	friendship
-ward	homeward

Examples

The article was a **compilation** of facts.

> **root + suffix**

compil(e) + -ation = something that has been compiled, or put together into an orderly form

We were concerned with the **legality** of our decision to change addresses.

> **root + suffix**

legal + -ity = pertaining to legal matters

Our college is one of the most **prestigious** in the state.

> **root + suffix**

prestig(e) + -ous = having prestige or distinction

> ## NOW PRACTICE . . . USING SUFFIXES 1

For each of the words listed, add a suffix so that the new word will complete the sentence. Write the new word in the space provided. Check a dictionary if you are unsure of the spelling.

1. converse

   Our phone _____ lasted ten minutes.

2. assist

   The medical _____ labeled the patient's blood samples.

3. qualify

   The job applicant outlined his _____ to the interviewer.

4. intern

   The doctor completed her _____ at Memorial Medical Center.

5. eat

   We did not realize that the blossoms of the plant could be _____.

6. audio

   She spoke so softly that her voice was not _____.

7. season

   It is usually very dry in July, but this year it has rained constantly. The weather isn't very _____.

8. permit

   The professor granted her _____ to miss class.

9. instruct

   The lecture on Freud was very _____.

10. remember

    The wealthy businessman donated the building in _____ of his deceased father.

> **NOW PRACTICE . . . USING SUFFIXES 2**

Read the following paragraph. For each pair of words in parentheses, underline the word that correctly completes the sentence.

How do new species form? Most evolutionary (1) (biologists / biological) believe that the most common source of new species, especially among animals, has been geographic isolation. When an (2) (impassable / impassor) barrier physically separates different parts of a population, a new species may result. Such physical separation could occur if, for example, some members of a population of land-dwelling organisms drifted, swam, or flew to a remote (3) (oceany / oceanic) island. Populations of water-dwelling organisms might be split when (4) (geological / geologist) processes such as volcanism or continental drift create new land barriers that divide previously (5) (continuous / continuation) seas or lakes. You can probably imagine many other scenarios that could lead to the geographic subdivision of a population.

—adapted from Audesirk, Audesirk, and Byers, *Life on Earth*, p. 237

SUMMING IT UP

WORD PARTS

WORD PARTS	LOCATION	HOW TO USE THEM
Prefixes	Beginnings of words	Notice how the prefix changes the meaning of the root or base word. (How does meaning change when *un-* is added to the word *reliable?*)
Roots	Beginning or middle of words	Use roots to figure out the basic meaning of the word.
Suffixes	Endings of words	Notice how the suffix changes the meaning of the root or base word. (How does meaning change when *-ship* is added to the word *friend?*)

3 Thesis, Main Ideas, Supporting Details, and Transitions

Most articles, essays, and textbook chapters contain numerous ideas. Some are more important than others. As you read, your job is to sort out the important ideas from those that are less important. For exams your instructors expect that you have discovered and learned what is important in assigned chapters. In class, your instructors expect you to be able to discuss the important ideas from an assignment. In this section, you will learn to identify the thesis of a reading assignment and to distinguish main ideas and supporting details. You will also learn about transitions that writers use to link ideas together.

3a IDENTIFYING THE THESIS

The **thesis** is what the entire reading selection is about. Think of it as the one most important idea that the entire article or assignment is written to explain. In articles and essays the thesis is quite specific and is often stated in one sentence, usually near the beginning of the article. In textbook chapters the thesis of the entire chapter is much more general. Individual sections of the chapter may have more specific theses. A psychology textbook chapter on stress, for example, may have as its thesis that stress can negatively affect us, but there are ways to control it. A section within the chapter may discuss the thesis that there are five main sources of stress. A magazine article on stress in the workplace, because it is much shorter, would have an even more specific thesis. It might, for instance, express the thesis that building strong relationships with coworkers can help to alleviate stress.

Now reread the article from *Wiretap* magazine on the topic of snitching that appears on p. 8. Do not continue with this section until you have read it.

The thesis of this reading is that the trend toward stopping snitching is dangerous and unhealthy. The remainder of the article presents evidence that supports this thesis.

> ## NOW PRACTICE . . . IDENTIFYING THESIS STATEMENTS

Underline the thesis statement in each group of sentences.

1. a. Monotheism is a belief in one supreme being.

   b. Polytheism is a belief in more than one supreme being.

   c. Theism is a belief in the existence of a god or gods.

   d. Monotheistic religions include Christianity, Judaism, and Islam.

2. a. Vincent Van Gogh is an internationally known and respected artist.

   b. Van Gogh's art displays an approach to color that was revolutionary.

   c. Van Gogh created seventy paintings in the last two months of his life.

   d. Van Gogh's art is respected for its attention to detail.

3. a. The Individuals with Disability Education Act offers guidelines for inclusive education.

   b. The inclusive theory of education says that children with special needs should be placed in regular classrooms and have services brought to them.

   c. The first movement toward inclusion was mainstreaming—a plan in which children with special needs were placed in regular classrooms for a portion of the day and sent to other classrooms for special services.

   d. Families play an important role in making inclusive education policies work.

4. a. Stress can have a negative effect on friendships and marital relationships.

   b. Stress can affect job performance.

   c. Stress is a pervasive problem in our culture.

   d. Some health problems appear to be stress related.

3b   FINDING MAIN IDEAS

MyReadingLab

To practice your
skills on main ideas
go to

➤ Study Plan
➤ Reading Skills
➤ Main Idea

A paragraph is a group of related sentences that express a single idea about a single topic. This idea is called the **main idea.** All the other sentences in the paragraph support this main idea. These sentences are called **supporting details.** Not all details in a paragraph are equally important.

In most paragraphs the main idea is expressed in a single sentence called the **topic sentence.** Occasionally, you will find a paragraph in which the main idea is not expressed in any single sentence. The main idea is **implied;** that is, it is suggested but not directly stated in the paragraph.

You can visualize a paragraph as shown in the accompanying diagram.

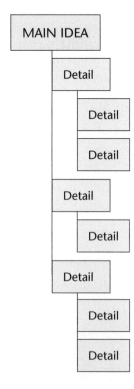

How to Find the Main Idea

We have defined a paragraph as a group of related ideas. The sentences are related to one another, and all are about the same person, place, thing, or idea. The common subject or idea is called the **topic**—what the entire paragraph is about. As you read the following paragraph, you will see that its topic is elections.

> Americans elect more people to office than almost any other society. Each even year, when most elections occur, more than 500,000 public officials are elected to school boards, city councils, county offices, state legislatures, state executive positions, the House of Representatives and the Senate, and of course, every fourth year, the presidency. By contrast with other countries, our elections are drawn-out affairs. Campaigns for even the most local office can be protracted over two or three months and cost a considerable amount of money. Presidential campaigns, including the primary season, last for at least ten months, with some candidates beginning to seek support many months and, as noted earlier, even years before the election.
>
> —Baradat, *Understanding American Democracy,* p. 163

Each sentence of this paragraph discusses or describes elections. To identify the topic of a paragraph, then, ask yourself: *"What or who is the paragraph about?"*

The **main idea** of a paragraph is what the author wants you to know about the topic. It is the broadest, most important idea that the writer develops throughout the paragraph. The entire paragraph explains, develops, and supports this main idea. A question that will guide you in finding the main idea is *"What key point is the author making about the topic?"* In the paragraph above, the writer's main idea is that elections in the United States are more numerous and more drawn out than in other countries.

The Topic Sentence

Often, but not always, one sentence expresses the main idea. This sentence is called the **topic sentence**.

To find the topic sentence, search for the one general sentence that explains what the writer wants you to know about the topic. A topic sentence is a broad, general statement; the remaining sentences of the paragraph provide details about or explain the topic sentence.

In the following paragraph, the topic is the effects of high temperatures. Read the paragraph to find out what the writer wants you to know about this topic. Look for one sentence that states this.

> Environmental psychologists have also been concerned with the effects that extremely high temperatures have on social interactions, particularly on aggression. There is a common perception that riots and other more common displays of violent behaviors are more frequent during the long, hot days of summer. This observation is largely supported by research evidence (Anderson, 1989; Anderson & Anderson, 1984; Rotton & Frey, 1985). C. A. Anderson (1987, 1989) reported on a series of studies showing that violent crimes are more prevalent in hotter quarters of the year and in hotter years, although nonviolent crimes were less affected. Anderson also concluded that differences in crime rates between cities are better predicted by temperature than by social, demographic (age, race, education), and economic variables. Baron and Ransberger (1978) point out that riots are most likely to occur when the outside temperature is only moderately high, between about 75° and 90°F. But when temperatures get much above 90°F, energy (even for aggression) becomes rapidly depleted, and rioting is less likely to occur.
>
> —Gerow, *Psychology: An Introduction,* p. 553

The paragraph opens with a statement and then proceeds to explain it by citing research evidence. The first sentence of the paragraph functions as a topic sentence, stating the paragraph's main point: High temperatures are associated with aggressive behavior. Here are some tips that will help you find the main idea.

1. **Identify the topic.** As you did earlier, figure out the general subject of the entire paragraph. In the preceding sample paragraph, "high temperatures and aggressive behavior" is the topic.

2. **Locate the most general sentence (the topic sentence).** This sentence must be broad enough to include all of the other ideas in the paragraph. The topic sentence in the sample paragraph ("Environmental psychologists have also been concerned with the effects that extremely high temperatures have on social interactions, particularly aggression.") covers all of the other details in the paragraph.

3. **Study the rest of the paragraph.** The main idea must make the rest of the paragraph meaningful. It is the one idea that ties all of the other details together. In the sample paragraph, sentence 2 explains and elaborates upon the topic sentence. Sentences 3, 4, 5, and 6 report results of research that suggest high temperature and aggressive behavior are related.

The topic sentence can be located anywhere in the paragraph. However, there are several positions where it is most likely to be found.

Locating the Topic Sentence

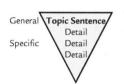

Topic Sentence First.   Most often the topic sentence is placed first in the paragraph. In this type of paragraph, the author first states his or her main point and then explains it.

> There is some evidence that colors affect you physiologically. For example, when subjects are exposed to red light respiratory movements increase; exposure to blue decreases respiratory movements. Similarly, eye blinks increase in frequency when eyes are exposed to red light and decrease when exposed to blue. This seems consistent with intuitive feelings about blue being more soothing and red being more arousing. After changing a school's walls from orange and white to blue, the blood pressure of the students decreased while their academic performance improved.
>
> —DeVito, *Interpersonal Communication*, p. 182

Here the writer first states that there is evidence of the physiological effects of color. The rest of the paragraph presents that evidence.

Topic Sentence Last.   The second most likely place for a topic sentence to appear is last in the paragraph. When using this arrangement, a writer leads up to the main point and then directly states it at the end.

> Is there a relationship between aspects of one's personality and one's state of physical health? Can psychological evaluations of an individual be used to predict physical as well as psychological disorders? Is there such a thing as a disease-prone personality? Our response is very tentative, and the data are not all supportive, but for the moment we can say yes, there does seem to be a positive correlation between some personality variables and physical health.
>
> —Gerow, *Psychology: An Introduction*, p. 700

In this paragraph, the author ponders the relationship between personality and health and concludes with the paragraph's main point: that they are related.

Topic Sentence in the Middle.   If it is placed neither first nor last, then the topic sentence appears somewhere in the middle of the paragraph. In this arrangement, the sentences before the topic sentence lead up to or introduce the main idea. Those that follow the main idea explain or describe it.

> There are 1,500 species of bacteria and approximately 8,500 species of birds. The carrot family alone has about 3,500 species, and there are 15,000 known species of wild orchids. Clearly, the task of separating various living things into their proper groups is not an easy task. Within the insect family, the problem becomes even more complex. For example, there are about 300,000 species of beetles. In fact, certain species are disappearing from the earth before we can even identify and classify them.
>
> —Wallace, *Biology: The World of Life*, p. 283

In this paragraph, the author first gives several examples of living things for which there are numerous species. Then he states his main point: Separating living things into species is not an easy task. The remainder of the paragraph offers an additional example and provides further information.

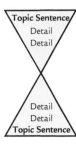

Topic Sentence First and Last. Occasionally the main idea is stated at the beginning of a paragraph and again at the end, or elsewhere in the paragraph. Writers may use this organization to emphasize an important idea or to explain an idea that needs clarification. At other times, the first and last sentences together express the paragraph's main idea.

> Many elderly people have trouble getting the care and treatment they need for ailments. Most hospitals, designed to handle injuries and acute illness that are common to the young, do not have the facilities or personnel to treat the chronic degenerative diseases of the elderly. Many doctors are also ill-prepared to deal with such problems. As Fred Cottrell points out, "There is a widespread feeling among the aged that most doctors are not interested in them and are reluctant to treat people who are as little likely to contribute to the future as the aged are reputed to do." Even with the help of Medicare, the elderly in the United States often have a difficult time getting the health care that they need.
>
> —Coleman and Cressey, *Social Problems,* p. 277

The first and last sentences together explain that many elderly people in the United States have difficulty obtaining needed health care.

> NOW PRACTICE . . . FINDING MAIN IDEAS 1

Underline the topic sentence(s) of each of the following paragraphs.

Paragraph 1

Evidence suggests that groups given the right to vote do not immediately exercise that right. In recent elections, young people have not voted at a high rate—always well below 50 percent. Since the passage of the Twenty-sixth Amendment in 1971, the addition of 18- to 20-year-olds to the electorate has contributed to a lower turnout. After the passage of the Nineteenth Amendment in 1920, many women were slow to use their new right. The difference in turnout between men and women has not been significant in recent decades, though. By the 1988 presidential election, it was fairly easy for most Americans to register and vote; yet only about 50 percent turned out to vote. What causes low turnout? How serious is it?

—Keefe et al., *American Democracy,* p. 178

Paragraph 2

The symbols that constitute language are commonly referred to as words—labels that we have assigned to concepts, or our mental representations. When we use the word *chair* as a symbol, we don't use it to label just one specific instance of a chair. We use the word as a symbol to represent our concept of chairs. As symbols, words need not stand for real things in the real world. We have words to describe objects or events that cannot be perceived, such as *ghost* or, for that matter, *mind*. With language we can communicate about owls and pussycats in teacups and a four-dimensional, time-warped hyperspace. Words stand for cognitions, or concepts, and we have a great number of them.

—Gerow, *Psychology: An Introduction,* p. 250

Paragraph 3

Body mass is made up of protoplasm, extracellular fluid, bone, and adipose tissue (body fat). One way to determine the amount of adipose tissue is to measure the whole-body density. After the on-land mass of the body is determined, the underwater body mass is obtained by submerging the person in water. Since water helps support the body by giving it buoyancy, the apparent body mass is less in water. A higher percentage of body fat will make a person more buoyant, causing the underwater mass to be even lower. This occurs because fat has a lower density than the rest of the body.

—Timberlake, *Chemistry,* p. 30

Paragraph 4

Early biologists who studied reflexes, kineses, taxes, and fixed action patterns assumed that these responses are inherited, unlearned, and common to all members of a species. They clearly depend on internal and external factors, but until recently, instinct and learning were considered distinct aspects of behavior. However, in some very clever experiments, Jack Hailman of the University of Wisconsin showed that certain stereotyped behavior patterns require subtle forms of experience for their development. In other words, at least some of the behavior normally called instinct is partly learned.

—Mix, *Biology, The Network of Life,* p. 532

Paragraph 5

On election day in 1972, at 5:30 p.m. Pacific Standard Time, NBC television news declared that Richard Nixon had been reelected president. This announcement came several hours before the polls were closed in the western part of the United States. In 1988, polls in a dozen western states were still open when CBS and ABC announced that George Bush had been elected president. These developments point to the continuing controversy over the impact of election night coverage on voter turnout.

—Keefe et al., *American Democracy,* p. 186

Paragraph 6

According to economic data, a tiny segment of the American population owns most of the nation's wealth. The wealthiest 1 percent (900,000 households with about $6 trillion net worth) own more than the least affluent 99 percent of Americans (84 million households with about $5 trillion net worth). Or, from another angle, the top 1 percent of the population owns about 38 percent of all wealth in the United States while the bottom 80 percent of the population accounts for about 17 percent of the national wealth (Mishel et al., 2001). To give you a more personalized view of the gap between rich and poor consider this: Bill Gates owns "more wealth than America's 100 million poorest people" (Greider et al., 1998:39).

—Thompson and Hickey, *Society in Focus,* p. 198

Paragraph 7

A gunnysack is a large bag, usually made of burlap. As a conflict strategy, gunnysacking refers to the practice of storing up grievances so we may unload them at another time. The immediate occasion for unloading may be relatively simple (or so it might seem at first), such as someone's coming home late without calling. Instead of arguing about this, the gunnysacker unloads all past grievances. As you probably know from experience, gunnysacking begets gunnysacking. When one person gunnysacks, the other person often reciprocates. Frequently the original problem never gets addressed. Instead, resentment and hostility escalate.

—DeVito, *Human Communication,* 9th edition, p. 217

Paragraph 8

As just about everyone today knows, e-mail has virtually become the standard method of communication in the business world. Most people enjoy its speed, ease and casual nature. But e-mail also has its share of problems and pitfalls, including privacy. Many people assume the contents of their e-mail are private, but there may in fact be any number of people authorized to see it. Some experts have even likened e-mail to postcards sent through U.S. mail: They pass through a lot of hands and before a lot of eyes, and, theoretically, many different people can read them.

—adapted from Ebert and Griffin, *Business Essentials,* p. 64

Paragraph 9

Patrescence, or becoming a father, usually is less socially noted than matrescence. The practice of **couvade** is an interesting exception to this generalization. Couvade refers to "a variety of customs applying to the behavior of fathers during the pregnancies of their wives and during and shortly after the births of their children" (Broude 1988:902). The father may take to his bed before, during, or after the delivery. He may also experience pain and exhaustion during and after the delivery. More common is a pattern of couvade that involves a set of prohibitions and prescriptions for male behavior. Couvade occurs in societies where paternal roles in child care are prominent. One interpretation views couvade as one phase of men's participation in parenting: Their good behavior as expectant fathers helps ensure a good delivery for the baby. Another interpretation of couvade is that it offers support for the mother. In Estonia, a folk belief is that a woman's birth pains will be less if her husband helps by taking some of them on himself.

—adapted from Miller, *Cultural Anthropology,* pp. 144–145

Paragraph 10

Everything moves. Even things that appear at rest move. They move relative to the sun and stars. As you're reading this you're moving at about 107,000 kilometers per hour relative to the sun. And you're moving even faster relative to the center of our galaxy. When we discuss the motion of something, we describe motion relative to something else. If you walk down the aisle of a moving bus, your speed relative to the floor of the bus is likely quite different from your speed relative to the road. When we say a racing car reaches a speed of 300 kilometers per hour, we mean relative to the track. Unless stated otherwise, when we discuss the speeds of things in our environment we mean relative to the surface of the earth; motion is relative.

—adapted from Hewitt, *Conceptual Physics,* p. 39

➤ NOW PRACTICE . . . FINDING MAIN IDEAS 2

Underline the topic sentence of each of the following paragraphs.

Symbols and Superstitions On the surface, many marketing images have virtually no literal connection to actual products. What does a cowboy have to do with a bit of tobacco rolled into a paper tube? How can a celebrity such as basketball star Michael Jordan enhance the image of a cologne? The meanings we impart to these symbols are largely influenced by our culture, so marketers need to take special care that the symbol they use in a foreign market has the meaning they intended. Even the same product may be used quite differently and take on a different meaning to people. In parts of rural India, for example, the refrigerator is a status symbol, so people want a snazzy-looking one that they can keep in the living room to show off to visitors.

For assistance in understanding how consumers interpret the meanings of symbols, some marketers are turning to a field of study known as **semiotics**, which examines how people assign meanings to symbols. For example, although the American cowboy on packs of Marlboro cigarettes is a well-known symbol of the frontier spirit in many countries, people in Hong Kong see him as a low-status laborer. Philip Morris has to make sure he's always pictured riding a white horse, which is a more positive symbol in that country. Even something as simple as a color takes on very different meanings around the globe. Pepsodent toothpaste found this out when it promised white teeth to people in Southeast Asia, where black or yellow teeth are status symbols.

Marketers also need to be concerned about taboos and superstitions. For example, the Japanese are superstitious about the number four. *Shi,* the word for "four," is also the word for "death," so Tiffany sells glassware and china in sets of five in Japan. In some Arab countries, alcohol and pork are forbidden to Islamic consumers (even stuffed pig toys are taboo), and advertisers may refrain from showing nudity or even the faces of women in photos, which some governments prohibit.

—Solomon and Stuart, *Marketing: Real People, Real Choices,* p. 108

➤ NOW PRACTICE . . . FINDING MAIN IDEAS 3

After reading the following passage, in the space provided write the letter of the choice that best completes each of the statements below.

Picking Partners

Just as males and females may find different ways to express emotions themselves, the process of partner selection also shows distinctly different patterns. For both males and females, more than just chemical and psychological processes influence the choice of partners. One of these factors is *proximity,* or being in the same place at the same time. The more you see a person in your hometown, at social gatherings, or at work, the more likely that an interaction will occur. Thus, if you live in New York, you'll probably end up with another New Yorker. If you live in northern Wisconsin, you'll probably end up with another Wisconsinite.

The old adage that "opposites attract" usually isn't true. You also pick a partner based on *similarities* (attitudes, values, intellect, interests). If your potential partner expresses interest or liking, you may react with mutual regard known as *reciprocity*. The more you express interest, the safer it is for someone else to return the regard, and the cycle spirals onward.

Another factor that apparently plays a significant role in selecting a partner is *physical attraction*. Whether such attraction is caused by a chemical reaction or a socially learned behavior, males and females appear to have different attraction criteria. Men tend to select their mates primarily on the basis of youth and physical attractiveness. Although physical attractiveness is an important criterion for women in mate selection, they tend to place higher emphasis on partners who are somewhat older, have good financial prospects, and are dependable and industrious.

—Donatelle, *Health: The Basics*, 5th ed., p. 105

_____ 1. The thesis of the entire selection is
    a. several factors influence choice of partners.
    b. physical attraction is more important to men than for women.
    c. proximity is the key to mate selection.
    d. opposites attract.

_____ 2. The topic sentence of the first paragraph begins with the words
    a. "For both."
    b. "One of these."
    c. "The more."
    d. "Just as."

_____ 3. The topic of the second paragraph is
    a. physical attraction.
    b. interaction.
    c. the old adage.
    d. similarities.

_____ 4. In the second paragraph, the topic sentence begins with the words
    a. "You also pick."
    b. "The more you express."
    c. "If your potential."
    d. "The old adage."

_____ 5. The topic sentence of the third paragraph is the
    a. first sentence.
    b. second sentence.
    c. third sentence.
    d. fourth sentence.

3c   FINDING THE IMPLIED MAIN IDEA

Although most paragraphs do have a topic sentence, some do not. This type of paragraph contains only details or specifics that, taken together, point to the main idea. The main idea, then, is implied but not directly stated. In such paragraphs you must infer, or reason out, the main idea. This is a process of adding up the details and deciding what they mean together or what main idea they all support or explain. Use the following steps to grasp implied main ideas.

- Identify the topic by asking yourself, "What is the one thing the author is discussing throughout the paragraph?"
- Decide what the writer wants you to know about the topic. Look at each detail and decide what larger idea each explains.
- Express this idea in your own words.

Here is a sample paragraph; use the above questions to identify the main idea.

> Severe punishment may generate such anxiety in children that they do not learn the lesson the punishment was designed to teach. Moreover, as a reaction to punishment that they regard as unfair, children may avoid punitive parents, who therefore will have fewer opportunities to teach and guide the child. In addition, parents who use physical punishment provide aggressive models. A child who is regularly slapped, spanked, shaken, or shouted at may learn to use these forms of aggression in interactions with peers.
>
> —Newcombe, *Child Development,* p. 354

The topic of this paragraph is punishment. The author's main point is that punishment has negative effects. You can figure out this writer's main idea even though no single sentence states this directly. You can visualize this paragraph as follows:

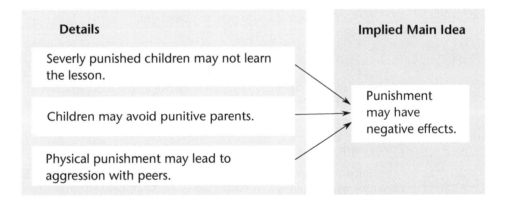

Details	Implied Main Idea
Severly punished children may not learn the lesson.	Punishment may have negative effects.
Children may avoid punitive parents.	
Physical punishment may lead to aggression with peers.	

NOW PRACTICE . . . FINDING IMPLIED MAIN IDEAS 1

After reading each of the paragraphs, complete the diagram that follows by filling in the missing information.

Paragraph A

The average American consumer eats 21 pounds of snack foods in a year, but people in the West Central part of the country consume the most (24 pounds per person) whereas those in the Pacific and Southeast regions eat "only" 19 pounds per person. Pretzels are the most popular snack in the mid-Atlantic area, pork rinds are most likely to be eaten in the South, and multigrain chips turn up as a favorite in the West. Not surprisingly, the Hispanic influence in the Southwest has influenced snacking preferences—consumers in that part of the United States eat about 50 percent more tortilla chips than do people elsewhere.

—adapted from Solomon, *Consumer Behavior,* p. 184

Paragraph B

The constellation [group of stars] that the Greeks named Orion, the hunter, was seen by the ancient Chinese as a supreme warrior called *Shen.* Hindus in ancient India also saw a warrior, called *Skanda,* who rode a peacock. The three stars of Orion's belt were seen as three fishermen in a

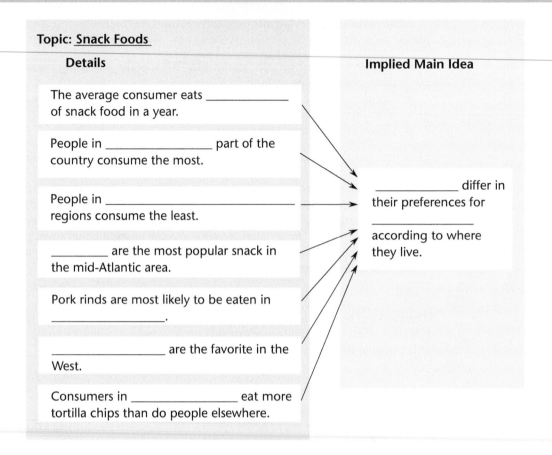

Topic: Snack Foods

Details

The average consumer eats _____ of snack food in a year.

People in _____ part of the country consume the most.

People in _____ regions consume the least.

_____ are the most popular snack in the mid-Atlantic area.

Pork rinds are most likely to be eaten in _____.

_____ are the favorite in the West.

Consumers in _____ eat more tortilla chips than do people elsewhere.

Implied Main Idea

_____ differ in their preferences for _____ according to where they live.

canoe by Aborigines of northern Australia. As seen from southern California, these three stars climb almost straight up into the sky as they rise in the east, which may explain why the Chemehuevi Indians of the California desert saw them as a line of three sure-footed mountain sheep.

—adapted from Bennett et al., *The Cosmic Perspective*, p. 28

Paragraph C

Initially, many computers entered homes as children's games. But the trend spread fast, from simple games to more sophisticated ones. Soon they became a favorite pastime both for children

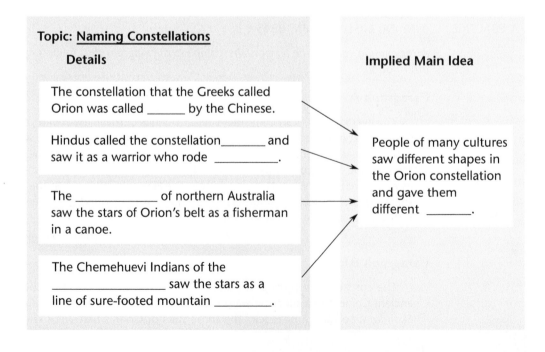

Topic: Naming Constellations

Details

The constellation that the Greeks called Orion was called _____ by the Chinese.

Hindus called the constellation_____ and saw it as a warrior who rode _____.

The _____ of northern Australia saw the stars of Orion's belt as a fisherman in a canoe.

The Chemehuevi Indians of the _____ saw the stars as a line of sure-footed mountain _____.

Implied Main Idea

People of many cultures saw different shapes in the Orion constellation and gave them different _____.

and young adults. This group of people showed an almost natural ability to adapt to computers; software developers saw the opportunity for the market and developed increasingly challenging games as well as educational programs. Many parents were then tempted to buy computers for home use and this, in turn, led to a situation where people of all ages and backgrounds saw the benefit of computers not only for young people but also for adults who used them for personal and business purposes.

—Bandyo-padhyay, *Computing for Non-specialists*, p. 4

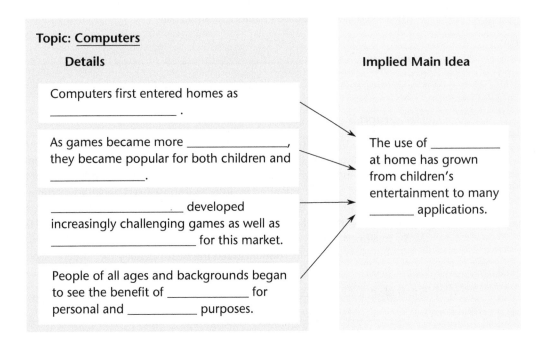

NOW PRACTICE . . . FINDING IMPLIED MAIN IDEAS 2

Write a sentence that states the main idea for each of the following paragraphs.

Paragraph 1

During the 1960s, police went from walking "beats" [regular routes] to riding in squad cars. While squad cars provided a faster response to emergency calls, they also changed the nature of social interaction between police officers and the public. Much police work had been highly personal, as officers strolled the sidewalks talking to storekeepers and homeowners, but it became much more impersonal, with less contact between officers and citizens. Since the 1960s, techno-logical advances have provided more elaborate means of communication and surveillance, better-equipped squad cars, and more sophisticated weaponry. Unfortunately criminals have benefited from increased technology as well. This increased technology and other developments have led many city leaders to question contemporary policing practices and some to accentuate the need to reemphasize police–community relations.

—Thompson and Hickey, *Society in Focus*, p. 162

Main idea: _____

_____

Paragraph 2

When a homemaker is killed in an auto accident, that person's family can often sue for the value of the services that were lost. Attorneys (who rely on economists) are often asked to make an attempt to estimate this value to present to the court. They add up the cost of purchasing babysitting, cooking, housecleaning, and tutoring services. The number turns out to be quite large, often in excess of $30,000 a year. Of course one of the problems in measuring the value of unremunerated housework in such a way is that we could often purchase the services of a full-time live-in housekeeper for less money than if we paid for the services of the various components of housekeeping. And what about quality? Some homemakers serve fabulous gourmet meals; others simply warm up canned and frozen foods. Should they be valued equally? Another problem lies in knowing when to stop counting. A person can hire a valet to help him or her get dressed in the morning. Should we therefore count the time spent in getting dressed as part of unpaid work? Both men and women perform services around the house virtually every day of the year. Should all of those unremunerated services be included in a "new" measure of GDP [Gross Domestic Product]? If they were, measured GDP would be increased dramatically.

—Miller, *Economics Today,* p. 185

Main idea: _____

_____

Paragraph 3

In 1970 the federal government passed the Comprehensive Drug Abuse, Prevention and Control Act (also known as the Controlled Substance Act). That act did not contain a rigid penalty system but rather established only upper bounds for the fines and prison terms to be imposed for offenses. In 1984 the act was amended in order to impose fixed penalties, particularly for dealers. For anyone caught with more than 1 kilogram of heroin, 50 grams of cocaine base, or 1,000 kilograms of marijuana, the applicable penalty was raised to imprisonment from 10 years to life plus a fine of $4 million. A variety of other prison penalties and fines were outlined in that amendment. Another amendment passed in 1988 included the death penalty for "drug kingpins."

—Miller, *Economics Today,* p. 513

Main idea: _____

_____

Paragraph 4

As recently as 20 years ago, textbooks on child psychology seldom devoted more than a few paragraphs to the behaviors of the neonate—the newborn through the first 2 weeks of life. It seemed as if the neonate did not do much worth writing about. Today, most child psychology texts devote substantially more space to discussing the abilities of newborns. It is unlikely that over the past 20 years neonates have gotten smarter or more able. Rather, psychologists have. They have devised new and clever ways of measuring the abilities and capacities of neonates.

—Gerow, *Psychology: An Introduction,* p. 319

Main idea: _____

_____

▶ NOW PRACTICE . . . FINDING IMPLIED MAIN IDEAS 3

After reading each of the following paragraphs, select the letter of the choice that best answers the questions that follow.

Paragraph A

John Kennedy, the first "television president," held considerably more public appearances than did his predecessors. Kennedy's successors, with the notable exception of Richard Nixon, have been even more active in making public appearances. Indeed, they have averaged more than one appearance every weekday of the year. Bill Clinton invested enormous time and energy in attempting to sell his programs to the public. George W. Bush has followed the same pattern.

—Edwards et al., *Government in America,* p. 422

_____ 1. What is the topic?

    a. the presidency

    b. the effects of television

    c. President Kennedy

    d. public appearances of the president

_____ 2. What main idea is the writer implying?

    a. U.S. presidents all enjoy being in the public eye.

    b. The successors of President Kennedy have tried to imitate him.

    c. Presidents have placed increasing importance on making public appearances.

    d. Presidents spend too much time making public appearances.

Paragraph B

When speaking on the telephone be sure to speak clearly, enunciating carefully. It is also a good practice to speak just a bit slower than if you were talking with someone face-to-face. When responding to an answering machine or voice mail, be brief but to the point. Give your name, telephone number, and a brief explanation of why you called. State what time would be best to return your call. It is also helpful to give your phone number a second time as a conclusion to your message.

—adapted from Cook, Yale, and Marqua, *Tourism: The Business of Travel,* p. 370

_____ 3. What is the topic?

    a. telephone manners

    b. public speaking

    c. telemarketing

    d. customer service

_____ 4. What is the writer saying about the topic?

    a. People today have terrible phone manners.

    b. Telephone manners are not as important as those used in face-to-face conversations.

    c. Speaking on the telephone requires clarity, brevity, and conciseness.

    d. Telephone messages should be kept to a minimum.

Paragraph C

All the nutrients in the world are useless to humans unless oxygen is also available. Because the chemical reactions that release energy from foods require oxygen, human cells can survive for only a few minutes without oxygen. Approximately 20% of the air we breathe is oxygen. It is made available to the blood and body cells by the cooperative efforts of the respiratory and cardiovascular systems.

—adapted from Marieb, *Anatomy and Physiology,* p. 9

_____ 5. What is the topic?

    a. humans

    b. nutrients

    c. oxygen

    d. the respiratory system

_____ 6. What main idea is the writer implying?

    a. All chemical reactions require oxygen.

    b. Oxygen is vital to human life.

    c. Less than a fourth of the air we breathe is oxygen.

    d. The respiratory system and the cardiovascular system work together.

_____ 7. Which one of the following details does *not* support the paragraph's implied main idea?

    a. All the nutrients in the world are useless to humans.

    b. The chemical reactions that release energy from foods use oxygen.

    c. Plants release oxygen into the air through the process of photosynthesis.

    d. The respiratory and cardiovascular systems supply oxygen to the blood and body cells.

Paragraph D

People's acceptance of a product may be largely determined by its packaging. In one study the very same coffee taken from a yellow can was described as weak, from a dark brown can as too strong, from a red can as rich, and from a blue can as mild. Even your acceptance of a person may depend on the colors worn. Consider, for example, the comments of one color expert: "If you have to pick the wardrobe for your defense lawyer heading into court and choose anything but blue, you deserve to lose the case. . . ." Black is so powerful it could work against the lawyer with the jury. Brown lacks sufficient authority. Green would probably elicit a negative response.

—adapted from DeVito, *Messages: Building Interpersonal Communication Skills*, p. 161

_____ 8. What is the topic?

    a. packaging

    b. marketing

    c. colors

    d. dressing for success

_____ 9. What is the writer saying about the topic?

    a. Colors influence how we think and act.

    b. A product's packaging determines whether or not we accept it.

    c. A lawyer's success depends on the color of his or her wardrobe.

    d. Color experts consider blue to be the most influential color.

_____ 10. Which one of the following details does *not* support the paragraph's implied main idea?

    a. The same coffee is judged differently depending on the color of the coffee can.

    b. The colors a person is wearing may influence your opinion of that person.

    c. Lawyers who wear blue in court deserve to be defeated.

    d. Green is not considered a good color to wear in the courtroom.

➤ NOW PRACTICE . . . FINDING STATED AND IMPLIED MAIN IDEAS

Turn to the article titled "Deadly Silence: Stop Snitching's Fatal Legacy" on p. 8. Using your own paper, number the lines from 1 to 15, to correspond to the 15 paragraphs in the article. For each paragraph number, if the main idea is stated, record the sentence number in which it appears (first, second, etc.). If the main idea is unstated and implied, write a sentence that expresses the main idea.

3d   RECOGNIZING SUPPORTING DETAILS

MyReadingLab

To practice your
skills on details,
go to

➤ Study Plan
➤ Reading Skills
➤ Supporting
   Details

Supporting details are those facts and ideas that prove or explain the main idea of a paragraph. While all the details in a paragraph do support the main idea, not all details are equally important. As you read, try to identify and pay attention to the most important details. Pay less attention to details of lesser importance. The key details directly explain the main idea. Other details may provide additional information, offer an example, or further explain one of the key details.

Figure A shows how details relate to the main idea and how details range in degree of importance. In the diagram, more important details are placed toward the left; less important details are closer to the right.

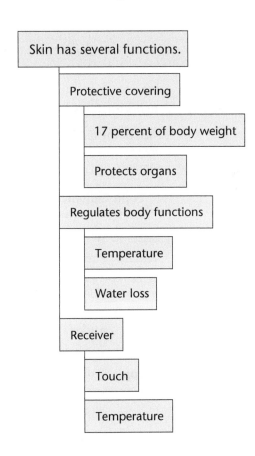

Figure A   **Figure B**

Read the following paragraph and study Figure B.

> The skin of the human body has several functions. First, it serves as a protective covering. In doing so, it accounts for 17 percent of the body weight. Skin also protects the organs within the body from damage or harm. The skin serves as a regulator of body functions. It controls body temperature and water loss. Finally, the skin serves as a receiver. It is sensitive to touch and temperature.

From this diagram you can see that the details that state the three functions of skin are the key details. Other details, such as "protects the organs," provide further information and are at a lower level of importance.

Read the following paragraph and try to pick out the more important details.

> Many cultures have different rules for men and women engaging in conflict. Asian cultures are more strongly prohibitive of women's conflict strategies. Asian women are expected to be exceptionally polite; this is even more important when women are in conflict with men and when the

conflict is public. In the United States, there is a verbalized equality; men and women have equal rights when it comes to permissible conflict strategies. In reality, there are many who expect women to be more polite, to pursue conflict in a nonargumentative way, while men are expected to argue forcefully and logically.

This paragraph could be diagrammed as follows (key details only):

Many cultures have different rules for men and women engaging in conflict.

Rules in Asian cultures

Rules in the United States

> NOW PRACTICE . . . RECOGNIZING SUPPORTING DETAILS 1

Each of the following topic sentences states the main idea of a paragraph. After each topic sentence are sentences containing details that may or may not support the topic sentence. Read each sentence and put an "S" beside those that contain details that support the topic sentence.

1. **Topic Sentence:** It is expected that most U.S. cities will continue to see population declines in the next ten or twenty years.

   _____ a. White, middle class people will continue to leave inner cities.

   _____ b. Population will continue to shift to suburbs and rural areas.

   _____ c. Those left behind in cities will be primarily African American, poor, and elderly.

   _____ d. Businesses will continue to move to the suburbs where most service and management workers live.

   _____ e. The federal government will continue to cut funding for cities.

2. **Topic Sentence:** *Mens rea,* a term that refers to a person's criminal intent when committing a crime, or his or her state of mind, can be evaluated in several ways.

   _____ a. Confessions by criminals are direct evidence of their criminal intent.

   _____ b. Circumstantial evidence can be used to suggest mental intent.

   _____ c. *Actus rea* is a person's actions that make up a crime.

   _____ d. A person may unknowingly commit a crime.

   _____ e. Expert witnesses may offer an opinion about a person's criminal intent.

3. **Topic Sentence:** Food irradiation is a process in which food is treated with radiation to kill bacteria.

   _____ a. Gamma radiation is made up of radioactive cobalt, cesium, and X-rays.

   _____ b. The radioactive rays pass through the food without damaging it or changing it.

   _____ c. The newest form of irradiation uses electricity as the energy source for irradiation.

   _____ d. Irradiation increases the shelf life of food because it kills all bacteria present in the food.

   _____ e. *E. coli,* salmonella, and listeria cause many illnesses each year.

4. **Topic Sentence:** Overtraining is the most common type of fitness-related injury, and it can be easily avoided.

_____ a. A physical fitness program will improve your health and well-being.

_____ b. Our bodies usually provide warning signs of potential muscle damage.

_____ c. People often injure themselves by doing too much too soon when they exercise.

_____ d. To avoid injury, do not rely solely on repetitive motion activities like running or step aerobics.

_____ e. Varying an exercise program can allow muscles time to rest and recover from strain.

5. **Topic Sentence:** Frank Lloyd Wright was a radically innovative architect.

_____ a. Wright believed that buildings fit their surroundings.

_____ b. He popularized the use of steel cantilevers in homes at a time when they were only used commercially.

_____ c. He built the Kaufmann Residence over a waterfall without disturbing it.

_____ d. Wright had plans to build a mile-high skyscraper but died before he could do so.

_____ e. Wright designed the Guggenheim Museum.

> **NOW PRACTICE . . . RECOGNIZING SUPPORTING DETAILS 2**

Underline only the most important details in each of the following paragraphs.

Paragraph 1

Physical dependence is what was formerly called addiction. It is characterized by *tolerance* and *withdrawal*. *Tolerance* means that more and more of the drug must be taken to achieve the same effect, as use continues. *Withdrawal* means that if use is discontinued, the person experiences unpleasant symptoms. When I quit smoking cigarettes, for example, I went through about five days of irritability, depression, and restlessness. Withdrawal from heroin and other narcotics is much more painful, involving violent cramps, vomiting, diarrhea, and other symptoms that continue for at least two or three days. With some drugs, especially barbiturates, cold-turkey (sudden and total) quitting can result in death, so severe is the withdrawal.

—Geiwitz, *Psychology,* p. 512

Paragraph 2

The two most common drugs that are legal and do not require a prescription are caffeine and nicotine. *Caffeine* is the active ingredient in coffee, tea, and many cola drinks. It stimulates the central nervous system and heart and therefore is often used to stay awake. Heavy use—say, seven to ten cups of coffee per day—has toxic effects, that is, it acts like a mild poison. Prolonged heavy use appears to be addicting. *Nicotine* is the active ingredient in tobacco. One of the most addicting of all drugs and one of the most dangerous, at least when obtained by smoking, it has been implicated in lung cancer, emphysema, and heart disease.

—Geiwitz, *Psychology,* p. 513

Paragraph 3

Hypnosis today is used for a number of purposes, primarily in psychotherapy or to reduce pain, and it is an acceptable technique in both medicine and psychology. In psychotherapy, it is most often used to eliminate bad habits and annoying symptoms. Cigarette smoking can be treated, for example, by the suggestion that the person will feel nauseated whenever he or she thinks of smoking. Sufferers of migraine headaches treated with hypnotic suggestions to relax showed a much greater tendency to improve than sufferers treated with drugs; 44 percent were headache-free after 12 months of treatment, compared to 12 percent of their drug-treated counterparts.

—Geiwitz, *Psychology,* p. 229

Paragraph 4

There are four main types of sunglasses. The traditional *absorptive* glasses soak up all the harmful sun rays. *Polarizing* sunglasses account for half the market. They're the best buy for knocking out glare, and reflections from snow and water, but they may admit more light rays than other sunglasses. *Coated* sunglasses usually have a metallic covering that itself reflects light. They are often quite absorptive, but a cheap pair of coated glasses may have an uneven or nondurable coating that could rub off after a short period of time. New on the market are the somewhat more expensive *photochromatic* sunglasses. Their chemical composition causes them to change color according to the brightness of the light: in the sun, they darken; in the shade, they lighten. This type of sunglasses responds to ultraviolet light only, and will not screen out infrared rays, so they're not the best bet for continual exposure to bright sun.

—George, *The New Consumer Survival Kit,* p. 14

Paragraph 5

In simplest outline, how is a President chosen? First, a candidate campaigns within his party for nomination at a national convention. After the convention comes a period of competition with the nominee of the other major party and perhaps the nominees of minor parties. The showdown arrives on Election Day. The candidate must win more votes than any other nominee in enough states and the District of Columbia to give him a majority of the electoral votes. If he does all these things, he has won the right to the office of President of the United States.

— "ABC's of How a President Is Chosen," *U.S. News and World Report,* p. 45

> ## NOW PRACTICE . . . RECOGNIZING SUPPORTING DETAILS 3

Reread the article "Deadly Silence: Stop Snitching's Fatal Legacy" on p. 8 and underline the most important supporting details in each paragraph.

3e   RECOGNIZING TRANSITIONS

Transitions are linking words or phrases used to lead the reader from one idea to another. If you get in the habit of recognizing transitions, you will see that they often guide you through a paragraph, helping you to read it more easily.

In the following paragraph, notice how the underlined transitions lead you from one important detail to the next.

The principle of rhythm and line also contributes to the overall unity of the landscape design. This principle is responsible for the sense of continuity between different areas of the landscape. One way in which this continuity can be developed is by extending planting beds from one area to another. For example, shrub beds developed around the entrance to the house can be continued around the sides and into the backyard. Such an arrangement helps to tie the front and rear areas of the property together. Another means by which rhythm is given to a design is to repeat shapes, angles, or lines between various areas and elements of the design.

—Reiley and Shry, *Introductory Horticulture,* p. 114

Not all paragraphs contain such obvious transitions, and not all transitions serve as such clear markers of major details. Often, however, transitions are used to alert you to what will come next in the paragraph. If you see the phrase *for instance* at the beginning of a sentence, then you know that an example will follow. When you see the phrase *on the other hand,* you can predict that a different, opposing idea will follow. Table 3.1 lists some of the most common transitions used within a paragraph and indicates what they tell you.

TABLE 3.1 COMMON TRANSITIONS

TYPES OF TRANSITIONS	EXAMPLES	WHAT THEY TELL THE READER
Time or Sequence	first, later, next, finally	The author is arranging ideas in the order in which they happened.
Example	for example, for instance, to illustrate, such as	An example will follow.
Enumeration	first, second, third, last, another, next	The author is marking or identifying each major point (sometimes these may be used to suggest order of importance).
Continuation	also, in addition, and, further, another	The author is continuing with the same idea and is going to provide additional information.
Contrast	on the other hand, in contrast, however	The author is switching to a different, opposite, or contrasting idea than previously discussed.
Comparison	like, likewise, similarly	The writer will show how the previous idea is similar to what follows.
Cause and Effect	because, thus, therefore, since, consequently	The writer will show a connection between two or more things, how one thing caused another, or how something happened as a result of something else.

> NOW PRACTICE . . . RECOGNIZING TRANSITIONS 1

Select the transitional word or phrase from the box below that best completes each of the following sentences.

another	however	more important
for example	because	

1. The function of taste buds is to enable us to select healthy foods. _____ function is to warn us away from foods that are potentially dangerous, such as those that are sour or bitter.

2. Michelangelo considered himself to be primarily a sculptor; _____, the Sistine Chapel ceiling painting is one of his best known works of art.

3. Failure to floss and brush teeth and gums can cause bad breath. _____, this failure can also lead to periodontal disease.

4. Businesses use symbols to stand for a product's qualities; _____, the golden arches have come to represent the McDonald's chain.

5. In the 1800s, the "Wild West" was made up of territories that did not belong to states. _____ there was no local government, vigilantes and outlaws ruled the land, answering only to U.S. marshals.

> NOW PRACTICE . . . RECOGNIZING TRANSITIONS 2

Select the transitional word or phrase from the box below that best completes each of the following sentences. Two of the transitions in the box may be used more than once.

on the other hand	for example	because	in addition
similarly	after	next	however
also			

1. Typically, those suffering from post-traumatic stress disorder are soldiers after combat. Civilians who have experienced events such as the World Trade Center destruction can _____ experience this syndrome.

2. Columbus was determined to find an oceanic passage to China _____ finding a direct route would mean increased trading and huge profits.

3. In the event of a heart attack, it is first important to identify the symptoms. _____, call 911 or drive the victim to the nearest hospital.

4. In the 1920s, courtship between men and women changed dramatically. _____, instead of paying calls at the woman's home with her parents there, men now invited women out on dates.

5. Direct exposure to sunlight is dangerous because the ultraviolet rays can lead to skin cancer. _____, tanning booths also emit ultraviolet rays and are as dangerous as, if not more dangerous than, exposure to sunlight.

6. Lie detector tests are often used by law enforcement to help determine guilt or innocence. _____, because these tests often only have an accuracy rate of between 60% and 80%, the results are not admissible in court.

7. The temporal lobes of the brain process sound and comprehend language. _____, this area of the brain is responsible for storing visual memories.

8. The theory of multiple intelligences holds that there are many different kinds of intelligence, or abilities. _____, musical ability, control of bodily movements (athletics), spatial understanding, and observational abilities are all classified as different types of intelligence.

9. During World War II, Japanese Americans were held in relocation camps. _____ the war was over, the United States paid reparations and issued an apology to those who were wrongfully detained.

10. Support continues to grow for the legalization of marijuana. _____, legalization has not yet been passed in any state and it is unlikely this will happen anytime soon.

NOW PRACTICE . . . RECOGNIZING TRANSITIONS 3

Many transitions have similar meanings and can sometimes be used interchangeably. Match each transition in column A with a similar transition in column B. Write the letter of your choice in the space provided.

Column A	Column B
_____ 1. because	a. therefore
_____ 2. in contrast	b. also
_____ 3. for instance	c. likewise
_____ 4. thus	d. after that
_____ 5. first	e. since
_____ 6. one way	f. finally
_____ 7. similarly	g. on the other hand
_____ 8. next	h. one approach
_____ 9. in addition	i. in the beginning
_____ 10. to sum up	j. for example

NOW PRACTICE . . . RECOGNIZING TRANSITIONS 4

Each of the following beginnings of paragraphs uses a transitional word or phrase to tell the reader what will follow in the paragraph. Read each, paying particular attention to the underlined word or phrase. Then, in the space provided, describe as specifically as you can what you would expect to find next in the paragraph.

1. Price is not the only factor to consider in choosing a pharmacy. Many provide valuable services that should be considered. For instance . . .

   _____

2. There are a number of things you can do to prevent a home burglary. First, . . .

   _____

3. Most mail order businesses are reliable and honest. However, . . .

   _____

   _____

4. One advantage of a compact stereo system is that all the components are built into the unit. Another . . .

   _____

5. To select the presidential candidate you will vote for, you should examine his or her philosophy of government. Next . . .

   _____

4 Organizational Patterns

MyReadingLab

To practice using organizational patterns, go to

➤ Study Plan
➤ Reading Skills
➤ Patterns of Organization

Most college students take courses in several different disciplines each semester. They may study psychology, anatomy and physiology, mathematics, and English composition all in one semester. During one day they may read a poem, solve math problems, and study early developments in psychology.

What few students realize is that a biologist and a psychologist, for example, think about and approach their subject matter in similar ways. Both carefully define terms, examine causes and effects, study similarities and differences, describe sequences of events, classify information, solve problems, and enumerate characteristics. The subject matter and language they use differ, but their approaches to the material are basically the same. Researchers, textbook authors, and your professors use standard approaches, or **organizational patterns**, to express their ideas.

In academic writing, commonly used organizational patterns include definition, classification, order or sequence, cause and effect, comparison and contrast, and listing/enumeration. Other important patterns include statement and clarification, summary, generalization and example, and addition.

These patterns can work for you in several ways:

- **Patterns** help you anticipate the author's thought development and thus focus your reading.
- **Patterns** help you remember and recall what you read.
- **Patterns** are useful in your own writing; they help you organize and express your ideas in a more coherent, comprehensible form.

The following sections describe each pattern listed above. In subsequent chapters, you will see how these patterns are used in specific academic disciplines.

4a DEFINITION

Each academic discipline has its own specialized vocabulary. One of the primary purposes of introductory textbooks is to introduce students to this new language. Consequently, definition is a commonly used pattern throughout most introductory-level texts.

Suppose you were asked to define the word *comedian* for someone unfamiliar with the term. First, you would probably say that a comedian is a person who entertains. Then you might distinguish a comedian from other types of entertainers by saying that a comedian is an entertainer who tells jokes and makes others laugh. Finally, you might mention, by way of example, the names of several well-known comedians who have appeared on television. Although you may have presented it informally, your definition would have followed the standard, classic pattern. The first part of your definition tells what general class or group the term belongs to (entertainers). The second part tells what distinguishes the term from other items in the same class or category. The third part includes further explanation, characteristics, examples, or applications.

You can visualize the definition pattern as follows:

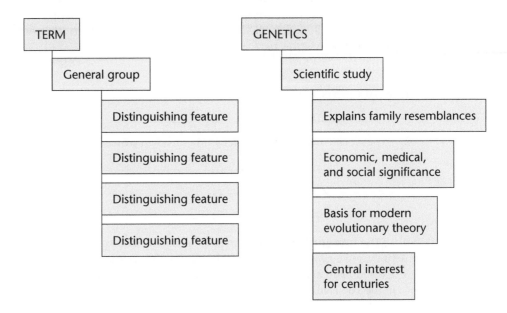

See how the term *genetics* is defined in the following paragraph, and notice how the term and the general class are presented in the first sentence. The remainder of the paragraph presents the distinguishing characteristics.

> **Genetics** is the scientific study of heredity, the transmission of characteristics from parents to offspring. Genetics explains why offspring resemble their parents and also why they are not identical to them. Genetics is a subject that has considerable economic, medical, and social significance and is partly the basis for the modern theory of evolution. Because of its importance, genetics has been a topic of central interest in the study of life for centuries. Modern concepts in genetics are fundamentally different, however, from earlier ones.
>
> —Mix, Farber, and King, *Biology, The Network of Life*, p. 262

Writers often provide clues called **transitions** that signal the organizational pattern being used. These signals may occur within single sentences or as connections between sentences. (Transitional words that occur in phrases are italicized in the box below to help you spot them.)

TRANSITIONS FOR THE DEFINITION PATTERN

genetics *is* . . .
bureaucracy *means* . . .
patronage *refers to* . . .
aggression *can be defined* as . . .
deficit is *another term* that . . .
balance of power *also means* . . .

➤ NOW PRACTICE . . . USING DEFINITION

Read each of the following paragraphs and answer the questions that follow.

A.   A **pidgin** is a contact language that emerges when different cultures with different languages come to live in close proximity and therefore need to communicate. Pidgins are generally limited to highly functional domains, such as trade, since that is what they were developed for. A pidgin therefore is no one's first language. Many pidgins of the Western hemisphere developed out of slavery, where owners needed to communicate with their slaves. A pidgin is always learned as a second language. Tok Pisin, the pidgin language of Papua New Guinea, consists of a mixture of many languages, some English, Samoan, Chinese, and Malayan. Tok Pisin has been declared one of the national languages of Papau New Guinea, where it is transforming into a **creole,** or a language descended from pidgin with its own native speakers and involving linguistic expansion and elaboration. About two hundred pidgin and creole languages exist today, mainly in West Africa, the Caribbean, and the South Pacific.

—Miller, *Cultural Anthropology*, pp. 308–309

1. What term is being defined?

_____

2. Explain the meaning of the term in your own words.

_____

_____

3. Give an example of the term. _____

B.   The **integumentary** system is the external covering of the body, or the skin. It waterproofs the body and cushions and protects the deeper tissues from injury. It also excretes salts and urea in perspiration and helps regulate body temperature. Temperature, pressure, and pain receptors located in the skin alert us to what is happening at the body surface.

—Marieb, *Essentials of Human Anatomy and Physiology*, p. 3

4. Define the integumentary system in your own words.

_____

5. List three things the integumentary system does.

_____

_____

4b   CLASSIFICATION

If you were asked to describe types of computers, you might mention PC's, laptops, and BlackBerries. By dividing a broad topic into its major categories, you are using a pattern known as *classification.*

This pattern is widely used in many academic subjects. For example, a psychology text might explain human needs by classifying them into two categories: primary and secondary. In a chemistry textbook, various compounds may be grouped and discussed according to common characteristics, such as the presence of hydrogen or oxygen. The classification pattern divides a topic into parts, on the basis of common or shared characteristics.

Here are a few examples of topics and the classifications or categories into which each might be divided.

- **Movies:** comedy, horror, mystery
- **Motives:** achievement, power, affiliation, competency
- **Plants:** leaves, stem, roots

Note how the following paragraph classifies the various types of cancers.

The name of the cancer is derived from the type of tissue in which it develops. Carcinoma (carc = cancer; omo = tumor) refers to a malignant tumor consisting of epithelial cells. A tumor that develops from a gland is called an adenosarcoma (adeno = gland). Sarcoma is a general term for any cancer arising from connective tissue. Osteogenic sarcomas (osteo = bone; genic = origin), the most frequent type of childhood cancer, destroy normal bone tissue and eventually spread to other areas of the body. Myelomas (myelos = marrow) are malignant tumors, occurring in middle-aged and older people, that interfere with the blood-cell-producing function of bone marrow and cause anemia. Chondrosarcomas (chondro = cartilage) are cancerous growths of cartilage.

—Tortora, *Introduction to the Human Body*, p. 56

You can visualize the classification pattern as follows:

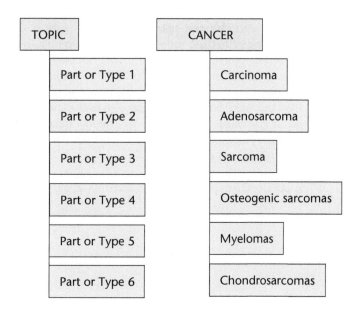

TRANSITIONS FOR THE CLASSIFICATION PATTERN

There are *several kinds* of chemical bonding . . .
There are *numerous types of* . . .
Reproduction can be *classified as* . . .
the human skeleton is *composed of* . . .
muscles *comprise* . . .
one type of communication . . .
another type of communication . . .
finally, there is . . .

NOW PRACTICE . . . USING CLASSIFICATION

Read each of the following paragraphs and answer the questions that follow.

A.   The reptiles made one of the most spectacular adaptive radiations in all of Earth history. One group, the pterosaurs, took to the air. These "dragons of the sky" possessed huge membranous wings that allowed them rudimentary flight. Another group of reptiles, exemplified by the fossil *Archaeopteryx,* led to more successful flyers: the birds. Whereas some reptiles took to the skies, others returned to the sea, including fish-eating plesiosaurs and ichthyosaurs. These reptiles became proficient swimmers, but retained their reptilian teeth and breathed by means of lungs.

—Tarbuck and Lutgens, *Earth Science*, p. 309

1. List the classification of reptiles included in this paragraph.

_____

2. Highlight the transitional words used in the paragraph.

_____

B.   From the hundreds of billions of galaxies, several basic types have been identified: spiral, elliptical, and irregular. The Milky Way and the Great Galaxy in Andromeda are examples of fairly large **spiral galaxies**. Typically, spiral galaxies are disk-shaped with a somewhat greater concentration of stars near their centers, but there are numerous variations. Viewed broadside, arms are often seen extending from the central nucleus and sweeping gracefully away. One type of spiral galaxy, however, has the stars arranged in the shape of a bar, which rotates as a rigid system. This requires that the outer stars move faster than the inner ones, a fact not easy for astronomers to reconcile with the laws of motion. Attached to each end of these bars are curved spiral arms. These have become known as **barred spiral galaxies**. The most abundant group, making up 60 percent of the total is the **elliptical galaxies**. These are generally smaller than spiral galaxies. Some are so much smaller, in fact, that the term dwarf has been applied. Because these dwarf galaxies are not visible at great distances, a survey of the sky reveals more of the conspicuous large spiral galaxies. As their name implies, elliptical galaxies have an ellipsoidal shape that ranges to nearly spherical, and they lack spiral arms. Only 10 percent of the known galaxies lack symmetry and are classified as **irregular galaxies**. The best-known irregular galaxies, the Large and Small Magellanic Clouds in the Southern Hemisphere, are easily visible with the unaided eye.

—Tarbuck and Lutgens, *Earth Science,* pp. 620–621

3. What are the three primary classifications of galaxies?

_____

4. What determines how a galaxy is classified?

_____

5. Highlight the transitional words used in the paragraph.

_____

4c   ORDER OR SEQUENCE

If you were asked to summarize what you did today, you probably would mention key events in the order in which they occurred. In describing how to write a particular computer program, you would detail the process step-by-step. In each case, you are presenting information in a particular sequence or order. Each of these examples illustrates a form of the organizational pattern known as *order* or *sequence*. Let's look at several types of order.

Chronology

Chronological order refers to the sequence in which events occur in time. This pattern is essential in the academic disciplines concerned with the interpretation of events in the past. History, government, and anthropology are prime examples. In various forms of literature, chronological order is evident; the narrative form, used in novels, short stories, and narrative essays, relies on chronological order.

You can visualize the chronological order pattern as follows:

The following paragraph uses chronology to describe how a conflict in Kosovo developed into an allied operation in Europe.

In 1999, a smoldering conflict in Kosovo, another of the provinces of the former Yugoslavia, led to war. In an effort to stop Slobodan Milosevic, the Serbian leader responsible for the devastation of Bosnia, from squelching a movement for autonomy in Kosovo, NATO, now 50 years old, launched an American-led bombing campaign. Milosevic responded with an even more violent "ethnic cleansing" campaign that drove hundreds of thousands of Kosovars from their homes. Even without the introduction of ground troops, this ultimately successful air assault was the largest allied operation in Europe since World War II.

—Nash et al., *The American People*, p. 1099

> ### TRANSITIONS FOR CHRONOLOGICAL ORDER
> *in* ancient times . . .
> *at* the start of the battle . . .
> *on* September 12 . . .
> the *first* primate species . . .
> *later* efforts . . .
> Other chronological transitions are *then, before, during, by the time, while, afterward, as, after, thereafter, meanwhile,* and *at that point.*

> NOW PRACTICE . . . USING ORDER OR SEQUENCE

Read each of the following textbook excerpts and answer the questions that follow.

A. Railroads: Pioneers of Big Business

Completion of efficient and speedy national transportation and communications networks encouraged mass production and mass marketing. Beginning in 1862, federal and state governments vigorously promoted railroad construction with land grants from the public domain. Eventually, railroads received lands one and a half times the size of Texas. Local governments gave everything from land for stations to tax breaks.

With such incentives, the first transcontinental railroad was finished in 1869. Four additional transcontinental lines and miles of feeder and branch roads were laid down in the 1870s and 1880s. By 1890, trains rumbled across 165,000 miles of tracks. Telegraph lines arose alongside them.

—Nash et al., *The American People*, pp. 611–613

1. What events does the excerpt detail?

   _____

2. What is the importance of these events?

   _____

3. Highlight the transitional words used in the excerpt.

   _____

B. **U.S. Intervention in Vietnam**

The pretext for full-scale intervention in Vietnam came in late July 1964. On July 30, South Vietnamese PT (patrol torpedo) boats attacked bases in the Gulf of Tonkin inside North Vietnamese waters. Simultaneously, the *Maddox,* an American destroyer, steamed into the area to disrupt North Vietnamese communication facilities. On August 2, possibly seeing the two separate missions as a combined maneuver against them, the North Vietnamese sent out several PT boats to attack the destroyer. The *Maddox* fired, sinking one of the attackers, then radioed the news to Washington. Johnson ordered another ship into the bay. On August 3 both destroyers reported another attack, although somewhat later, the commander of the *Maddox* radioed that he was not sure. Nonetheless, the president ordered American planes to retaliate by bombing inside North Vietnam.

—Wilson et al., *The Pursuit of Liberty*, p. 493

4. What events in history does this paragraph describe?

   _____

   _____

5. Highlight the transitional words used in the paragraph.

   _____

   _____

Process

In disciplines that focus on procedures, steps, or stages by which actions are accomplished, the process pattern is often employed. These subjects include mathematics, natural and life sciences, computer science, and engineering. The pattern is similar to chronology, in that the steps or stages follow each other in time. Transitional words and phrases often used in conjunction with this pattern are similar to those used for chronological order. You can visualize the process pattern as follows:

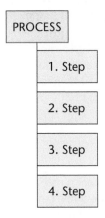

Note how this pattern is used in a paragraph explaining what occurs in the brain during sleep.

> Let us track your brain waves through the night. As you prepare to go to bed, an EEG records that your brain waves are moving along at a rate of about 14 cycles per second (cps). Once you are comfortably in bed, you begin to relax and your brain waves slow down to a rate of about 8 to 12 cps. When you fall asleep, you enter your *sleep cycle,* each of whose stages shows a distinct EEG pattern. In Stage 1 sleep, the EEG shows brain waves of about 3 to 7 cps. During Stage 2, the EEG is characterized by *sleep spindles,* minute bursts of electrical activity of 12 to 16 cps. In the next two stages (3 and 4) of sleep, you enter into a very deep state of relaxed sleep. Your brain waves slow to about 1 to 2 cps, and your breathing and heart rate decrease. In a final stage, the electrical activity of your brain increases; your EEG looks very similar to those recorded during stages 1 and 2. It is during this stage that you will experience REM sleep, and you will begin to dream.
>
> —Zimbardo and Gerrig, *Psychology and Life,* p. 115

➤ **NOW PRACTICE . . . USING PROCESS**

Read each of the following textbook excerpts and answer the questions that follow.

A.   Should you eat less fat? Scientists doing medical research think you probably should; they recommend no more than 30% fat in our diets, whereas the average American diet is estimated to contain 34% fat. Perhaps you're convinced that you should cut down on fatty foods, but you can't imagine watching the Super Bowl without a big bag of chips at your side. The chemists at Procter & Gamble have been trying to resolve your dilemma by developing an edible substance with the rich taste and smooth texture of fat molecules but without the calories. Olestra seems to meet these criteria.

Fat digestion is an enzyme-mediated process that breaks fat molecules into glycerol and fatty acids, which are then able to enter the bloodstream. Olestra is a hexa-, hepta-, or octa-ester of fatty acids (derived from vegetable oil, such as soybean oil or cottonseed oil) and sucrose. Because the body contains no digestive enzymes that convert Olestra's fat-like molecules into their smaller components of sucrose and fatty acids, and because Olestra is too large to enter the bloodstream undigested, the compound passes through systems unchanged.

—Bishop, *Introduction to Chemistry,* p. 749

1. What process does this passage explain?

_____

2. Why is Olestra not digested?

_____

_____

B.   BMI [body mass index] is an index of the relationship of height and weight. It is one of the most accurate indicators of a person's health risk due to excessive weight, rather than "fatness" per se. Although many people recoil in fright when they see they have to convert pounds to kilograms and inches to meters to calculate BMI, it really is not as difficult as it may seem. To get your kilogram weight, just divide your weight in pounds (without shoes or clothing) by 2.2. To convert your height to meters squared, divide your height in inches (without shoes) by 39.4, then square this result. Sounds pretty easy and it actually is. Once you have these basic values, calculating your BMI involves dividing your weight in kilograms by your height in meters squared.

$$BMI = \frac{\text{Weight (in lbs)} \times 2.2 \text{ (to determine weight in kg)}}{(\text{Height [in inches]} \div 39.4)^2 \text{ (to determine height in meters squared)}}$$

Healthy weights have been defined as those associated with BMIs of 19 to 25, the range of the lowest statistical health risk. A BMI greater than 25 indicates overweight and potentially significant health risks. The desirable range for females is between 21 and 23; for males, it is between 22 and 24. A body mass index of over 30 is considered obese. Many experts believe this number is too high, particularly for younger adults.

—Donatelle, *Access to Health,* p. 264

3. What process is being described in this paragraph?

_____

4. How do you convert height in inches to meters squared?

_____

5. What does BMI measure and why is it useful?

_____

_____

Order of Importance

Ideas can be organized in a pattern that expresses order of priority or preference. Ideas are arranged in one of two ways: from most to least important, or from least to most important. In the following paragraph, the causes of the downward trend in the standard of living are arranged in order of importance.

The United States' downward trend in standard of living has many different causes, of which only a few major ones can be identified here. Most important is probably deindustrialization, the massive loss of manufacturing jobs as many U.S. corporations move their production to poor, labor-cheap countries. But deindustrialization hurts mostly low-skilled manufacturing workers. Most of the well-educated, high-skilled employees in service industries are left unscathed. Deindustrialization alone is therefore not enough to explain the economic decline. Another major factor is the great increase in consumption and decrease in savings. Like their government, people spend more than they earn and become deeply in debt. Those who do practice thrift still have an average rate of savings significantly lower than in countries with fast-growing economies. The habits of high consumption and low saving may have resulted from the great affluence after the Second World War up until the early 1970s (Harrison, 1992).

—Thio, *Sociology,* p. 255

Order of importance is used in almost every field of study.

TRANSITIONS FOR ORDER OF IMPORTANCE

is *less* essential than . . .
more revealing is . . .
of *primary* interest is . . .
Other transitions that show the order of
importance are *first, next, last, most
important, primarily,* and *secondarily.*

> **NOW PRACTICE . . . USING ORDER OF IMPORTANCE**

Read the following paragraph and answer the questions that follow.

Media resources are being reassembled in a new pattern, with three main parts. The first is the traditional mass media that will continue to be for a long time the most important element in the pattern in terms of their reach and influence. The second consists of the advanced electronic mass media, operating primarily within the new information utility, and competing increasingly with older media services. Finally, there are newer forms of personal electronic media, formed by clusters of like-minded people to fulfill their own professional or individual information needs. Internet chat rooms and personalized Web pages are fast-expanding examples of this development. Each of these parts of the evolving mass-communications pattern deserves separate scrutiny.

—Dizard, *Old Media, New Media,* p. 179

1. What does this paragraph describe?

_____

2. Write the transitional words used in the paragraph.

_____

3. Why is traditional mass media the most important type of resource?

_____

4. Which type of media resource competes the most with the traditional mass media?

_____

5. What are some examples of personal electronic media?

_____

Spatial Order

Information organized according to its physical location, or position or order in space, exhibits a pattern that is known as **spatial order**. Spatial order is used in academic disciplines in which physical descriptions are important. These include numerous technical fields, engineering, and the biological sciences.

You can see how the following description of a particular type of blood circulation relies on spatial relationships.

Pulmonary circulation conducts blood between the heart and the lungs. Oxygen-poor, CO_2-laden blood returns through two large veins (venae cavae) from tissues within the body, enters the right atrium, and is then moved into the right ventricle of the heart. From there, it is pumped into the pulmonary artery, which divides into two branches, each leading to one of the lungs. In the lung, the arteries undergo extensive branching, giving rise to vast networks of capillaries where gas exchange takes place, with blood becoming oxygenated while CO_2 is discharged. Oxygen-rich blood then returns to the heart via the pulmonary veins.

—Mix, Farber, and King, *Biology: The Network of Life*, pp. 663–664

Diagramming is of the utmost importance in working with this pattern; often, a diagram accompanies text material. For example, a diagram makes the functions of the various parts of the human brain easier to understand. Lecturers often refer to a visual aid or chalkboard drawing when providing spatial descriptions.

TRANSITIONS FOR SPATIAL ORDER

the *left side* of the brain . . .
the *lower* portion . . .
the *outer* covering . . .
beneath the surface . . .
Other spatial transitions are *next to, beside, to the left, in the center,* and *externally.*

> **NOW PRACTICE . . . USING SPATIAL ORDER**

Read the following passage and answer the questions that follow.

Skeletal muscle tissue is named for its location—attached to bones. Skeletal muscle tissue is also *voluntary* because it can be made to contract by conscious control. A single skeletal muscle fiber (cell) is cylindrical and appears *striated* (striped) under a microscope; when organized in a tissue, the fibers are parallel to each other. Each muscle fiber has a plasma membrane, the **sarcolemma**, surrounding the cytoplasm, or **sarcoplasm**. Skeletal muscle fibers are multinucleate (more than one nucleus), and the nuclei are near the sarcolemma.

—Tortora, *Introduction to the Human Body*, p. 77

1. Briefly describe skeletal muscle tissue.

   _____

   _____

2. Highlight the transitional words in the paragraph.

   _____

3. How are skeletal muscle fibers or cells arranged in a tissue?

   _____

4. Where can the sarcolemma (or plasma membrane) be found in muscle fibers?

   _____

5. Where are the nuclei in the skeletal muscle fibers located?

   _____

   _____

4d   CAUSE AND EFFECT

The **cause-and-effect** pattern expresses a relationship between two or more actions, events, or occurrences that are connected in time. The relationship differs, however, from chronological order in that one event leads to another by *causing* it. Information that is organized in terms of the cause-and-effect pattern may:

- explain causes, sources, reasons, motives, and action
- explain the effect, result, or consequence of a particular action
- explain both causes and effects

You can visualize the cause and effect pattern as follows:

Cause and effect is clearly illustrated by the following passage, which gives the sources of fashions or the reasons why fashions occur.

> Why do fashions occur in the first place? One reason is that some cultures, like ours, *value change:* what is new is good, even better. Thus, in many modern societies clothing styles change yearly, while people in traditional societies may wear the same style for generations. A second reason is that many industries promote quick changes in fashion to increase sales. A third reason is that fashions usually trickle down from the top. A new style may occasionally originate from lower-status groups, as blue jeans did. But most fashions come from upper-class people who like to adopt some style or artifact as a badge of their status. But they cannot monopolize most status symbols for long. Their style is adopted by the middle class, maybe copied or modified for use by lower-status groups, offering many people the prestige of possessing a high-status symbol.
>
> —Thio, *Sociology,* p. 534

The cause-and-effect pattern is used extensively in many academic fields. All disciplines that ask the question "Why" employ the cause-and-effect thought pattern. It is widely used in the sciences, technologies, and social sciences.

Many statements expressing cause-and-effect relationships appear in direct order, with the cause stated first and the effect following: "When demand for a product increases, prices rise." However, reverse order is sometimes used, as in the following statement: "Prices rise when a product's demand increases."

The cause-and-effect pattern is not limited to an expression of a simple one-cause, one-effect relationship. There may be multiple causes, or multiple effects, or both multiple causes and multiple effects. For example, both slippery road conditions and your failure to buy snow tires (causes) may contribute to your car sliding into the ditch (effect).

In other instances, a chain of causes or effects may occur. For instance, failing to set your alarm clock may force you to miss your 8:00 a.m. class, which in turn may cause you not to submit your term paper on time, which may result in a penalty grade.

TRANSITIONS FOR THE CAUSE-AND-EFFECT PATTERN

stress *causes* . . .
aggression *creates* . . .
depression *leads to* . . .
forethought *yields* . . .
mental retardation *stems from* . . .
life changes *produce* . . .
hostility *breeds* . . .
avoidance *results in* . . .
Other cause-and-effect transitions are *therefore, consequently, hence, for this reason,* and *since.*

➤ NOW PRACTICE . . . USING CAUSE AND EFFECT

Read each of the following paragraphs and answer the questions that follow.

A.   All objects continually radiate energy. Why, then, doesn't the temperature of all objects continually decrease? The answer is that all objects also continually absorb radiant energy. If an object is radiating more energy than it is absorbing, its temperature does decrease; but if an object is absorbing more energy than it is emitting, its temperature increases. An object that is warmer than its surroundings emits more energy than it receives, and therefore it cools; an object colder than its surroundings is a net gainer of energy, and its temperature therefore increases. An object whose temperature is constant, then, emits as much radiant energy as it receives. If it receives none, it will radiate away all its available energy, and its temperature will approach absolute zero.

—Hewitt, *Conceptual Physics,* p. 272

1. Explain why some objects that radiate energy increase in temperature.

    _____

    _____

2. What happens to an object that radiates energy but does not absorb any?

    _____

3. Highlight the transitional words used in the paragraph.

    _____

4. What causes an object's temperature to remain constant?

    _____

5. What is the effect of an object being warmer than its surroundings?

    _____

B.   It's the end of the term and you have dutifully typed the last of several papers. After hours of nonstop typing, you find that your hands are numb, and you feel an intense, burning pain that makes the thought of typing one more word almost unbearable. If you are like one of the thousands of students and workers who every year must quit a particular task due to pain, you may be suffering from a **repetitive stress injury (RSI)**. These are injuries to nerves, soft tissue or joints that result from the physical stress of repeated motions. One of the most common RSIs is **carpal tunnel syndrome**, a product of both the information age and the age of technology in general. Hours spent typing at the computer, flipping groceries through computerized scanners, or other jobs "made simpler" by technology can result in irritation to the median nerve in the wrist, causing numbness, tingling, and pain in the fingers and hands.

—Donatelle, *Access to Health,* p. 516

6. What is the cause of RSIs?

    _____

7. What kind of damage causes carpal tunnel syndrome?

    _____

8. What do students often do that can cause RSIs?

    _____

9. What kinds of symptoms can result from RSI?

    _____

10. Highlight the transitional words used in the passage.

    _____

4e   COMPARISON AND CONTRAST

The **comparison organizational pattern** is used to emphasize or discuss similarities between or among ideas, theories, concepts, or events, whereas the **contrast pattern** emphasizes differences. When a speaker or writer is concerned with both similarities and differences, a combination pattern is used. You can visualize these three variations of the pattern as follows:

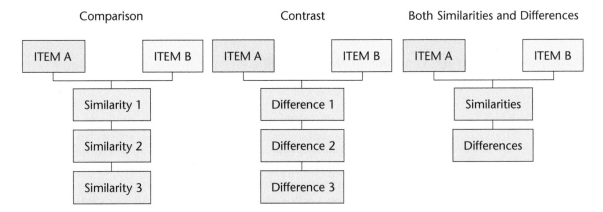

The comparison-and-contrast pattern is widely used in the social sciences, where different groups, societies, cultures, or behaviors are studied. Literature courses may require comparisons among poets, among several literary works, or among stylistic features. A business course may examine various management styles, compare organizational structures, or contrast retailing plans.

A contrast is shown in the following paragraph, which describes the purchasing processes of small and large businesses.

> Small businesses are likely to have less formal purchasing processes. A small retail grocer might, for example, purchase a computer system after visiting a few suppliers to compare prices and features, while a large grocery store chain might collect bids from a specified number of vendors and then evaluate those bids on pre-established criteria. Usually, fewer individuals are involved in the decision-making process for a small business. The owner of the small business, for example, may make all decisions, and a larger business may operate with a buying committee of several people.
>
> —Kinnear, Bernhardt, and Krentler, *Principles of Marketing*, p. 218

Depending on whether a speaker or writer is concerned with similarities, differences, or both similarities and differences, the pattern might be organized in different ways. Suppose a professor of American literature is comparing the work of two American poets, Walt Whitman and Robert Frost. Each of the following organizations is possible:

1. **Compare and then contrast the two.** That is, first discuss how Frost's poetry and Whitman's poetry are similar, and then discuss how they are different.
2. **Discuss by author.** Discuss the characteristics of Whitman's poetry, then discuss the characteristics of Frost's poetry, then summarize their similarities and differences.
3. **Discuss by characteristic.** For example, first discuss the two poets' use of metaphor, next discuss their use of rhyme, and then discuss their common themes.

TRANSITIONS THAT SHOW CONTRAST

unlike Whitman, Frost . . .
less wordy *than* Whitman . . .
contrasted with Whitman, Frost . . .
Frost *differs from* . . .
Other transitions of contrast are *in contrast, however, on the other hand, as opposed to,* and *whereas.*

> **TRANSITIONS THAT SHOW COMPARISON**
> *similarities between* Frost and Whitman . . .
> Frost is *as* powerful *as* . . .
> *like* Frost, Whitman . . .
> *both* Frost and Whitman . . .
> Frost *resembles* Whitman in that . . .
> Other transitions of comparison are *in a like manner,*
> *similarly, likewise, correspondingly,* and *in the same way.*

➤ **NOW PRACTICE . . . USING COMPARISON AND CONTRAST**

Read each of the following paragraphs and answer the questions that follow.

A.   When considering the relationship of Congress and the president, the basic differences of the two branches must be kept in mind. Members of Congress are elected from narrower constituencies than is the president. The people usually expect the president to address general concerns such as foreign policy and economic prosperity, while Congresspersons are asked to solve individual problems. There are structural differences as well. Congress is a body composed of hundreds of independent people, each with a different power base, and it is divided along partisan lines. Thus, it is difficult for Congress to act quickly or to project unity and clear policy statements.

                              —Baradat, *Understanding American Democracy,* p. 300

1. What two branches of the government are discussed?

   _____

2. Does this paragraph mainly use comparison, contrast, or both?

   _____

3. Explain how the two branches are similar and/or different.

   _____

   _____

4. Why is it difficult for Congress to act quickly?

   _____

   _____

5. Highlight the transitional words in the paragraph.

   _____

B.   What are the main characteristics of this new postindustrial society? Unlike the industrial society from which we are emerging, its hallmark is not raw materials and manufacturing. Rather, its basic component is *information*. Teachers pass on knowledge to students, while lawyers, physicians, bankers, pilots, and interior decorators sell their specialized knowledge of law, the body, money, aerodynamics, and color schemes to clients. Unlike the factory workers in an industrial society, these workers don't *produce* anything. Rather, they transmit or use information to provide services that others are willing to pay for.

                              —Henslin, *Social Problems,* p. 154

6. What two things are being compared or contrasted?

   _____

7. What is the postindustrial society based upon?

   _____

8. What did most workers in the industrial society do at their jobs?

_____

9. How is information connected to money in the postindustrial society?

_____

10. Highlight the transitional words used in the paragraph.

_____

4f   LISTING/ENUMERATION

If asked to evaluate a film you saw, you might describe the characters, plot, and technical effects. These details about the film could be arranged in any order; each detail provides further information about the film, but they have no single order in which they must be discussed. This arrangement of ideas is known as **listing** or **enumeration**—giving bits of information on a topic by stating them one after the other. Often there is no particular method of arrangement for those details.

You can visualize the listing/enumeration patterns as follows:

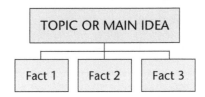

The following list of managers' difficulties in problem solving could have been presented in any order without altering the meaning of the paragraph.

> Although accurate identification of a problem is essential before the problem can be solved, this stage of decision making creates many difficulties for managers. Sometimes managers' preconceptions of the problem prevent them from seeing the situation as it actually is. They produce an answer before the proper question has ever been asked. In other cases, managers overlook truly significant issues by focusing on unimportant matters. Also, managers may mistakenly analyze problems in terms of symptoms rather than underlying causes.
>
> —Pride, Hughes, and Kapoor, *Business,* p. 189

This pattern is widely used in college textbooks in most academic disciplines. In its loosest form, the pattern may be simply a list of items: factors that influence light emission, characteristics of a particular poet, a description of an atom, a list of characteristics that define poverty.

Somewhat tighter is the use of listing to explain, support, or provide evidence. Support may be in the form of facts, statistics, or examples. For instance, the statement, "The incidence of white collar crime has dramatically increased over the past ten years" would be followed by facts and statistics documenting the increase.

> **TRANSITIONS FOR LISTING**
>
> *one* aspect of relativity . . .
> *a second feature* of relativity . . .
> *also,* relativity . . .
> there are *several characteristics of* . . .
> *(1)* . . . , *(2)* . . . , *and (3)* . . . ,
> *(a)* . . . , *(b)* . . . , *and (c)* . . . ,
> Other transitional words and phrases are *in addition, first, second, third, finally,* and *another.*

> **NOW PRACTICE . . . USING LISTING**

Read the following paragraphs and answer the questions that follow.

A.   Minorities come into existence, then, when, due to expanded political boundaries or migration, people with different customs, languages, values or physical characteristics come under control of the same state organization. There, some groups who share physical and cultural traits discriminate against those with different traits. The losers in this power struggle are forced into minority group status; the winners enjoy the higher status and greater privileges that their dominance brings. Wagley and Harris noted that all minorities share these five characteristics: (1) They are treated unequally by the dominant group. (2) Their physical or cultural traits are held in low esteem by the dominant group. (3) They tend to feel strong group solidarity because of their physical or cultural traits—and the disabilities these traits bring. (4) Their membership in a minority group is not voluntary but comes through birth. (5) They tend to marry within their group. Sharing cultural or physical traits, having similar experiences of discrimination, and marrying within their own group create a shared identity—sometimes even a sense of common destiny. These shared experiences, however, do not mean that all minority groups have the same goals.

—Henslin, *Social Problems*, p. 252

1. What does this paragraph list?

_____

2. How do minority groups come into existence?

_____

_____

_____

B.   Voters make two basic decisions at election time. The first is whether to vote. Americans' right to vote is well established, but in order to do so citizens must go through the registration process. America's unique registration system is one major reason why turnout in American elections is much lower than in most other democracies. The 1996 election was another in a long string of low-turnout elections. Second, those who choose to vote must decide for whom to cast their ballots. Over a generation of research on voting behavior has helped political scientists understand the dominant role played by three factors in voters' choices: party identification, candidate evaluations, and policy positions.

—Edwards, *Government in America*, p. 330

3. What does this paragraph list?

_____

_____

4. Highlight the transitional words used in the paragraph.

_____

5. What is the major reason why voter turnout is low in America?

_____

SUMMING IT UP

PATTERNS AND TRANSITIONS

PATTERN	CHARACTERISTICS	TRANSITIONS
Definition	Explains the meaning of a word or phrase	Is, refers to, can be defined as, means, consists of, involves, is a term that, is called, is characterized by, occurs when, are those that, entails, corresponds to, is literally
Classification	Divides a topic into parts based on shared characteristics	Classified as, comprises, is composed of, several varieties of, different stages of, different groups that, includes, one, first, second, another, finally, last
Chronological Order	Describes events, processes, procedures	First, second, later, before, next, as soon as, after, then, finally, meanwhile, following, last, during, in, on, when, until
Process	Describes the order in which things are done or how things work	First, second, next, then, following, after that, last, finally
Order of Importance	Describes ideas in order of priority or preference	Less, more, primary, first, next, last, most important, secondarily
Spatial Order	Describes physical location or position in space	Above, below, beside, next to, in front of, behind, inside, outside, opposite, within, nearby
Cause and Effect	Describes how one or more things cause or are related to another	*Causes:* because, because of, for, since, stems from, one cause is, one reason is, leads to, causes, creates, yields, produces, due to, breeds, for this reason *Effects:* consequently, results in, one result is, therefore, thus, as a result, hence
Comparison and Contrast	Discusses similarities and/or differences among ideas, theories, concepts, objects, or persons	*Similarities:* both, also, similarly, like, likewise, too, as well as, resembles, correspondingly, in the same way, to compare, in comparison, share *Differences:* unlike, differs from, in contrast, on the other hand, instead, despite, nevertheless, however, in spite of, whereas, as opposed to
Listing/Enumeration	Organizes lists of information: characteristics, features, parts, or categories	The following, several, for example, for instance, one, another, also, too, in other words, first, second, numerals (1., 2.), letters (a., b.), most important, the largest, the least, finally
Statement and Clarification	Indicates that information explaining an idea or concept will follow	In fact, in other words, clearly, evidently, obviously
Summary	Indicates that a condensed review of an idea or piece of writing is to follow	In summary, in conclusion, in brief, to summarize, to sum up, in short, on the whole
Generalization and Example	Provides examples that clarify a broad, general statement	For example, for instance, that is, to illustrate, thus
Addition	Indicates that additional information will follow	Furthermore, additionally, also, besides, further, in addition, moreover, again

5 Making Inferences

MyReadingLab

To practice making inferences, go to

➤ Study Plan
➤ Reading Skills
➤ Inference

Look at the photograph below, which appeared in a psychology textbook. What do you think is happening here? What is the man's occupation? What are the feelings of the participants?

In order to answer these questions, you had to use any information you could get from the photo and make guesses based on it. The facial expression, body language, clothing, and other objects present in this photo provided clues. This reasoning process is called "making an inference."

5a MAKING INFERENCES FROM THE GIVEN FACTS

An **inference** is a reasoned guess about what you don't know made on the basis of what you do know. Inferences are common in our everyday lives. When you get on an expressway and see a long, slow-moving line of traffic, you might predict that there is an accident or roadwork ahead. When you see a puddle of water under the kitchen sink, you can infer that you have a plumbing problem. The inferences you make may not always be correct, even though you based them on the available information. The water under the sink might have been the result of a spill. The traffic you encountered on the expressway might be normal for that time of day, but you didn't know it because you aren't normally on the road then. An inference is only the best guess you can make in a situation, given the information you have.

> **NOW PRACTICE . . . MAKING INFERENCES 1**

Study the photograph below. Use your skills in making inferences to write a statement explaining what is happening in this photograph.

_____

_____

_____

_____

_____

> **NOW PRACTICE . . . MAKING INFERENCES 2**

Read each of the following statements. Place a check mark in front of each sentence that follows that is a reasonable inference that can be made from the statement.

1. Twice as many couples seek marriage counseling as did 20 years ago.
    _____ a. There are more married people now than 20 years ago.
    _____ b. There has been an increased demand for licensed marriage counselors.
    _____ c. Marriage is more legalistic than it used to be.
    _____ d. Couples are more willing to discuss their differences than they were 20 years ago.

2. More than half of all Americans are overweight.
    _____ a. Many Americans are at high risk for heart disease.
    _____ b. Teaching children about nutrition and exercise should be a high priority in public schools.

_____ c. Americans place great emphasis on appearance.

_____ d. The weight-loss industry is an important sector of business.

3. Many courts now permit lawyers to file papers and handle some court work over the Internet.

_____ a. Courtrooms will no longer be needed.

_____ b. Attorneys will be able to check the status of their cases from their home computers.

_____ c. Some cases may proceed more quickly now.

_____ d. More lawyers will carry laptops.

5b   MAKING INFERENCES FROM WRITTEN MATERIAL

When you read the material associated with your college courses, you need to make inferences frequently. Writers do not always present their ideas directly. Instead, they often leave it to you to add up and think beyond the facts they present. You are expected to reason out or infer the meaning an author intended (but did not say) on the basis of what he or she did say. In a sense, the inferences you make act as bridges between what is said and what is not said, but is meant.

5c   HOW TO MAKE INFERENCES

Each inference you make depends on the situation, the facts provided, and your own knowledge and experience. Here are a few guidelines to help you see beyond the factual level and make solid inferences.

Understand the Literal Meaning

Be sure you have a firm grasp of the literal meaning. You must understand the stated ideas and facts before you can move to higher levels of thinking, which include inference making. You should recognize the topic, main idea, key details, and organizational pattern of each paragraph you have read.

Notice Details

As you are reading, pay particular attention to details that are unusual or stand out. Often such details will offer you clues to help you make inferences. Ask yourself:

- What is unusual or striking about this piece of information?
- Why is it included here?

Read the following excerpt, which is taken from a business marketing textbook, and mark any details that seem unusual or striking.

Marketing in Action

Dressing Up the Basics in Idaho

In almost any grocery store across the United States, consumers can purchase ten pounds of Idaho-grown potatoes for less than $5.00. Despite this fact, Rolland Jones Potatoes, Incorporated, has been extremely successful selling a "baker's dozen" of Idaho potatoes for $18.95. The potatoes are wrapped in a decorative box that uses Easter grass.

The Baker's Dozen of Idaho potatoes is only one example of a growing phenomenon. Laura Hobbs, marketing specialist for the Idaho Department of Agriculture, reports that more than 200

Idaho farms produce specialty or value-added products. These goods typically consist of basic farm commodities that have been "dressed-up" with packaging. Consumers can choose from these products: microwave popcorn that comes on the cob and pops right off the cob, a bag of complete chili ingredients that makers claim won't cause embarrassing side-effects, and chocolate-covered "Couch Potato Chips."

Idaho farmers are supported by two groups, the Idaho Specialty Foods Association and Buy Idaho, whose goals are to help producers market and promote unique items. With the help of the groups, Idaho farmers are getting quite savvy. The marketers have discovered, for example, that packaging certain items together can increase their attractiveness. Hagerman's Rose Creek Winery found that sales of its wines soared when they were packaged in gift baskets with jars of Sun Valley brand mustard.

According to Hobbs, consumers attracted to the unique packaging provide a market for an endless variety of products, all of which are standard commodities transformed into new products through packaging. The value added through the unique packaging also provides opportunities to charge prices in ranges far above the prices of standard products—like $18.95 for 12 potatoes!

—Kinnear, Bernhardt, and Krenther, *Principles of Marketing*, p. 301

Did you mark details such as the price of $18.95 for potatoes, corn that pops right off the cob, and chocolate-covered potato chips?

Add Up the Facts

Consider all of the facts taken together. To help you do this, ask yourself such questions as the following:

- What is the writer trying to suggest from this set of facts?
- What do all these facts and ideas seem to point toward or add up to?
- Why did the author include these facts and details?

Making an inference is somewhat like assembling a complicated jigsaw puzzle; you try to make all the pieces fit together to form a recognizable picture. Answering these questions will require you to add together all the individual pieces of information, which will enable you to arrive at an inference.

When you add up the facts in the article "Dressing Up the Basics in Idaho," you realize that the writer is suggesting that people are willing to pay much more than a product is worth if it is specially packaged.

Be Alert to Clues

Writers often provide you with numerous hints that can point you toward accurate inferences. An awareness of word choices, details included (and omitted), ideas emphasized, and direct commentary can help you determine a textbook author's attitude toward the topic at hand. In the foregoing excerpt, the authors offer clues that reveal their attitude toward increased prices for special packaging. Terms such as *dressed-up* and the exclamation point at the end of the last sentence suggest that the authors believe that the products mentioned are not worth their price.

Consider the Author's Purpose

Also study the author's purpose for writing. If an author's purpose is to persuade you to purchase a particular product, as in an advertisement, as you begin reading you already have a clear idea of the types of inferences the writer hopes you will make. For instance, here is a magazine ad for a sound system:

If you're in the market for true surround sound, a prematched system is a good way to get it. The components in our system are built for each other by our audio engineers. You can be assured of high performance and sound quality.

Verify Your Inference

Once you have made an inference, check that it is accurate. Look back at the stated facts to be sure that you have sufficient evidence to support the inference. Also, be certain that you have not overlooked other equally plausible or more plausible inferences that could be drawn from the same set of facts.

> NOW PRACTICE . . . MAKING INFERENCES 3

Study the cartoon below and place a check mark after each statement that is a reasonable inference that can be made from the cartoon.

_____ 1. The cartoonist thinks workers are physically abused.

_____ 2. The cartoonist is critical of those in management.

_____ 3. Many conflicts exist between workers and supervisors.

_____ 4. The cartoonist believes that people change when they become managers.

_____ 5. The cartoonist is a labor relations specialist.

"We get it, Tom—you're management now."

> NOW PRACTICE . . . MAKING INFERENCES 4

Read each of the following statements. Place a check mark in front of each sentence that follows that is a reasonable inference that can be made from the statement.

1. Political candidates must now include the Internet in their campaign plans.

_____ a. Political candidates may host online chats to assess voter opinion.

_____ b. Informal debates between candidates may be conducted online.

_____ c. Internet campaigning will drastically increase overall campaign expenditures.

_____ d. Television campaigning is likely to remain the same.

2. Half of the public education classrooms in the United States are now hooked up to the Internet.

     _____ a. Children are more computer literate than their parents were when they were in school.

     _____ b. Students now have access to current world news and happenings.

     _____ c. Books are no longer considered the sole source of information on a subject.

     _____ d. Teachers have become better teachers now that they have Internet access.

3. The Internet can make doctors more efficient through the use of new software and databases that make patient diagnosis more accurate.

     _____ a. The cost of in-person medical care is likely to decrease.

     _____ b. Doctors may be able to identify patients with serious illness sooner.

     _____ c. Doctors are likely to pay less attention to their patients' descriptions of symptoms.

     _____ d. Information on the symptoms and treatment of rare illnesses is more readily available.

➤ NOW PRACTICE . . . MAKING INFERENCES 5

Read each of the following passages. Using inference, determine whether the statements following each passage are true or false. Place an ✕ next to each untrue statement.

A.   The United Nations Population Division predicts that by 2025, world population will increase to about 9 billion people. More disturbing, whereas the United Nations earlier predicted that the world population would stabilize at around 10 billion, it has revised its estimate to close to 11 billion, or even as high as 14 billion. These projections have prompted concerns that overpopulation and food scarcity are the principal threats to the planet's future. The United Nations sponsored an International Conference on Population and Development held in Cairo in 1994. There, a World Programme of Action was developed to shift the focus of dismal demographic projections toward concern about a gender-sensitive, humanistic approach to population control.

                                        —Thompson and Hickey, *Society in Focus,* p. 544

     _____ 1. If the projections are inaccurate, the world community no longer needs to be concerned about overpopulation.

     _____ 2. Previous approaches to population control have not been gender sensitive.

     _____ 3. If population increases more rapidly than predicted, there will be even greater food shortages.

     _____ 4. The United Nations has developed adequate responses to food scarcity.

     _____ 5. By 2050, world population will have increased to 20 billion.

B.   Blowfish is one of the most prized delicacies in the restaurants of Japan. This fish is prized not only for its taste, but for the tingling sensation one gets around the lips when eating it. In blowfish TTX (a neurotoxin) is concentrated in certain organs, including the liver and gonads. Its preparation takes great skill and can only be done by licensed chefs who are skilled at removing the poison-containing organs without crushing them, which can lead to contamination of normally edible parts. The toxin cannot be destroyed by cooking. Lore has it that the most skilled chefs intentionally leave a bit of the poison in, so that diners can enjoy the tingling sensation caused by blockage of nerve signals from the sense receptors on the lips.

                                —adapted from Germann and Stanfield, *Principles of Human Physiology,* p. 185

     _____ 6. Consuming TTX has potentially dangerous consequences.

     _____ 7. The United States has strict rules about the preparation of blowfish.

     _____ 8. Japanese diners enjoy blowfish partly because of the sense of danger involved.

     _____ 9. TTX causes blockage of signals from nerves.

     _____ 10. Blowfish is always unsafe to eat.

C.   Through your parents, teachers, and the media, your culture instills in you a variety of beliefs, values, and attitudes—about success (how you define it and how you should achieve it); the relevance of a person's religion, race, or nationality; the ethical principles you should follow in business and in your personal life. These teachings provide benchmarks against which you can measure yourself. Your ability to, for example, achieve what your culture defines as success, will contribute to a positive self-concept. Your failure to achieve what your culture teaches (for example, not being married by the time you're thirty) will contribute to a negative self-concept.

—DeVito, *Essentials of Human Communication*, pp. 36–37

_____ 11. People with positive self-concepts often have achieved their culture's notion of success.

_____ 12. Most cultures do not believe that race or religion are relevant.

_____ 13. People often ignore their culture's beliefs about ethical principles.

_____ 14. Self-concept is affected by both success and failure.

_____ 15. Your self-concept can never change.

NOW PRACTICE . . . MAKING INFERENCES 6

Read each of the following paragraphs. A number of statements follow them; each statement is an inference. Label each inference as either:

PA—Probably accurate—there is substantial evidence in the paragraph to support the statement.

IE—Insufficient evidence—there is little or no evidence in the paragraph to support the statement.

A.   While working for a wholesale firm, traveling to country stores by horse and buggy, Aaron Montgomery Ward conceived the idea of selling directly to country people by mail. He opened his business in 1872 with a one-page list of items that cost one dollar each. People could later order goods through a distributed catalog and the store would ship the merchandise cash on delivery (COD). The idea was slow to catch on because people were suspicious of a strange name. However, in 1875 Ward announced the startling policy of "satisfaction guaranteed or your money back." Contrasting with the former retailing principle of caveat emptor (Latin for "buyer beware"), this policy set off a boom in Ward's business.

—Frings, *Fashion: From Concepts to Consumer*, p. 11

_____ 1. Aaron Ward had experience in sales before he began his own business.

_____ 2. Country people were targeted because they do not have access to stores in cities.

_____ 3. Ward's mistake was to give every item on the list the same price.

_____ 4. Other stores in operation at the time did not offer money back guarantees.

_____ 5. Other mail order businesses quickly followed Ward's success.

B.   Artist Georgia O'Keefe was born in Sun Prairie, Wisconsin, and spent her childhood on her family's farm. While in high school, she had a memorable experience that gave her a new perspective on the art-making process. As she passed the door to the art room, O'Keefe stopped to watch as a teacher held up a jack-in-the-pulpit plant so that the students could appreciate its unusual shapes and subtle colors. Although O'Keefe had enjoyed flowers in the marshes and meadows of Wisconsin, she had done all of her drawing and painting from plaster casts or had copied them from photographs or reproductions. This was the first time she realized that one could draw and paint from real life. Twenty-five years later she produced a powerful series of paintings based on flowers.

—adapted from Preble and Preble, *Artforms*, p. 34

_____ 6. O'Keefe's artistic style was influenced by her high-school art teacher.

_____ 7. O'Keefe's paintings from plaster casts were unsuccessful.

_____ 8. O'Keefe was deeply influenced by nature.

_____ 9. O'Keefe was not influenced by modern art.

_____ 10. O'Keefe never copied flowers from other paintings.

> ### Top 10 Commercial Jingles
>
> 1. "You Deserve a Break Today" (McDonald's, 1974)
> 2. "Be All That You Can Be" (U.S. Army, 1983)
> 3. "Pepsi Cola Hits the Spot" (1954)
> 4. "M'mmm M'mmm Good" (Campbell's Soup, mid-1930s)
> 5. "See the USA in Your Chevrolet" (1978)
> 6. "I Wish I Were an Oscar Mayer Weiner" (1963)
> 7. "Double Your Pleasure, Double Your Fun" (Wrigley's Doublemint Gum, 1986)
> 8. "Winston Tastes Good Like a Cigarette Should" (1954)
> 9. "It's the Real Thing" (Coca-Cola, 1975)
> 10. "A Little Dab'll Do Ya" (Brylcreem, mid-1950s)
>
> [source: Ad Age]

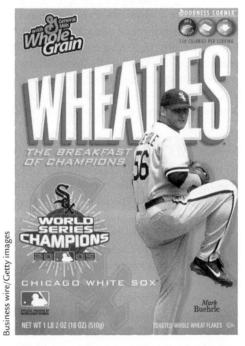

Business wire/Getty images

"Have you had your Wheaties today?"

Why are jingles so catchy?

7   Jingles are written to be as easy to remember as nursery rhymes. The shorter the better, the more repetition the better, the more rhymes the better. If you're being indecisive in the deodorant aisle and you suddenly hear a voice in your head singing "by . . . Mennen," you might drop a Speed Stick (manufactured by Mennen) into your basket without a second thought. Jingles are designed to infiltrate your memory and stay there for years, sometimes popping up from out of nowhere. You probably fondly remember all of the words to the Oscar Mayer B-O-L-O-G-N-A song, the "plop plop fizz fizz" chorus of the Alka-Seltzer jingle, and countless other melodies from your childhood.

8   Psyohologists and neurologists who study the effects of music on the brain have found that music with a strong emotional connection to the listener is difficult to forget. It was this discovery that led

marketers to license pop songs for advertising instead of commissioning original jingles. It turns out that some pop songs contain **earworms**: pleasantly melodic, easy-to-remember "hooks" that have the attributes of a typical jingle. Earworms, also known by their German name, "ohrwurm," are those tiny, 15- to 30-second pieces of music that you can't get out of your head no matter how hard you try (the phenomenon is also called Song Stuck Syndrome, repetuneitis, the Jukebox Virus and melodymania). The word "earworm" was popularized by James Kellaris, a marketing professor at the University of Cincinnati, who has done a great deal (for better or worse) to bring this phenomenon to the forefront of the study of advertising techniques.

9   We don't know much about what causes earworms, but it could be the repeating of the neural circuits that represent the melody in our brains. It might also have to do with some of the findings of researchers Alan Baddely and Graham Hitch, and the model of **working memory**, the part of the brain that practices and repeats verbal information [source: Models of Working Memory]. In 1947 Baddely and Hitch discovered what they called the **phonological loop**, which is composed of the **phonological store** (your "inner ear," which remembers sounds in chronological order) and the **articulatory rehearsal system** (your "inner voice" which repeats these sounds in order to remember them). This area of the brain, is vital in early childhood for developing vocabulary and in adulthood for learning new languages.

10   Researchers have noted that the shorter and simpler the melody, the more likely it is to get stuck in your head—that is why some of the most common earworms are jingles and the choruses of pop songs. Earworms tend to occur more often in musicians than nonmusicians and in women more than men. Those suffering from obsessive-compulsive disorder can be particularly irritated by earworms. Sometimes, actually hearing the offending refrain (or replacing it with something equally infectious) can clear an earworm from the mind, but, unfortunately, there is no surefire way to get rid of them.

11   But now that jingles have been largely supplanted in advertising by pop songs, do they still have a future? Before we can answer that, we'll look more closely at their decline in popularity.

The Future of Jingles

12   Jingles were an advertiser's dream for the same reason the public can grow to hate them: You can't get them out of your head. But, as with most other stimuli, the more you experience them, the less of an effect they have on you. The widespread use of jingles on radio and TV has caused the newest generation of consumers to see them as hokey.

13   As we've mentioned, the commercial licensing of pop songs caused the decline of the jingle. In 1987, the Beatles tune "Revolution" was licensed for a Nike shoe campaign, which would prove to be the start of a revolution in advertising. As markets became increasingly clogged with indistinguishable products, it was no longer possible (or relevant) to tout the absolute supremacy of a product. To gain a loyal brand following, a good product was simply not enough—a company now had to represent a lifestyle or an identity. Piggybacking on emotional and cultural experience became the most effective way to sell products. It's widely known that most humans have a deep emotional connection

"The most refreshing taste around. . . . the one that never lets you down."

Give Me a Break, Give Me a Break . . .

Professor Kellaris has noted that experience is highly individual, but through several surveys he's been able to compile a list of the tunes (not necessarily jingles) most frequently cited as earworms. He calls it "The Playlist from Hell" [source: Earworms Research].

- The "Baby Back Ribs" Chili's jingle
- Baha Men: "Who Let the Dogs Out?"
- Queen: "We Will Rock You"
- The "Give Me a Break" Kit-Kat jingle
- Lalo Schifrin: "Mission: Impossible Theme"
- The Village people: "YMCA"
- Tag Team: "Whoomp, There It Is"
- The Tokens: "The Lion Sleeps Tonight"
- Richard Sherman: "It's a Small World"

---

to music—so instead of trying to form a new connection with consumers, why not let the *Rolling Stones, Mike and the Mechanics, Fall Out Boy,* or *Bob Seger* do it for you?

14   Music purists derided the commercialization of their favorite tunes, and musicians who wanted to be considered "serious artists" vowed never to allow their songs to be used in a marketing campaign. In the 1980s, Sting famously rebuffed an offer to use the *Police* song "Don't Stand So Close To Me" in a deodorant commercial (but he and his music later went on to star in a Jaguar campaign in 2000). But for all the cries of ruination, these ad campaigns have significantly helped revive the music of several critically acclaimed but widely unknown musicians—like Nick Drake, *Stereolab and Spiritualized.* In fact, marketers are quick to point out that much of the hype surrounding the licensing of pop songs for commercials comes from major record labels. Major labels are in crisis mode, desperately seeking new ways to promote their albums. Deals with advertisers—and prime-time shows like "Grey's Anatomy"—have helped record companies find new ways to promote their music and create additional revenue streams.

15   Product placement, the conspicuous inclusion of name-brand products in TV shows and movies, has also gained hold in recent years. With the invention of the digital video recorder (DVR), viewers can now fast-forward through commercials, forcing companies to find more clever ways to advertise their products.

16   Fashion is cyclical, though, and advertising is no exception to the rule. The ubiquity that led to the demise of jingles and the rise of licensed music is causing the pendulum to swing the other way. The cost of licensing music is getting higher as it becomes more popular, and jingles are being rediscovered for their promotional value in small and local markets. There may never be another "I'm stuck on Band-Aid, 'cause Band-Aid's stuck on me," but the jingle has proven itself as a tried-and-true technique for advertisers trying to worm their way into our brains.

7b   ANNOTATING

In many situations, highlighting alone is not a sufficient means of identifying what to learn. It does not give you any opportunity to comment on or react to the material. For this, you might want to use annotation. Annotating is an active reading process. It forces you to keep track of your comprehension as well as react to ideas. The chart on page 106 suggests various types of annotation used in marking a political science textbook chapter.

➤ NOW PRACTICE . . . ANNOTATING 1

Review the chart on p. 106 and then add annotations to the reading "How Commercial Jingles Work" on page 101.

MARGINAL ANNOTATION	TYPES OF ANNOTATION	EXAMPLE
	Circling unknown words	. . . redressing the apparent (asymmetry) of their relationship
	Marking definitions	def ⎡ To say that the balance of power favors one party over another is to introduce a disequilibrium. ⎦
	Marking examples	ex ⎡ . . . concessions may include negative sanctions, trade agreements . . . ⎦
	Numbering lists of ideas, causes, reasons, or events	components of power include ① self-image, ② population, ③ natural resources, and geography ④
	Placing asterisks next to important passages	* ⎡ Power comes from three primary sources . . .
	Putting question marks next to confusing passages	? → war prevention occurs through institutionalization of mediation . . .
	Making notes to yourself	Chech def in soc text power is the ability of an actor on the international stage to . . .
	Marking possible test items	T There are several key features in the relationship . . .
	Drawing arrows to show relationships	⎡ . . . natural resources . . . , . . . control of industrial ↓ manufacture capacity
	Writing comments, noting disagreements and similarities	Can terrorism be prevented through similar balance? war prevention through balance of power is . . .
	Marking summary statements	sum ⎡ the greater the degree of conflict, the more intricate will be . . . ⎦

➤ NOW PRACTICE . . . ANNOTATING 2

Add annotations to the reading "Economic Change, Ideology, and Private Life" on page 85.

7c   PARAPHRASING

A **paraphrase** is a restatement of a passage's ideas in your own words. The author's meaning is retained, but your wording, *not* the author's, is used. We use paraphrasing frequently in everyday speech. For example, when you relay a message from one person to another you convey the meaning but do not use the person's exact wording. A paraphrase can be used to make a passage's meaning clearer and often more concise. Paraphrasing is also an effective learning and review strategy in several situations.

First, paraphrasing is useful for portions of a text for which exact, detailed comprehension is required. For example, you might paraphrase the steps in solving a math problem, the process by which a blood transfusion is administered, or the levels of jurisdiction of the Supreme Court. Below is a paraphrase of a paragraph from "How Commercial Jingles Work."

A SAMPLE PARAPHRASE

PARAGRAPH	PARAPHRASE
There is some debate about this historical tidbit, though. Some point to a 1905 song called "In My Merry Oldsmobile," by Gus Edwards and Vincent Bryan, as the world's first jingle. But the song itself predates commercial radio—Oldsmobile appropriated it for radio in the late 1920s. So, we could probably more accurately call it the world's first pop song licensed for advertising.	Some dispute that jingles began with the Wheaties commercial. Some people think the first jingle was a song titled "In My Merry Oldsmobile," written in 1905 by Gus Edwards and Vincent Bryan. However, the song was published before the fisrt radio commercial. Oldsmobile decided to use the song in their commercials in the late 1920s. Actually, then, the song was the first to be licensed and used in advertising.

Paraphrasing is also a useful way to be certain you understand difficult or complicated material. If you can express the author's ideas in your own words, you can be certain you understand it, and if you find yourself at a loss for words—except for those of the author—you will know your understanding is incomplete.

Paraphrasing is also a useful strategy when working with material that is stylistically complex, poorly written, or overly formal, awkward, or biased. Use the following suggestions to paraphrase effectively.

1. **Read slowly and carefully.**
2. **Read the material through entirely before writing anything.**
3. **As you read, pay attention to exact meanings and relationships among ideas.**
4. **Paraphrase sentence by sentence.**
5. **Read each sentence and express the key idea in your own words.** Reread the original sentence; then look away and write your own sentence. Then reread the original and add anything you missed.
6. **Don't try to paraphrase word by word. Instead, work with ideas.**
7. **For words or phrases you are unsure of** or that are not words you feel comfortable using, check a dictionary to locate a more familiar meaning.
8. **You may combine several original sentences into a more concise paraphrase**.

> NOW PRACTICE . . . USING PARAPHRASING 1

Read each paragraph and the paraphrases following them. Answer the questions about the paraphrases.

Paragraph A

The use of silence can be an effective form of communication, but its messages and implications differ cross culturally. In Siberian households, the lowest status person is the in-marrying daughter, and she tends to speak very little. However, silence does not always indicate powerlessness. In American courts, comparison of speaking frequency between the judge, jury, and lawyers shows that lawyers, who have the least power, speak most, while the silent jury holds the most power.

—Miller, *Cultural Anthropology,* p. 302

Paraphrase 1

Silence carries a message as well as serves as a form of communication. Young married Siberian women speak very little, lawyers (who are powerless) speak a great deal, and the jury (which is most powerful) is silent.

Paraphrase 2

Silence is a way to communicate, but its meaning varies from culture to culture. In Siberia, women have low status in their husband's family and speak very little. In American courts, however, the most powerful group, the jury, is silent, while the least powerful—attorneys—speak the most.

Paraphrase 3

Silence has many meanings. Siberian women speak very little, indicating their low status. Lawyers speak a great deal, while a jury is silent.

1. Which is the best paraphrase of the paragraph? _____

2. Why are the other paraphrases less good? Answers will vary.

_____

_____

_____

_____

_____

Paragraph B

Today, the dominant family form in the United States is the child-free family, where a couple resides together and there are no children present in the household. With the aging of the baby boomer cohort, this family type is expected to increase steadily over time. If current trends continue, nearly three out of four U.S. households will be childless in another decade or so.

—Thompson and Hickey, *Society in Focus,* p. 355

Paraphrase 1

A child-free family is one where two adults live together and have no children. It is the dominant family form.

Paraphrase 2

The child-free family is dominant in the U.S. Baby boomers are having fewer children. Three out of four homes do not have children in them.

Paraphrase 3

The child-free family is dominant in the U.S. As baby boomers get older, there will be even more of these families. Three-quarters of all U.S. homes will be childless ten years from now.

3. Which is the best paraphrase of the paragraph?_____

4. Why are the other paraphrases less good?

_____

_____

_____

_____

NOW PRACTICE . . . PARAPHRASING 2

Write a paraphrase of paragraph 3 in the reading "How Commercial Jingles Work" on page 102.

7d   OUTLINING TO ORGANIZE IDEAS

Outlining is a writing strategy that can assist you in organizing information and pulling ideas together. It is also an effective way to pull together information from two or more sources—your textbook and class lectures, for example. Finally, outlining is a way to assess your comprehension and strengthen your recall. Use the following tips to write an effective outline.

MyReadingLab

To practice outlining, go to

➤ Study Plan
➤ Reading Skills
➤ Outlining and Summarizing

1. **Read an entire section and then jot down notes.** Do not try to outline while you are reading the material for the first time.
2. **As you read, be alert for organizational patterns** (see Chapter 4). These patterns will help you organize your notes.
3. **Record all the most important ideas in the briefest possible form.**
4. **Think of your outline as a list of the main ideas and supporting details of a selection.** Organize it to show how the ideas are related or to reflect the organization of the material.
5. **Write in your own words; do not copy sentences or parts of sentences from the selection.** Use words and short phrases to summarize ideas. Do not write in complete sentences.
6. **Use a system of indentation to separate main ideas and details.** As a general rule, the greater the importance of an idea, the closer it is placed to the left margin. Ideas of lesser importance are indented and appear closer to the center of the page. Your notes might follow a format such as this:

OUTLINE FORMAT

```
                    TOPIC
                Main Idea
                    Supporting detail
                        fact
                        fact
                    Supporting detail
                Main Idea
                    Supporting detail
                    Supporting detail
                        fact
                        fact
```

To further illustrate the techniques of outlining, study the notes shown in the sample outline below. They are based on a portion (paragraph 1 and the table included in the reading) of the textbook excerpt "Ending Relationships" on page 5.

A SAMPLE OUTLINE

I. Ending Relationships

   A. How to Break Up (Disengage)

      1. Five Strategies

         a) use a positive tone and express positive feelings

         b) blame the other person (negative identity management)

         c) give reasons for breakup (justification)

         d) reduce the strength of the relationship by avoiding the person or spending less time with him or her (behavioral de-escalation)

         e) reduce exclusivity (de-escalation)

      2. Strategy used depends on a person's goal

> **NOW PRACTICE . . . OUTLINING 1**

Read the following passage and complete the outline.

Gender Characteristics

Masculinity refers to attributes considered appropriate for males. In American society, these tradition- ally include being aggressive, athletic, physically active, logical, and dominant in social relationships with females. Conversely, femininity refers to attributes associated with appropriate behavior for females, which in America include passivity, docility, fragility, emotionality, and subordination to males. Research con- ducted by Carol Gilligan and her students at Harvard's Gender Studies Department indicate that children are acutely aware of and feel pressure to conform to these powerful gender traits by the age of 4. Some people insist that gender traits such as male aggressiveness are innate characteristics linked to sex and do not depend on cultural definitions. However, the preponderance of research indicates that females and males can be equally aggressive under different social and cultural conditions and that levels of aggression vary as widely within the sexes as between them.

—adapted from Thompson and Hickey, *Society in Focus,* p. 285

Gender Characteristics

A. Masculinity

    1. attributes society believes appropriate for males

    2. include _____

    _____

B. Femininity

    1. _____

    2. include _____

    and subordination to males

C. _____ are aware of and feel pressure to conform to gender

    expectations by _____

D. Link to Sex

    1. some people believe linked to sex

    2. research shows both sexes can be equally aggressive and levels of

    _____

> **NOW PRACTICE . . . OUTLINING 2**

Finish outlining the textbook excerpt "Ending a Relationship" on page 5.

7e   MAPPING TO SHOW RELATIONSHIPS

Mapping is a way of drawing a diagram to describe how a topic and its related ideas are connected. Mapping is a visual means of learning by writing; it organizes and consolidates information.

This section discusses four types of maps: conceptual maps, process diagrams, part and function diagrams, and time lines.

Conceptual Maps

A conceptual map is a diagram that presents ideas spatially rather than in list form. It is a "picture" of how ideas are related. Use the following steps in constructing a conceptual map.

1. **Identify the topic and write it in the center of the page.**
2. **Identify ideas, aspects, parts, and definitions that are related to the topic.** Draw each one on a line radiating from the topic.
3. **As you discover details that further explain an idea already recorded, draw new lines branching from the idea that the details explain.**

A conceptual map of Part One of this book is shown below. This map shows only the major topics included in Part One. Maps can be much more detailed and include more information than the one shown, depending on the purpose for drawing it.

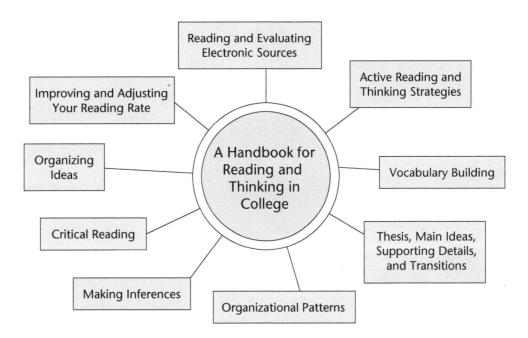

> **NOW PRACTICE . . . DRAWING A CONCEPTUAL MAP 1**

Read the following paragraph about social institutions. Complete the conceptual map that presents the ideas contained in this paragraph.

Society cannot survive without social institutions. A social institution is a set of widely shared beliefs, norms and procedures necessary for meeting the basic needs of society. The most important institutions are family, education, religion, economy, and politics. They have stood the test of time, serving society well. The family institution leads countless people to produce and raise children to ensure that they can eventually take over from the older generation the task of keeping society going. The educational institution teaches the young to become effective contributors to the welfare—such as the order, stability, or prosperity—of society. The religious institution fulfills spiritual needs, making earthly lives seem more meaningful and therefore more bearable or satisfying. The economic institution provides food, clothing, shelter, employment, banking, and other goods and services that we need to live. The political institution makes and enforces laws to prevent criminals and other similar forces from destabilizing society.

—Thio, *Sociology,* pp. 35–36

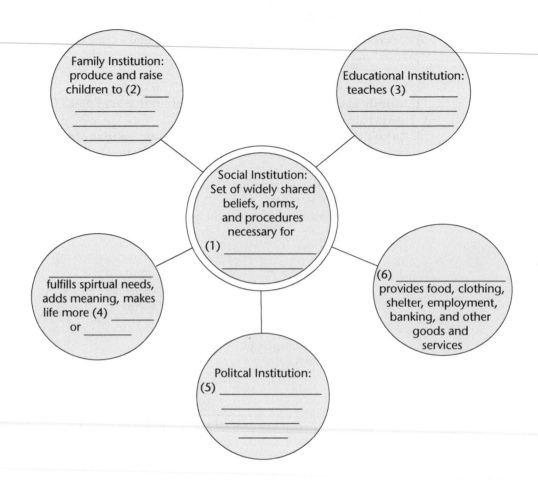

> NOW PRACTICE . . . DRAWING A CONCEPTUAL MAP 2

Draw a conceptual map for the textbook excerpt "Ending a Relationship" on page 5.

Process Diagrams

In the technologies and the natural sciences, as well as in many other courses, *processes* are an important part of the course content. A diagram that visually describes the steps, variables, or parts of a process will make learning easier. For example, the diagram below visually describes the steps in the search process for using library sources.

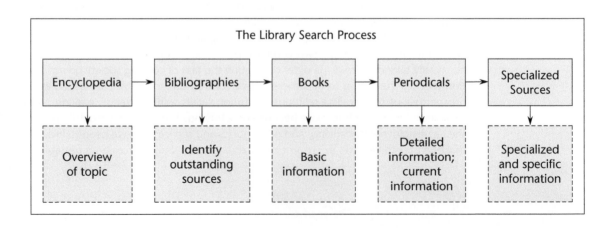

> **NOW PRACTICE . . . DRAWING A PROCESS DIAGRAM 1**

The following paragraph describes how a bill becomes a law. Read the paragraph and then complete the process diagram that illustrates this procedure.

Federal criminal laws must originate in the House of Representatives or the U.S. Senate. A senator or representative introduces a proposal (known as a bill) to create a new law or modify an existing law. The merits of the bill are debated in the House or Senate and a vote is taken. If the bill receives a majority vote, it is passed on to the other house of Congress where it is again debated and put to a vote. If any changes are made, the amended bill must be returned to the house of Congress where it

Drawing a Process Diagram – 1

The Making of Federal Criminal Laws

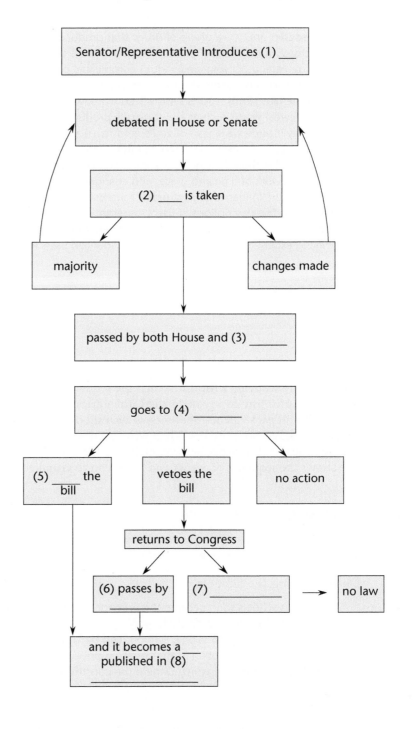

originated and voted on again. This process continues until the House and Senate agree on a single version of the bill. The bill is then forwarded to the president, who can sign the bill into law, veto it or take no action, in which case the bill dies automatically when Congress adjourns. If the president vetoes a bill, Congress can pass the law over the president's veto by a two-thirds vote of both houses. Whether approved by the president and the Congress or by the Congress alone, a bill becomes a law when it is published in the *U.S. Criminal Codes.*

—Fagin, *Criminal Justice,* p. 107

➤ NOW PRACTICE . . . DRAWING A PROCESS DIAGRAM 2

The following paragraph describes the sequential effects of taking the psychedelic drug LSD. Read the paragraph and then draw a process diagram that describes this response sequence. Compare your diagram with those of several other students.

Psychedelics are . . . a group of drugs that produce hallucinations and various other phenomena that very closely mimic certain mental disorders. These drugs include lysergic acid diethylamide (LSD), mescaline, peyote, psilocybin, and various commercial preparations such as Sernyl and Ditran.

Of these, LSD is probably the best known, although its use has apparently diminished since its heyday in the late 1960s. LSD is synthesized from lysergic acid produced by a fungus (ergot) that is parasitic on cereal grains such as rye. It usually produces responses in a particular sequence. The initial reactions may include weakness, dizziness and nausea. These symptoms are followed by a distortion of time and space. The senses may become intensified and strangely intertwined—that is, sounds can be "seen" and colors "heard." Finally, there may be changes in mood, a feeling of separation of the self from the framework of time and space, and changes in the perception of the self. The sensations experienced under the influence of psychedelics are unlike anything encountered within the normal range of experiences. The descriptions of users therefore can only be puzzling to nonusers. Some users experience bad trips or "bummers," which have been known to produce long-term effects. Bad trips can be terrifying experiences and can occur in experienced users for no apparent reason.

—Donatelle, *Health,* p. 179

Time Lines

When you are studying a topic in which the sequence or order of events is a central focus, a time line is a helpful way to organize the information. Time lines are especially useful in history courses. To map a sequence of events, draw a single line and mark it off in year intervals, just as a ruler is marked off in inches. Then write events next to the correct year. For example, the following time line displays major events during the presidency of Franklin D. Roosevelt. The time line shows the sequence of events and helps you to visualize them clearly.

➤ NOW PRACTICE . . . DRAWING A TIME LINE

The following passage reviews the chronology of events in public school desegregation. Read the selection and then draw a time line that will help you to visualize these historical events.

Desegregating the Schools

The nation's schools soon became the primary target of civil-rights advocates. The NAACP concentrated first on universities, successfully waging an intensive legal battle to win admission for qualified blacks to graduate and professional schools. Led by Thurgood Marshall, NAACP lawyers then took on the broader issue of segregation in the country's public schools. Challenging the 1896 Supreme Court decision (*Plessy v. Ferguson*) which upheld the constitutionality of separate but equal public facilities,

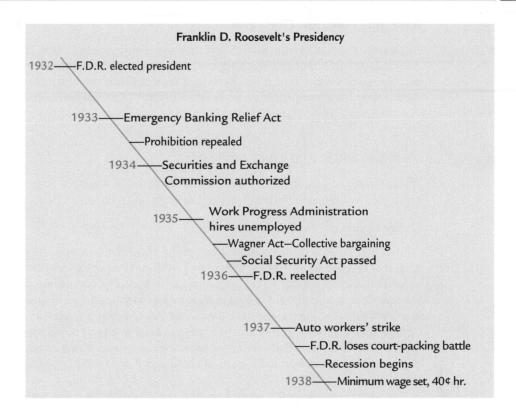

Franklin D. Roosevelt's Presidency

1932——F.D.R. elected president

1933——Emergency Banking Relief Act

——Prohibition repealed

1934——Securities and Exchange Commission authorized

1935—— Work Progress Administration hires unemployed

——Wagner Act–Collective bargaining

——Social Security Act passed

1936——F.D.R. reelected

1937——Auto workers' strike

——F.D.R. loses court-packing battle

——Recession begins

1938——Minimum wage set, 40¢ hr.

Marshall argued that even substantially equal but separate schools did profound psychological damage to black children and thus violated the Fourteenth Amendment.

A unanimous Supreme Court agreed in its 1954 decision in the case of *Brown v. Board of Education of Topeka.* Chief Justice Earl Warren, recently appointed by President Eisenhower, wrote the landmark opinion which flatly declared that "separate educational facilities are inherently unequal." To divide grade-school children "solely because of their race," Warren argued, "generates a feeling of inferiority as to their status in the community that may affect their hearts and minds in a way unlikely ever to be undone." Despite this sweeping language, Warren realized that it would be difficult to change historic patterns of segregation quickly. Accordingly, in 1955 the Court ruled that implementation should proceed "with all deliberate speed" and left the details to the lower federal courts.

The process of desegregating the schools proved to be agonizingly slow. Officials in the border states quickly complied with the Court's ruling, but states deeper in the South responded with a policy of massive resistance. Local White Citizen's Councils organized to fight for retention of racial separation; 101 congressmen and senators signed a Southern Manifesto in 1956 which denounced the *Brown* decision as "a clear abuse of judicial power." School boards, encouraged by this show of defiance, found a variety of ways to evade the Court's ruling. The most successful was the passage of pupil-placement laws . . . .

Southern leaders mistook Ike's silence for tacit support of segregation. In 1957, Governor Orville Faubus of Arkansas called out the national guard to prevent the integration of Little Rock's Central High School on grounds of a threat to public order . . . .

Despite the snail's pace of school desegregation, the *Brown* decision led to other advances. In 1957, the Eisenhower administration proposed the first general civil-rights legislation since Reconstruction. Strong southern resistance and compromise by both the administration and Senate Democratic leader Lyndon B. Johnson of Texas weakened the bill considerably. The final act, however, did create a permanent Commission for Civil Rights, one of Truman's original goals. It also provided for federal efforts aimed at "securing and protecting the right to vote." A second civil-rights act in 1960 slightly strengthened the voting-rights section.

—Divine, *America Past and Present,* pp. 890–891

Part and Function Diagrams

In courses that deal with the use and description or classification of physical objects, labeled drawings are an important learning tool. In a human anatomy and physiology course, for example, the easiest way to learn the parts and functions of the brain is to draw it. To study it, you would sketch the brain and test your recall of each part and its function.

> NOW PRACTICE . . . DRAWING A PART AND FUNCTION DIAGRAM

The following paragraph describes the layers of the earth. Read the paragraph and then draw a diagram that will help you to visualize how the earth is structured.

Outer Layers of the Earth

The Earth's crust and the uppermost part of the mantle are known as the *lithosphere*. This is a fairly rigid zone that extends about 100 km below the Earth's surface. The crust extends some 60 km or so under continents, but only about 10 km below the ocean floor. The continental crust has a lower density than the oceanic crust. It is primarily a light granitic rock rich in the silicates of aluminum, iron, and magnesium. In a simplified view, the continental crust can be thought of as layered: On top of a layer of igneous rock (molten rock that has hardened, such as granite) lies a thin layer of sedimentary rocks (rocks formed by sediment and fragments that water deposited, such as limestone and sandstone); there is also a soil layer deposited during past ages in the parts of continents that have had no recent volcanic activity or mountain building.

Sandwiched between the lithosphere and the lower mantle is the partially molten material known as the *asthenosphere,* about 150 km thick. It consists primarily of iron and magnesium silicates that readily deform and flow under pressure.

—Berman and Evans, *Exploring the Cosmos*, p. 145

7f   SUMMARIZING TO CONDENSE IDEAS

MyReadingLab

To practice summarizing, go to

> Study Plan
> Reading Skills
> Outlining and Summarizing

Like outlining, summarizing is an excellent way to learn from your reading and to increase recall. A **summary** is a brief statement that reviews the key points of what you have read. It condenses an author's ideas or arguments into sentences written in your own words. A summary contains only the gist of the text, with limited explanation, background information, or supporting detail. Writing a summary is a step beyond recording the author's ideas; a summary must pull together the writer's ideas by condensing and grouping them. Before writing a summary, be sure you understand the material and have identified the writer's major points. Then use the following suggestions:

1. **As a first step, highlight or write brief notes on the material.**
2. **Write one sentence that states the writer's overall concern or most important idea.** To do this, ask yourself what one topic the material is about. Then ask what point the writer is trying to make about that topic. This sentence will be the topic sentence of your summary.
3. **Be sure to paraphrase, using your own words rather than those of the author.**
4. **Review the major supporting information that the author gives to explain the major idea.**
5. **The amount of detail you include, if any, depends on your purpose for writing the summary.** For example, if you are writing a summary of a television documentary for a research paper, it might be more detailed than if you were writing it to jog your memory for a class discussion.
6. **Normally, present ideas in the summary in the same order in which they appeared in the original material.**
7. **If the writer presents a clear opinion or expresses an attitude toward the subject matter, include it in your summary.**

8. **If the summary is for your own use only and is not to be submitted as an assignment, do not worry about sentence structure.** Some students prefer to write summaries using words and phrases rather than complete sentences.

A sample summary of the article "Ending a Relationship", which appears on page 5, is shown below.

A SAMPLE SUMMARY

It is inevitable that some relationships do end. As a relationship ends, there are two concerns: how to end it and how to deal with the breakup. There are five ways to end a relationship, called disengagement strategies. They are: use a positive tone, blame the other person, give reasons for the breakup, reduce the intensity of the relationship, and reduce the exclusivity of the relationship. Breakups always cause stress. Six ways to deal with a breakup are to avoid loneliness and depression, avoid jumping into a new relationship, build self-esteem, get rid of hurtful reminders, seek help and support from family and friends, and avoid repeating the same mistakes.

➤ **NOW PRACTICE . . . SUMMARIZING 1**

Complete this summary of the passage about psychedelic drugs on page 114.

Psychedelic drugs cause _____ and can cause reactions mimicking _____. Examples of these drugs include _____. LSD is the best known and was most popular in _____. It is created from _____, which comes from a _____. Initially, it causes weakness, _____, and _____ and later a distortion of time and space. It causes senses to be _____. The drug affects _____, creates a feeling of distance, and creates changes in _____. The sensations resulting are outside _____. _____ can have _____ consequences and the reason for them is not understood.

—Donatelle, *Health: The Basics,* p. 179

➤ **NOW PRACTICE . . . SUMMARIZING 2**

Write a summary of the section titled "Why are jingles so catchy?" (paragraphs 7–11) of the article "How Commercial Jingles Work" on page 103.

8 Improving and Adjusting Your Reading Rate

The speed at which you read, called your reading rate, is measured in words per minute (WPM). What should your reading rate be? Is it better to be a fast or slow reader? You should be able to read at 100, 200, 300, and even 400 words per minute, depending on what you are reading and why you are reading it. You should be both a slow and a fast reader; when you are reading difficult, complicated material you should read slowly. When reading easy material or material that you do not have to remember for a test, you can afford to read faster. This section will offer some suggestions for improving your reading rate and explain how to adjust your reading rate.

8a   IMPROVING YOUR READING RATE

Here are a few suggestions for improving your overall reading rate.

1. **Try to read a little faster.** Sometimes by just being conscious of your reading rate, you can improve it slightly.
2. **Be sure to preview** (see Chapter 1, Section 1b). Previewing familiarizes you with the material and allows you to understand what you are reading more easily, thereby enabling you to read slightly faster.
3. **Improve your concentration.** If your mind wanders while you are reading, it will cost you time. Eliminate distractions, read in a place conducive to study, use writing to keep you mentally and physically alert, and alternate between different types of reading assignments.
4. **Set time goals.** Before you begin an assignment, decide approximately how much time it should take. Without a time goal, it is easy to drift and wander through an assignment rather than working straight through it efficiently.

8b   ADJUSTING YOUR RATE TO MEET COMPREHENSION DEMANDS

Do you read the newspaper in the same way and at the same speed at which you read a biology textbook? Do you read an essay for your English class in the same way and at the same speed at which you read a mystery novel? Surprisingly, many people do.

If you are an efficient reader, however, you read the newspaper more quickly and in a different way than you read a biology textbook. The newspaper is usually easier to read, and you have a different purpose for reading it. Efficient readers adapt their speed and comprehension levels to suit the material.

Rate and comprehension are the two main factors that you must keep in balance; as your reading rate increases, your comprehension may decrease. Your goal is to achieve a balance that suits the nature of the material and your purpose for reading it. The following steps will help you learn to vary your reading rate.

1. **Assess how difficult the assignment is.** Factors such as the difficulty of the vocabulary, length, and organization all affect text difficulty. Usually, longer or poorly organized material is more difficult to read than shorter or well-organized material. Numerous typographical aids (italics, headings, etc.) can make material easier to read. As you preview an assignment, notice these features and estimate how difficult the material will be to read. There is no rule

to use when adjusting your speed to compensate for differing degrees of difficulty. Instead, use your judgment to adjust your reading rate and style to the material.

2. **Assess your familiarity with and interest in the subject.** Your knowledge of and interest in a subject influence how fast you can read it. Material you are interested in or that you know something about will be easier for you to read, and you can increase your speed.

3. **Define your purpose.** The reason you are reading an assignment should influence how you read it. Different situations demand different levels of comprehension and recall. For example, you can read an article in *Time* magazine assigned as a supplementary reading in your sociology class faster than you can read your sociology text, because the magazine assignment does not require as high a level of recall and analysis.

4. **Decide what, if any, follow-up activity is required.** Will you have to pass a multiple-choice exam on the content? Will you be participating in a class discussion? Will you summarize the information in a short paper? The activities that follow your reading determine, in part, the level of comprehension that is required. Passing an exam requires a very high level of reading comprehension, whereas preparing for a class discussion requires a more moderate level of comprehension or retention.

Table 8.1 on this page shows the level of comprehension required for various types of material and gives approximate reading rates that are appropriate for each level.

TABLE 8.1 LEVELS OF COMPREHENSION

DESIRED LEVEL OF COMPREHENSION	TYPE OF MATERIAL	PURPOSE IN READING	RANGE OF READING RATES
Complete, 100%	Poetry, legal documents, argumentative writing	Analysis, criticism, evaluation	Less than 200 WPM
High, 80–100%	Textbooks, manuals, research documents	High comprehension, recall for exams, writing research reports, following directions	200–300 WPM
Moderate, 60–80%	Novels, paperbacks, newspapers, magazines	Entertainment, enjoyment, general information	300–500 WPM

➤ NOW PRACTICE . . . ADJUSTING YOUR READING RATE

For each of the following situations, define your purpose and indicate the level of comprehension that seems appropriate.

1. Reading a credit card agreement or an insurance policy before signing it.

   Purpose: _____

   _____

   Comprehension level: _____

2. Reading a critical essay that analyzes a Shakespearean sonnet you are studying in a literature class.

   Purpose: _____

   _____

   Comprehension level: _____

3. Reading an encyclopedia entry on poverty to narrow down a term paper assignment to a manageable topic.

   Purpose: _____

   _____

   Comprehension level: _____

4. Reading a newspaper article on a recent incident in the Middle East for your political science class.

   Purpose: _____

   _____

   Comprehension level: _____

5. Reading an excerpt from a historical novel set in the Civil War period for your American history class.

   Purpose: _____

   _____

   Comprehension level: _____

9 Reading and Evaluating Electronic Sources

Most of today's college students and teachers learned to read using print text. We have been reading print text much longer than electronic text; consequently our brains have developed numerous strategies or "work orders" for reading traditional printed material.

Electronic text has a wider variety of formats and presents us with more variables than traditional text. Because electronic text is a relatively new form of text, our brains need to develop new strategies in order to understand Web sites. And because Web sites vary widely in both purpose and reliability, it is important that your reading be critical.

9a DEVELOPING NEW WAYS OF THINKING AND READING

The first step in reading electronic text easily and effectively is to understand how it is different from print text. A print source is linear—it goes in a straight line from idea to idea. Electronic sources, in contrast, tend to be multidirectional. Using links, you can skip around easily. (See the accompanying figure.) Therefore, reading electronic sources demands a different type of thinking from reading print sources.

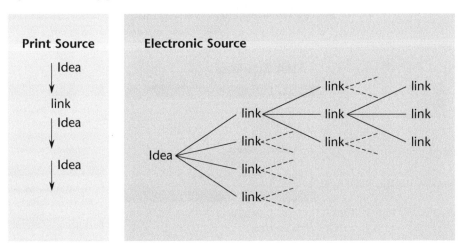

Using electronic text also requires new reading strategies. You need to change and adapt how you read. To do this, focus on your purpose, pay attention to how information is organized, and use links to find the information you need.

Focus on Your Purpose

Focus clearly on your purpose for visiting the site. What information do you need? Because you must create your own path through the site, fix in your mind what you are looking for. If you don't, you may wander aimlessly, waste valuable time, or even become lost, following numerous links that lead you farther and farther away from the site at which you began.

Pay Attention to How Information Is Organized

Because you can navigate through a Web site in many different ways, it is important to have the right expectations and to make several decisions before you begin. Some Web sites are much better organized than others. Some have clear headings and labels that make it easy to discover how to proceed; others do not and will require more thought before you begin. For example, if you are reading an article with as many as 10 or 15 underlined words (links), there is no prescribed order to follow and these links are not categorized in any way. Below are some suggestions on how to stay organized when using a Web site.

1. **Use the site map, if provided, to discover what information is available and how it is organized.** A sample site map for the American Management Association Web site is shown below. Notice that the links are categorized according to the types of information (seminars, books, membership) a user may need.
2. **Consider the order in which you want to take in information.** Choose an order in which to explore links; avoid randomly clicking on link buttons. Doing so is somewhat like randomly choosing pages to read out of a reference book. Do you need definitions first? Do you want historical background first? Your decision will be partly influenced by your learning style.
3. **Consider writing brief notes to yourself as you explore a complicated Web site.** Alternatively, you could print the home page and jot notes on it. You can also save Web pages on to a disk or save them on your computer as a text file.
4. **Expect shorter, less detailed sentences and paragraphs.** Much online communication tends to be briefer and more concise than in traditional sources. As a result, you may have to mentally fill in transitions and make inferences about the relationships among ideas. For example, you may have to infer similarities and differences or recognize cause-and-effect connections on your own.

Use Links to Find the Information You Need

Links are unique to electronic text. The suggestions below will help you use links to find the information you need.

1. **Plan on exploring links to find complete and detailed information.** Both remote links (those that take you to another site) and related links (within a site) are intended to provide more detailed information on topics introduced on the home page.
2. **As you follow links, be sure to bookmark your original site and other useful sites you come across so you can find them again.** Bookmarking is a feature of your Internet browser that allows you to record Web site addresses and access them later by simply clicking on the site name. Different Web browsers use different terms for this function. Firefox and Safari use the term *Bookmarks;* Microsoft Explorer calls it *Favorites.* In addition, the browsers have a *History* or "Back" feature that allows a user to retrace the steps of the current search.
3. **If you use a site or a link that provides many pages of continuous paragraphs, print the material and read it offline.**
4. **If you find you are lacking background on a topic, use links to help fill in the gaps, or search for a different, less technical Web site on the same topic.**

> NOW PRACTICE . . . NEW WAYS OF THINKING AND READING 1

Visit one of the following Web sites. Locate the information needed and take brief notes to record what you find.

URL	Information to Locate

1. **http://www.consumer.gov**   List three tips for buying a used car.

_____

_____

_____

_____

2. **http://www.bls.gov.oco/**   What is the job outlook for CAD operators?

_____

3. **http://thomas.loc.gov/**   Why are lights and ringing bells used in parts of the
   home/lawsmade.toc.html   Capitol building and U.S. House and Senate
                                     office buildings?

_____

_____

_____

_____

> NOW PRACTICE . . . NEW WAYS OF THINKING AND READING 2

For one of the Web sites you visited above or a new site of your choice, follow at least three links and then answer the following questions.

1. What type of information did each contain?

_____

2. Was each source reliable? How do you know?

_____

3. Which was the easiest to read and follow? Why?

_____

9b   DISCOVERING THE PURPOSE OF WEB SITES

There are millions of Web sites and they vary widely in purpose. Table 9.1 below summarizes five primary types of Web sites.

9c   EVALUATING WEB SITES

Once you have become familiar with the organization of a Web site and determined its purpose, you should evaluate it. To do this, consider its content, accuracy, authority, objectivity, timeliness, and usability.

Evaluate the Content of a Web Site

When evaluating the content of a Web site, evaluate its appropriateness, its level of technical detail, its completeness, and its links.

Evaluate Appropriateness. To be worthwhile a Web site should contain the information you need. It should answer one or more of your search questions. If the site only touches upon answers to your questions but does not address them in detail, check the links on the site to see if they will lead you to more detailed information. If they do not, search for a more useful site.

Evaluate the Level of Technical Detail. A Web site should contain a level of technical detail that is suited to your purpose. Some sites may provide information that is too sketchy for your search purposes; others assume a level of background knowledge or technical sophistication that you lack. For example, if you are writing a short, introductory-level paper on threats to the survival of marine animals, information on the Web site of the Scripps Institution of Oceanography (**http://www.sio.ucsd.edu**) may be too technical and contain more information

TABLE 9.1 TYPES OF WEB SITES

TYPE	PURPOSE	DESCRIPTION	URL EXTENSION
Informational	To present facts, information, and research data	May contain reports, statistical data, results of research studies, and reference materials	.edu or .gov
News	To provide current information on local, national, and international news	Often supplements print newspapers, periodicals, and television news programs	.com
Advocacy	To promote a particular cause or point of view	Usually concerned with a controversial issue; often sponsored by nonprofit groups	.org
Personal	To provide information about an individual and his or her interests and accomplishments	May list publications or include the individual's résumé	URL will vary; may contain .com or .org or may contain a tilde (~)
Commercial	To promote goods or services	May provide news and information related to their products	.com

PART TWO

Readings for Academic Disciplines

Introduction: Reading Across the Disciplines

Brian was a first-year student taking a full-time course load: Introductory Psychology, College Writing, Biology, and World History. He had received good grades in high school and was confident he would do well at a community college where he was majoring in pre-elementary education. After about the fourth week of the term, Brian realized he was not doing as well as he expected to do in his courses. He spent approximately 30 hours per week studying, but was not earning top grades. He got C's on three biology labs, a B minus on a response essay for his writing class, a 70 on his first history exam, and 65, 75, and 70 on the first three psychology quizzes. Brian knew he would probably pass all of his courses, but his goal was to earn grades that would ensure his transfer to a four-year college of his choice.

Brian visited the campus Academic Skills Center and requested tutors for three of his courses. After the first few tutoring sessions he realized that his tutors used a unique approach to each of the disciplines. Specifically, they seemed to read, study, and think differently in each. Brian learned to vary his approach to the material he was studying in different courses. Before, he had studied each course the same way; now he has realized that different disciplines require specialized thinking skills.

Brian's realization is confirmed by a national research study titled "Understanding University Success"; it identified the critical thinking skills essential to success in various disciplines. The table on this page demonstrates that different disciplines require different types of thinking and includes many of the skills identified in the research study. Study the table to get an idea of the types of thinking skills involved in each disciplinary grouping.

READINGS FOR ACADEMIC DISCIPLINES

Each college course you take will be different; in each you will be asked to master a unique set of information, learn new terminology, and demonstrate what you have learned. This section of the text provides you with opportunities to practice reading material from a wide range of disciplines, learn new terminology, and demonstrate your mastery of content through a variety of test-taking methods.

ADAPTING YOUR THINKING TO ACADEMIC DISCIPLINES

DISCIPLINE	SPECIALIZED TYPES OF THINKING REQUIRED	EXAMPLES
Social Sciences (sociology, psychology, anthropology, economics)	Evaluate ideas, make generalizations, be aware of bias, follow and evaluate arguments	Studying patterns of child development, examining causes of age discrimination, comparing cultures
Mathematics	Think sequentially, reason logically, evaluate solutions	Solving word problems, understanding theorems

(continued on next page)

(continued from preceding page)

DISCIPLINE	SPECIALIZED TYPES OF THINKING REQUIRED	EXAMPLES
Natural and Life Sciences (biology, chemistry, physiology, physics, astronomy, earth science)	Grasp relationships, ask questions, understand processes, evaluate evidence	Studying the theory of evolution, examining the question of life in outer space
Arts (music, painting, sculpture)	Evaluate the work of others, express your own ideas, critique your own work	Evaluating a sculpture, revising a musical score
Applied Fields (career fields, technology, business)	Follow processes and procedures, make applications, make and evaluate decisions	Evaluating a patient (nursing), finding a bug in a computer program (computer technology)

Part Two contains readings for each of the following disciplines: social sciences, communication/speech, anthropology, arts/humanities/literature, public policy/contemporary issues, political science/government/history, business/advertising/economics, technology/computers, health-related fields, life sciences, physical sciences/mathematics, and workplace/career fields.

When taking courses in these fields, you will read textbooks, but you will also read a variety of print and online sources, as well. To give you practice reading a wide range of sources, most chapters in Part Two contain one textbook reading, and two non-textbook readings. The readings are preceded by information, tips, and questions intended to guide your reading. They are followed by questions that will help you evaluate your reading and practice with different test-taking formats. The types of questions and activities are intended to prepare you for future work in the different disciplines. They are in different formats so as to familiarize you with the variety of testing and evaluation methods used in these disciplines. Included are multiple-choice, fill-in-the-blank, true-false, and matching tests, as well as open-ended questions and brief writing assignments. Here is a review of the types of questions and activities you will work with.

- **Understanding the Thesis and Other Main Ideas.** These questions help you identify the most important information in each reading.
- **Identifying Details.** These questions help you discover the relationship between main ideas and details and distinguish between more and less important details.
- **Recognizing Methods of Organization and Transitions.** This activity guides you in discovering organizational patterns and using transitions.
- **Reviewing and Organizing Ideas.** This activity shows you how to learn the material in a reading. You will learn and practice a number of different review and study strategies, including mapping, summarizing, outlining, and paraphrasing.
- **Figuring Out Inferred Meanings and Thinking Critically.** These two sections demonstrate the types of thinking and reasoning that are expected in college courses. The questions take you beyond the literal (factual) content of the selection and guide you in applying many of the critical thinking skills you learned in Part One.
- **Building Vocabulary.** This section gives you practice in learning the terminology that is an essential part of each new academic discipline. You will learn how to use both context and word parts to master new terminology.
- **Selecting a Learning/Study Strategy.** Choosing appropriate learning and study methods is important in every discipline. This activity guides you in identifying appropriate ways to learn and study the material in a selection.

- **Exploring Ideas Through Discussion and Writing.** Because class participation is an important part of many college courses, this activity provides topics that can be used for class discussion. As many college courses involve writing papers and research reports and taking written exams, this activity also provides an opportunity for you to begin to apply your writing skills to various disciplines.
- **Beyond the Classroom to the Web.** Many instructors expect their students to extend and apply their learning to situations outside the classroom. This activity extends your learning beyond the reading selection and provides ways you can use or apply new information.

10 Social Sciences

The **social sciences** are concerned with the study of people, their history and development, and how they interact and function together. These disciplines deal with the political, economic, social, cultural, and behavioral aspects of people. Social scientists study how we live, how we act, how we dress, how we get along with others, and how our culture is similar to and different from other cultures. By reading in the social sciences, you will learn a great deal about yourself and those around you. In "Applying Principles of Learning to Video Games" you will read about efforts to use video game design principles in academic learning. "The New Flirting Game" examines a much more personal form of human interaction—flirtation. "Coming Into My Own" considers a social problem—racial discrimination—and shows how a black neurosurgeon dealt with it. Use the following tips when reading in the social sciences.

TIPS FOR READING IN THE SOCIAL SCIENCES

- **Pay attention to terminology.** The social sciences use precise terminology to describe their subject matter. Learn terms that describe behavior, name stages and processes, and label principles, theories, and models. Also learn the names of important researchers and theorists. As you read, highlight new terms. You can transfer them later to index cards or a vocabulary log for that course.

- **Understand explanations and theories.** The social sciences are devoted, in part, to explaining how people behave as they do. In this chapter you will read an explanation of how people flirt and why people tell stories, for example. As you read theories and explanations, ask these questions: What behavior is being explained? What evidence is offered that it is correct? Of what use is the explanation?

- **Look for supporting evidence.** As you read, look for details, examples, anecdotes, or research evidence that demonstrates that the writer's explanations are reasonable or correct. When reading "The New Flirting Game" look for the author's examples of women's flirting behaviors, for instance. Often, too, in the social sciences, the examples and applications are highly interesting and will help you remember the theories they illustrate.

- **Make comparisons and connections.** Try to see relationships and make comparisons. Draw connections between topics. Draw charts or maps that compare different explanations, for example.

- **Make practical applications.** As you read, consider how the information is useful to you in real-life situations. Make marginal notes of situations that illustrate what you are reading about. Write comments, for example, about what you have observed about flirting or about instances of racial discrimination.

SELECTION 1

Applying Principles of Learning to Video Games

Samuel E. Wood, Ellen Green Wood, and Denise Boyd

This reading selection from a textbook titled *Mastering the World of Psychology* discusses how video game design principles can be used to make academic learning and instruction more engaging.

➤ PREVIEWING THE READING

Using the steps listed on page 4, preview the reading selection. When you have finished, complete the following items.

1. What is the subject of this selection?

    _____

2. List the five principles of learning that are described in this selection.

    a. _____

    b. _____

    c. _____

    d. _____

    e. _____

MAKING CONNECTIONS

Think about a board game or a video game that you enjoy playing. What makes it engaging to you?

➤ READING TIP

As you read, look for and highlight the ways that game-based instruction can enhance learning.

Applying Principles of Learning to Video Games

1   Imagine that you are a **cybernetic** human who has narrowly escaped from the final battle in an alien war against planet Earth, only to find yourself marooned on a mysterious space station known as *Mastering the World of Psychology,* [the title of the textbook from which this reading was taken] or *MWP3E,* as it is more often called. To get back to Earth, you must unlock the secrets of *MWP3E.* You soon learn that *MWP3E* is inhabited by a ruthless alien army made up of killing machines who will stop at nothing to protect their secrets, even if they must resort to destroying every living being in the galaxy, including themselves, by means of a merciless horde of parasites. Your task seems impossible, but you have many weapons at your disposal. Do you think you are up to the challenge?

2   If you are one of the millions of college students who enjoy playing the video game *Halo,* these words have a familiar ring. Of course, learning psychology isn't among the obstacles that the game's heroes have to overcome. Suppose, though, that your psychology course was structured like a role-playing video game. Do you think you would learn more than you might from a conventional course?

3   Many educators argue that video game design principles should be incorporated into computer-assisted and online courses. To critics who scoff at the idea of game-based instruction, proponents point out that educational board games, for example, are a staple of both elementary and secondary classrooms. Thus, advocates say, using video games in classrooms represents nothing more than an update of an instructional resource that has been employed by teachers throughout the ages.

4   One of the most vocal advocates of applying video game design principles to instruction, Professor Rod Riegle of Illinois State University, launched what he claims to be the first role-playing game (RPG) online course in 2000. Riegle's undergraduate education course features an interactive learning environment that includes sights, sounds, and language that are similar to those found in fantasy-based electronic games. Students are cast as "Change Agents" who must do battle against "Status Quo," a fictional character who represent forces in education that oppose new technologies and methods of instruction. Assignments consist of four **hierarchical** quests that require mastery of progressively difficult concepts and technological skills. When each quest is completed to Riegle's satisfaction, he awards students a title. "Future Lords" are students who have completed Quest 1, and "Hidden Masters" are those who have finished Quest 2. Those who have completed Quest 3 are known as "Infonauts," and their classmates who have finished Quest 4 are called "CyberGuides."

hierarchical (paragraph 4) organized according to different levels

5   Professor Riegle's course is very popular among students at Ilinois State University. However, before other educators adopt Riegle's strategies, most of them want to know how game-based instruction affects students' learning. Experiments carried out by Richard Mayer, an educational psychologist at the University of California at Santa Barbara, suggest that a game-based learning environment such as Riegle's RPG course could be quite effective if the instructor takes care to ensure that the structure of the course itself does not distract students from the content that they are expected to learn. However, the strongest argument in favor of game-based instruction is its potential for enhancing student engagement. To understand how a course that is structured like a video game might increase student engagement, we must understand why video games are engaging. Here's how the principles of learning can be used to explain how video games attract and hold players' interest.

- *Learning through association of stimuli:* The cues associated with games—their names, images, and sounds—trigger the emotions players experience while playing them, a set of feelings that are implied when we use the word "fun."
- *Learning through rewards:* With every new game, players experience both success and failure, and the consequences of their actions are immediate. Rewards of this kind exert a powerful influence on future behavior.
- *Learning through discovery:* The "Aha!" experiences that happen when players suddenly realize how to predict the appearance of an obstacle, learn how to escape from a trap, or find a shortcut from one level to the next have an important role in the "fun" experience of playing a video game.
- *Learning through exploration:* Whether players win or lose, each time they play a game, they become more familiar with its features. This knowledge helps them develop and execute strategies.

■ *Learning through observation:* Playing video games with friends is yet another source of learning that keeps players coming back for more. Internet sites and magazines devoted to game-playing strategies are also important sources of observational learning. A possible downside of this principle is that players may imitate risky behaviors exhibited by a game's characters (e.g., reckless driving).

6   Applying learning principles to explain why video games are engaging calls attention to the practical value of psychological research. However, be forewarned that you will read about many experiments that seem to be far removed from everyday learning experiences. Remember, though, that the goal of psychologists is to identify general principles that explain and predict behavior across a variety of situations. Thus, these principles can be used to explain diverse learned behaviors—from those exhibited by maze-running laboratory rats to those of the 48% of college students who admit that they sometimes play video games when they should be studying and the 30% or so who say that they even play games while in class (Jones, 2003).

A.   UNDERSTANDING THE THESIS AND OTHER MAIN IDEAS

Select the best answer.

_____   1. The authors' primary purpose in this selection is to
  a. promote video games as part of online instruction.
  b. compare conventional teaching methods with online instruction.
  c. identify different types of games that are used successfully in classrooms.
  d. explore the connection between learning and game-based instruction.

_____   2. The topic of paragraph 3 is
  a. psychology.
  b. online courses.
  c. game-based instruction.
  d. elementary education.

_____   3. The main idea of paragraph 4 is expressed in the
  a. first sentence.
  b. second sentence.
  c. third sentence.
  d. sixth sentence.

_____   4. The primary question that is answered in paragraph 5 is:
  a. Do students like Professor Riegle's online course?
  b. What courses are most appropriate for game-based learning?
  c. How does game-based instruction influence students' learning?
  d. How can video games be adapted for use in the classroom?

_____   5. The purpose of the bulleted list in paragraph 5 is to explain
  a. why video games interfere with learning.
  b. principles of learning that apply to video games.
  c. methods of video game development.
  d. principles of psychological research.

B.   IDENTIFYING DETAILS

Indicate whether each statement is true (T) or false (F).

_____   1. Professor Riegle claims to have launched the first role-playing game (RPG) online course.

_____ 2. Professor Riegle is an educational psychologist at the University of California at Santa Barbara.

_____ 3. The game character representing forces that oppose new technologies is known as "Status Quo."

_____ 4. Professor Riegle's game is called *MWP3E*.

_____ 5. Professor Riegle's RPG course is for undergraduate students in education.

C.   RECOGNIZING METHODS OF ORGANIZATION AND TRANSITIONS

Complete the following statements by filling in the blanks.

1. In paragraph 3, the authors use the generalization and example pattern to explain why some educators like the idea of game-based instruction. Two transitional phrases that indicate this pattern are _____ and _____.

2. In paragraph 5, the authors use the _____ pattern to introduce the principles of learning as applied to video games.

3. In paragraph 6, the authors signal a change in thought with the transitional word _____.

D.   REVIEWING AND ORGANIZING IDEAS: MAPPING

Complete the following map by filling in the blanks.

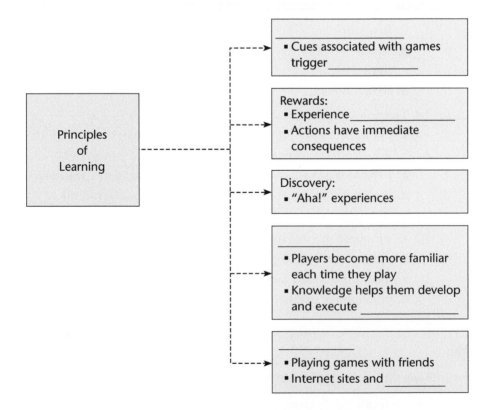

➤ E.   FIGURING OUT INFERRED MEANINGS

Indicate whether each statement is true (T) or false (F).

_____   1. The video game described in the opening paragraphs is meant to resemble the game *Halo*.

_____   2. Educational board games have been used successfully in classrooms for many years.

_____   3. It can be inferred that critics of RPG courses object primarily to the violence in such games.

_____   4. The structure and content of a course must be compatible for an RPG course to be effective.

_____   5. RPG courses are designed mainly for students who already play video games in class.

➤ F.   THINKING CRITICALLY

Select the best answer.

_____   1. The tone of this selection can best be described as
   a. disapproving.
   b. informative.
   c. incredulous.
   d. sensational.

_____   2. In paragraph 5, the authors use the word "Aha!" to describe the
   a. sarcastic reaction of critics of game-based learning.
   b. frustration students sometimes associate with learning.
   c. sudden moment of understanding during a game or learning experience.
   d. irony of a connection between video games and learning.

_____   3. The intended audience for this selection is most likely to be
   a. psychology students.
   b. college professors.
   c. video game designers.
   d. educational consultants.

_____   4. The authors support their thesis with all of the following *except*
   a. examples and illustrations.
   b. statistical data.
   c. expert opinion.
   d. personal experience.

➤ G.   BUILDING VOCABULARY

➤ Context
Using context and a dictionary, if necessary, determine the meaning of each word as it is used in the selection.

_____   1. ruthless (paragraph 1)
   a. careful
   b. merciless

c. weak

d. harmless

_____ 2. horde (paragraph 1)

a. punishment

b. field

c. swarm

d. portion

_____ 3. scoff (paragraph 3)

a. ridicule

b. imitate

c. establish

d. overlook

_____ 4. staple (paragraph 3)

a. label

b. lesson

c. essential item

d. fastener

_____ 5. exert (paragraph 5)

a. depart

b. put forth

c. define

d. breathe

> **Word Parts**

A REVIEW OF PREFIXES, ROOTS, AND SUFFIXES

AD- means *toward*

PRO- means *supporting, favoring*

VOC- means *call*

-ENT means *one who*

Use your knowledge of word parts and the review above to fill in the blanks in the following sentences.

In this selection, the word *proponents* (paragraph 3) refers to people who _____

something. Another word in this paragraph that means the same thing is

_____, which is used here to describe those who speak in favor of using

game-based instruction.

> **H. SELECTING A LEARNING/STUDY STRATEGY**

Assume you will be tested on this reading on an upcoming exam. Evaluate the usefulness of the map you completed on page 140 as a study tool. How would you use it to study?

> **I. EXPLORING IDEAS THROUGH DISCUSSION AND WRITING**

1. Evaluate the introduction to this selection. How successful was it in capturing your attention?

2. Think of a game that you enjoy playing, either a more traditional board game such as Monopoly or an online game. Apply the five learning principles to the game you have chosen and assess how well it reflects each principle.

3. Do you think game-based instruction would enhance your interest in learning? Identify specific courses that you think could benefit from game-based instruction. Which of your courses would *not* be enhanced by unconventional methods of instruction? Explain your answers.

J.   BEYOND THE CLASSROOM TO THE WEB

Explore the site for a Economics 101 game http://econ100.uncg.edu/dcl/econ100/. *Be sure to go through each menu item to learn as much as possible about the game. How does this game reflect the principles outlined in the reading? Do you think you would enjoy learning about economics through this game?*

✔ Tracking Your Progress

Selection 1

Section	Number Correct	Score
A. Thesis and Main Ideas (5 items)	_____ x 5	_____
B. Details (5 items)	_____ x 4	_____
C. Organization and Transitions (4 items)	_____ x 3	_____
E. Inferred Meanings (5 items)	_____ x 4	_____
F. Thinking Critically (4 items)	_____ x 3	_____
G. Vocabulary		
1. Context (5 items)	_____ x 3	_____
2. Word Parts (2 items)	_____ x 1	_____
TOTAL SCORE	_____ %	

<table>
<tr><td>SELECTION
2</td><td># The New Flirting Game
Deborah A. Lott</td></tr>
</table>

SELECTION 2

The New Flirting Game

Deborah A. Lott

This article first appeared in *Psychology Today*. Read it to discover how psychologists study the age-old custom of flirtation.

PREVIEWING THE READING

Using the steps listed on page 4, preview the reading selection. When you have finished, complete the following items.

1. The subject of this reading is _____.

2. List at least three questions you expect to be able to answer after reading the article:

   a. _____

   b. _____

   c. _____

MAKING CONNECTIONS

Are these people flirting with each other? How can you tell?

READING TIP

As you read, look for and highlight the qualities and characteristics of flirting. Highlighting will make it easier to review the reading and find information you need.

The New Flirting Game

1   We flirt with the intent of assessing potential lifetime partners, we flirt to have easy, no-strings-attached sex, and we flirt when we are not looking for either. We flirt because, most simply, flirtation can be a liberating form of play, a game with suspense and ambiguities that brings joys of its

social psychologist
a person who
studies how
groups behave
and how individuals
are affected by the
group

own. As Philadelphia-based social psychologist Tim Perper says, "Some flirters appear to want to prolong the interaction because it's pleasurable and erotic in its own right, regardless of where it might lead."

2   Here are some of the ways the game is currently being played.

Taking the Lead

3   When it comes to flirting today, women aren't waiting around for men to make the advances. They're taking the lead. Psychologist Monica Moore, Ph.D., of Webster University in St. Louis, Missouri, has spent more than 2000 hours observing women's flirting maneuvers in restaurants, singles bars and at parties. According to her findings, women give nonverbal cues that get a flirtation rolling fully two-thirds of the time. A man may think he's making the first move because he is the one to literally move from wherever he is to the woman's side, but usually he has been summoned.

evolutionary
psychologists
people who track
how human
behavior and
psychological traits
have developed and
changed over the
course of history

4   By the standards set out by evolutionary psychologists, the women who attract the most men would most likely be those with the most symmetrical features or the best hip-to-waist ratios. Not so, says Moore. In her studies, the women who draw the most response are the ones who send the most signals. "Those who performed more than 35 displays per hour elicited greater than four approaches per hour," she notes, "and the more variety the woman used in her techniques, the more likely she was to be successful."

Sexual Semaphores

semaphores
visual, nonverbal
systems for
sending
information or
signals

5   Moore tallied a total of 52 different nonverbal courtship behaviors used by women, including glancing, gazing (short and sustained), primping, preening, smiling, lip licking, pouting, giggling, laughing and nodding, as if to nonverbally indicate, "Yes! yes!" A woman would often begin with a room-encompassing glance, in actuality a casing-the-joint scan to seek out prospects. When she'd zeroed in on a target she'd exhibit the short darting glance—looking at a man, quickly looking away, looking back and then away again. There was something shy and indirect in this initial eye contact.

6   But women countered their shy moves with other, more aggressive and overt tactics. Those who liked to live dangerously took a round robin approach, alternately flirting with several different men at once until one responded in an unequivocal fashion. A few women hiked their skirts up to bring more leg into a particular man's field of vision. When they inadvertently drew the attention of other admirers, they quickly pulled their skirts down. If a man failed to get the message, a woman might parade, walking across the room towards him, hips swaying, breasts pushed out, head held high.

Who's Submissive?

ethologists
people who study
behavior patterns

7   Moore observed some of the same nonverbal behaviors that Eibl Eibesfeldt and other ethologists had deemed universal among women: the eyebrow flash (an exaggerated raising of the eyebrows of both eyes, followed by a rapid lowering), the coy smile (a tilting of the head downward, with partial averting of the eyes and, at the end, covering of the mouth), and the exposed neck (turning the head so that the side of the neck is bared.

8   But while many ethologists interpret these signs as conveying female submissiveness, Moore has an altogether different take. "If these behaviors serve to orchestrate courtship, which they do, then how can they be anything but powerful?" she observes. "Who determined that to cover your mouth is a submissive gesture? Baring the neck may have a lot more to do with the neck being an erogenous zone than its being a submissive posture." Though women in Moore's sample used the coy smile, they also maintained direct eye contact for long periods and smiled fully and unabashedly.

9   Like Moore, Perper believes that ethologists have overemphasized certain behaviors and misinterpreted them as signifying either dominance or submission. For instance, says Perper, among flirting American heterosexual men and women as well as homosexual men, the coy smile is less frequent than direct eye contact and sustained smiling. He suggests that some cultures may use the coy smile more than others, and that it is not always a sign of deference.

10   In watching a flirtatious couple, Perper finds that a male will perform gestures and movements that an ethologist might consider dominant, such as sticking out his chest and strutting around, but he'll also give signs that could be read as submissive, such as bowing his head lower than the woman's. The

woman may also do both. "She may drop her head, turn slightly, bare her neck, but then she'll lift her eyes and lean forward with her breasts held out, and that doesn't look submissive at all," Perper notes.

11   Men involved in these encounters, says Perper, don't describe themselves as "feeling powerful." In fact, he and Moore agree, neither party wholly dominates in a flirtation. Instead, there is a subtle, rhythmical and playful back and forth that culminates in a kind of physical **synchronization** between two people. She turns, he turns; she picks up her drink, he picks up his drink.

synchronization happening at the same time

12   Still, by escalating and de-escalating the flirtation's progression, the woman controls the pace. To slow down a flirtation, a woman might orient her body away slightly or cross her arms across her chest, or avoid meeting the man's eyes. To stop the dance in its tracks, she can yawn, frown, sneer, shake her head from side to side as if to say "No," pocket her hands, hold her trunk rigidly, avoid the man's gaze, stare over his head, or resume flirting with other men. If a man is really dense, she might hold a strand of hair up to her eyes as if to examine her split ends or even pick her teeth.

Learning the Steps

13   If flirting today is often a conscious activity, it is also a learned one. Women pick up the moves early. In observations of 100 girls between the ages of 13 and 16 at shopping malls, ice skating rinks and other places adolescents congregate, Moore found the teens exhibiting 31 of the 52 courtship signals deployed by adult women. (The only signals missing were those at the more overt end of the spectrum, such as actual caressing.) Overall, the teens' gestures looked less natural than ones made by mature females: they laughed more boisterously and preened more obviously, and their moves were broader and rougher.

alpha female the "first" female in a group, the leader whose behavior is copied by the others in the group

14   The girls clearly modeled their behavior on the leader of the pack. When the **alpha female** stroked her hair or swayed her hips, her companions copied quickly. "You never see this in adult women," says Moore, "Indeed, women go to great lengths to stand out from their female companions."

15   Compared with adults, the teens signaled less frequently—7.6 signs per hour per girl, as opposed to 44.6 per woman—but their maneuvers, though clumsy, were equally effective at attracting the objects of their desire, in this case, teen boys.

16   Some of the exhilaration of flirting, of course, lies in what is hidden, the tension between what is felt and what is revealed. Flirting pairs volley back and forth, putting out ambiguous signals, neither willing to disclose more than the other, neither wanting to appear more desirous to the other.

17   To observers like Moore and Perper, flirtation often seems to most resemble the antics of children on the playground or even perhaps the ritual peek-a-boo that babies play with their caregivers. Flirters jostle, tease and tickle, even sometimes stick out a tongue at their partner or reach around from behind to cover up their eyes. As Daniel Stern, researcher, psychiatrist, and author of *The Interpersonal World of the Infant* (Karnac, 1998), has pointed out, the two groups in our culture that engage in the most sustained eye contact are mothers and infants, and lovers.

18   And thus in a way, the cycle of flirting takes us full circle. If flirting sets us off on the road to producing babies, it also whisks us back to the pleasures of infancy.

A.   UNDERSTANDING THE THESIS AND OTHER MAIN IDEAS

Select the best answer.

_____ 1. The author's primary purpose in "The New Flirting Game" is to

    a. expose the shallowness and superficiality of flirting behavior.

    b. teach women and men the modern methods of flirting.

    c. compare flirting behaviors of today with those of previous generations.

    d. describe how and why women and men flirt.

_____ 2. The main idea of paragraph 1 is that women and men flirt

    a. to find lifetime partners.

    b. to have uncomplicated sex.

    c. as a game.

    d. for many different reasons.

_____ 3. The main idea of paragraph 3 is expressed in the
   a. first sentence.
   b. third sentence.
   c. fourth sentence.
   d. last sentence.

_____ 4. The topic of paragraph 6 is
   a. risky behavior.
   b. male responses.
   c. flirting tactics.
   d. flirting mistakes.

_____ 5. The main idea of paragraph 8 is that
   a. nonverbal flirting behaviors convey female submissiveness.
   b. women use both a smile and eye contact when flirting.
   c. the neck is an erogenous zone.
   d. nonverbal flirting behaviors are often powerful rather than submissive.

_____ 6. The statement that best expresses the main idea of paragraph 13 is
   a. "If flirting today is often a conscious activity, it is also a learned one."
   b. "Women pick up the moves early."
   c. "The only signals missing were those at the more overt end of the spectrum."
   d. "Overall, the teens' gestures looked less natural than ones made by mature females."

_____ 7. The main idea of paragraph 17 is that
   a. flirters are immature.
   b. flirtation resembles play.
   c. eye contact is important to mothers and infants.
   d. the eye contact between lovers is like that between mothers and infants.

B. IDENTIFYING DETAILS

Select the best answer.

_____ 1. According to Dr. Moore's research, the women who attract the most men are those
   a. with the most symmetrical features.
   b. with the best hip-to-waist ratios.
   c. who send the most signals.
   d. who are least interested in attracting men.

_____ 2. All of the following courtship behaviors are considered "sexual semaphores" _except_
   a. glancing and gazing.
   b. using suggestive language.
   c. primping and preening.
   d. smiling and laughing.

_____ 3. As described in the reading, one way that a woman can slow the pace of a flirtation is by
   a. staring directly into the man's eyes.
   b. nodding as if in agreement.
   c. orienting her body toward him.
   d. crossing her arms across her chest.

_____ 4. Nonverbal flirting behaviors that are considered universal among women include all of the following *except* the
   a. eyebrow flash.
   b. coy smile.
   c. wink.
   d. exposed neck.

_____ 5. As compared to the flirting behavior of adult women, the adolescent girls observed by Dr. Moore did all of the following *except*
   a. exhibit many of the same courtship signals.
   b. look less natural in their gestures.
   c. go to greater lengths to stand out from their female companions.
   d. signal less frequently.

_____ 6. According to Dr. Moore's findings, women give nonverbal cues that begin a flirtation
   a. one-third of the time.
   b. one-half of the time.
   c. two-thirds of the time.
   d. three-fourths of the time.

C.   RECOGNIZING METHODS OF ORGANIZATION AND TRANSITIONS

Complete the following statements by filling in the blanks.

1. Locate a phrase in paragraph 9 that indicates an example is to follow.

   _____

2. In paragraphs 13–15, Dr. Moore's observations of adult women and adolescent girls are discussed using an organizational pattern called _____.
   A transitional phrase that helps identify the organizational pattern in this section is

   _____.

D.   REVIEWING AND ORGANIZING IDEAS: PARAPHRASING

Complete the following paraphrase of paragraph 8 by filling in the blanks with the correct words or phrases.

Although many _____ believe these _____ convey female _____, Dr. Moore disagrees. She says that since these _____ seem to promote _____, they must be _____. She also disagrees that _____ is a _____ gesture and states that _____ may have more to do with it being an _____ than to it being a _____ posture. Women in Moore's _____ used the _____ but they also maintained _____ for extended periods and _____ fully and openly.

E.   FIGURING OUT INFERRED MEANINGS

Indicate whether each statement is true (T) or false (F).

_____ 1. Some people enjoy flirting simply for the fun of it.

_____ 2. The people in the studies mentioned in the reading knew they were being observed.

_____ 3. Evolutionary psychology and social psychology are the same thing.

_____ 4. Flirting behaviors are the same in all cultures.

_____ 5. Teenage girls learn most of their flirting behaviors from watching adult women.

➤ F.   THINKING CRITICALLY

Select the best answer.

_____ 1. The author supports the thesis of "The New Flirting Game" primarily with
   a. cause and effect relationships.
   b. research evidence.
   c. personal experience.
   d. statistics.

_____ 2. The author's tone throughout the article can best be described as
   a. serious and concerned.
   b. judgmental and opinionated.
   c. pessimistic and depressing.
   d. light and factual.

_____ 3. Another appropriate title for this reading would be
   a. "The Modern Moral Decline."
   b. "Commitment in the Twenty-First Century."
   c. "The Art and Science of Flirting."
   d. "Nonverbal Communication Between Women and Men."

_____ 4. In paragraph 3, the phrase "but usually he has been summoned" means that the man
   a. is usually the one who makes the first move.
   b. is expected to move from his location to the woman's.
   c. has been waved at from across the room.
   d. doesn't realize that he is responding to the woman's nonverbal invitation.

_____ 5. The author ends the reading with
   a. a pleasing comparison.
   b. a warning.
   c. an appeal to action.
   d. a sympathetic note.

➤ G.   BUILDING VOCABULARY

➤ Context
Using context and a dictionary, if necessary, determine the meaning of each word as it is used in the selection.

_____ 1. elicited (paragraph 4)
   a. expected from
   b. brought forth
   c. directed at
   d. returned to

_____ 2. encompassing (paragraph 5)

    a. avoiding

    b. emptying

    c. filling

    d. including

_____ 3. overt (paragraph 6)

    a. obvious

    b. secret

    c. friendly

    d. private

_____ 4. dominance (paragraph 9)

    a. control

    b. stubbornness

    c. friendliness

    d. extroversion

_____ 5. culminates (paragraph 11)

    a. fears

    b. concludes

    c. recovers

    d. begins

_____ 6. congregate (paragraph 13)

    a. depart

    b. arrange

    c. plan

    d. gather

➤ Word Parts

> **A REVIEW OF PREFIXES MEANING "NOT"**
> Each of the following prefixes means _not_.
> DE-
> IN-
> MIS-
> NON-
> UN-

Match each word in Column A with its meaning in Column B. Write your answers in the spaces provided.

Column A Prefix + Root	Column B Meaning
_____ 1. nonverbal	a. not on purpose
_____ 2. indirect	b. not understood correctly
_____ 3. unequivocal	c. without embarrassment
_____ 4. inadvertently	d. not spoken
_____ 5. unabashedly	e. without doubt
_____ 6. misinterpreted	f. without doubt or misunderstanding

➤ **Unusual Words/Understanding Idioms**
Indicate whether each statement is true (T) or false (F).

_____ 1. In paragraph 1, the phrase **no-strings-attached** sex means sex that is uncomplicated by expectations of commitment.

_____ 2. In paragraph 12, the phrase **to stop the dance in its tracks** means to bring an end to the flirtation.

➤ **H.   SELECTING A LEARNING/STUDY STRATEGY**

Discuss how visualization might help you learn the characteristics of flirting presented in this article.

➤ **I.   EXPLORING IDEAS THROUGH DISCUSSION AND WRITING**

1. The author uses terms that imply games or sports, such as the phrases "a round robin approach" (paragraph 6) and "volley back and forth" (paragraph 16). How do these phrases support her central thesis?

2. What images do the words *maneuvers* (paragraph 3) and *deployed* (paragraph 13) bring to mind?

3. Why is the reading called "The *New* Flirting Game"? What do you think the old flirting game consisted of?

➤ **J.   BEYOND THE CLASSROOM TO THE WEB**

Visit "Developing Flirt-Ability" at **http://www.askheartbeat.com**.

Skim several articles. Compare the reliability of the articles on this Web site with Lott's article. Which is more likely to provide helpful information on dating and relationships? Why?

✔ **Tracking Your Progress**

Selection 2

Section	Number Correct		Score
A. Thesis and Main Ideas (7 items)	_____	x 4	_____
B. Details (6 items)	_____	x 3	_____
C. Organization and Transitions (3 items)	_____	x 2	_____
E. Inferred Meanings (5 items)	_____	x 3	_____
F. Thinking Critically (5 items)	_____	x 3	_____
G. Vocabulary			
1. Context (6 items)	_____	x 2	_____
2. Word Parts (6 items)	_____	x 1	_____
	TOTAL SCORE	_____%	

SELECTION 3

Coming Into My Own

Ben Carson

This reading was taken from an autobiography titled *Gifted Hands: The Ben Carson Story*. In his book, Carson, a well-known neurosurgeon, describes his journey from his childhood in inner-city Detroit to a position as director of pediatric neurosurgery at Johns Hopkins Hospital.

➤ PREVIEWING THE READING

Using the steps listed on page 4, preview the reading selection. When you have finished, answer the following questions.

1. What is the setting of the first half of the reading?

   _____

2. What is the subject's profession in this reading?

   _____

MAKING CONNECTIONS

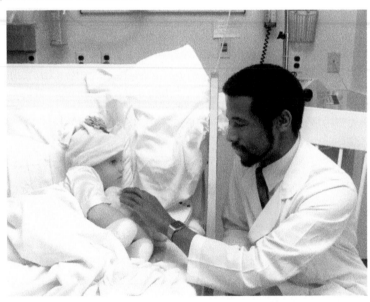

Dr. Benjamin Carson at Johns Hopkins Hospital. What do you suppose Dr. Carson is doing in this photo?

➤ READING TIP

As you read, notice situations that reveal racial discrimination or prejudice and how the author responded to them.

Coming Into My Own

orderly
an attendant who
does routine,
nonmedical
work in a hospital

1   The nurse looked at me with disinterest as I walked toward her station. "Yes?" she asked, pausing with a pencil in her hand. "Who did you come to pick up?" From the tone of her voice I immediately knew that she thought I was an **orderly**. I was wearing my green scrubs, nothing to indicate I was a doctor.

intern
a recent medical school graduate undergoing supervised practical training

Intensive Care Unit
a specialized section of a hospital containing the equipment, medical and nursing staff, and monitoring devices necessary to provide care to extremely ill patients

entrepreneurs
businesspeople

2   "I didn't come to pick up anyone." I looked at her and smiled, realizing that the only Black people she had seen on the floor had been orderlies. Why should she think anything else? "I'm the new intern."

3   "New intern? But you can't—I mean—I didn't mean to" the nurse stuttered, trying to apologize without sounding prejudiced.

4   "That's OK," I said, letting her off the hook. It was a natural mistake. "I'm new, so why should you know who I am?"

5   The first time I went into the Intensive Care Unit, I was wearing my whites (our monkey suits, as we interns called them), and a nurse signaled me. "You're here for Mr. Jordan?"

6   "No, ma'am, I'm not."

7   "You sure?" she asked as a frown covered her forehead. "He's the only one who's scheduled for respiratory therapy today."

8   By then I had come closer and she could read my name badge and the word *intern* under my name.

9   "Oh, I'm so very sorry," she said, and I could tell she was.

10   Although I didn't say it, I would like to have told her, "It's all right because I realize most people do things based on their past experiences. You've never encountered a Black intern before, so you assumed I was the only kind of Black male you'd seen wearing whites, a respiratory therapist." I smiled again and went on.

11   It was inevitable that a few White patients didn't want a Black doctor, and they protested to Dr. Long. One woman said, "I'm sorry, but I do not want a Black physician in on my case."

12   Dr. Long had a standard answer, given in a calm but firm voice. "There's the door. You're welcome to walk through it. But if you stay here, Dr. Carson will handle your case."

13   At the time people were making these objections, I didn't know about them. Only much later did Dr. Long tell me as he laughed about the prejudices of some patients. But there was no humor in his voice when he defined his position. He was adamant about his stance, allowing no prejudice because of color or ethnic background.

14   Of course, I knew how some individuals felt. I would have had to be pretty insensitive not to know. The way they behaved, their coldness, even without saying anything, made their feelings clear. Each time, however, I was able to remind myself they were individuals speaking for themselves and not representative of all Whites. No matter how strongly a patient felt, as soon as he voiced his objection he learned that Dr. Long would dismiss him on the spot if he said anything more. So far as I know, none of the patients ever left!

15   I honestly felt no great pressures. When I did encounter prejudice, I could hear Mother's voice in the back of my head saying things like, "Some people are ignorant and you have to educate them."

16   The only pressure I felt during my internship, and in the years since, has been a self-imposed obligation to act as a role model for Black youngsters. These young folks need to know that the way to escape their often dismal situations is contained within themselves. They can't expect other people to do it for them. Perhaps I can't do much, but I can provide one living example of someone who made it and who came from what we now call a disadvantaged background. Basically I'm no different than many of them.

17   As I think of Black youth, I also want to say I believe that many of our pressing racial problems will be taken care of when we who are among the minorities will stand on our own feet and refuse to look to anybody else to save us from our situations. The culture in which we live stresses looking out for number one. Without adopting such a self-centered value system, we can demand the best of ourselves while we are extending our hands to help others.

18   I see glimmers of hope. For example, I noticed that when the Vietnamese came to the United States they often faced prejudice from everyone—White, Black, and Hispanics. But they didn't beg for handouts and often took the lowest jobs offered. Even well-educated individuals didn't mind sweeping floors if it was a paying job.

19   Today many of these same Vietnamese are property owners and entrepreneurs. That's the message I try to get across to the young people. The same opportunities are there, but we can't start out as vice president of the company. Even if we landed such a position, it wouldn't do us any good anyway because we wouldn't know how to do our work. It's better to start where we can fit in and then work our way up.

> **A.   UNDERSTANDING THE THESIS AND OTHER MAIN IDEAS**

Select the best answer.

_____   1. The writer of "Coming Into My Own" can best be described as
   a. a black respiratory therapist.
   b. a white female nurse.
   c. a black male doctor.
   d. the white patient of a black doctor.

_____   2. The statement from the reading that best supports the writer's primary thesis is
   a. "From the tone of her voice I immediately knew that she thought I was an orderly." (paragraph 1)
   b. "It was inevitable that a few White patients didn't want a Black doctor." (paragraph 11)
   c. "I can provide one living example of someone who made it and who came from what we now call a disadvantaged background." (paragraph 16)
   d. "I see glimmers of hope." (paragraph 18)

_____   3. According to the writer, the only pressure he felt during and after his internship has been from
   a. himself as he strives to be a role model for black youngsters.
   b. white nurses and doctors who treat him as less than equal.
   c. his parents and other family members because of their high expectations for him.
   d. members of other ethnic groups who resent his success.

_____   4. The statement that best expresses the main idea of paragraph 17 is
   a. People should look to themselves rather than others to improve their situations.
   b. Adopting a self-centered value system is the only way to succeed in our culture.
   c. The racial problems in our society are primarily caused by misunderstanding.
   d. Extending help to others is not as important as getting ahead.

_____   5. The topic of paragraph 18 is
   a. low-paying jobs.
   b. Vietnamese immigrants.
   c. prejudice among ethnic groups.
   d. education levels of immigrants.

_____   6. The main point of paragraph 19 is expressed in the
   a. first sentence.   c. fourth sentence.
   b. second sentence.   d. last sentence.

> **B.   IDENTIFYING DETAILS**

Indicate whether each statement is true (T) or false (F).

_____   1. The writer/intern was mistaken for both an orderly and a respiratory therapist.

_____   2. The white patients who were prejudiced were careful to hide their feelings.

_____   3. Many patients left the hospital immediately rather than be treated by a black doctor.

_____   4. The writer came from a privileged background.

_____   5. Many Vietnamese immigrants who started in low-paying jobs now own property.

Appendix

Assessing Your Reading Progress

This appendix contains a Reading Progress Graph.

Use the Reading Progress Graph to chart your progress as you work through the reading selections in the book. For each reading selection you complete, record the date and the selection number. Then write your Total Score from the Tracking Your Progress boxes in the appropriate columns.

Reading Progress Graph

Reading Progress Chart

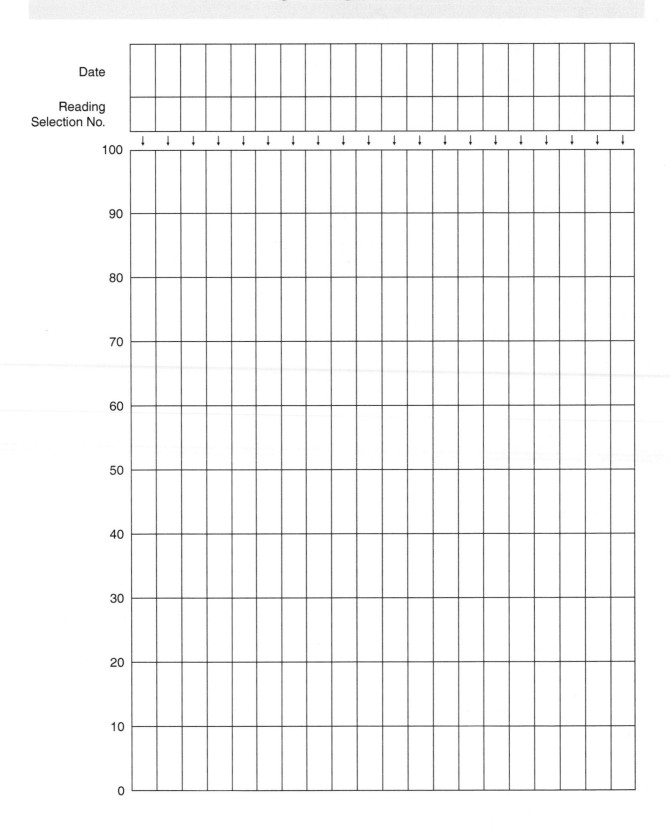

Reading Progress Chart *(continued)*

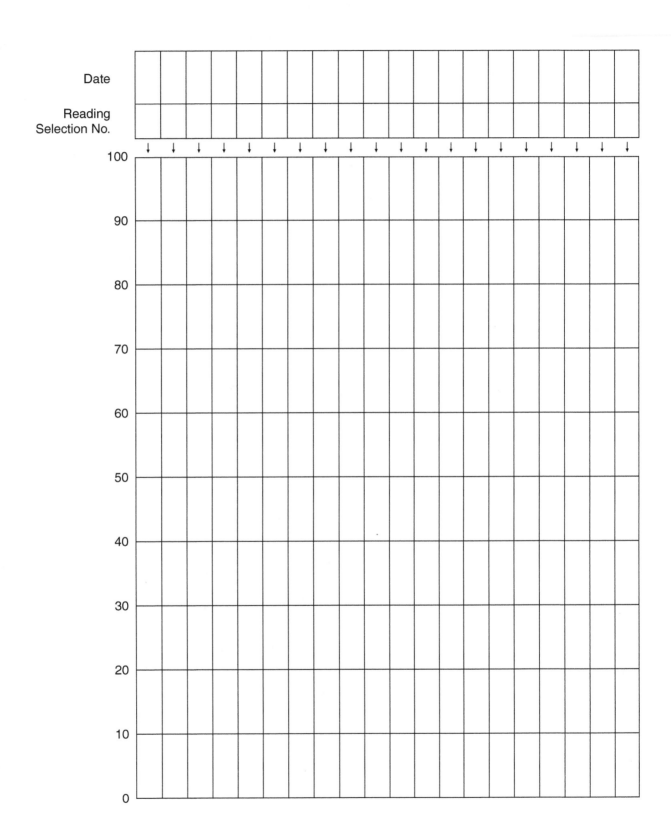

Credits

Text Credits

Chapter 1

5: Joseph A. DeVito, from *The Interpersonal Communication Book,* 9/e. Published by Allyn and Bacon, Boston, MA. Copyright © 2001 by Pearson Education. Copyright © 2001 by Pearson Education. Reprinted by permission of the publisher.
8: Ayah Young, "Deadly Silence: Stop Snitching's Fatal Legacy. Reprinted from WiretapMag.org.

Chapter 2

16: F. Philip Rice and Kim Gale Dolgin, from *The Adolescent: Development, Relationships, and Culture*, 10/e, pp. 250–251. Boston: Allyn and Bacon, 2002.
17: Teresa Audesirk, Gerald Audesirk, and Bruce E. Byers, from *Life on Earth*, 3/e, pp. 622–624, 632. Copyright © 2003. Adapted by permission of Pearson Education, Inc., Upper Saddle River, NJ.
19: Mark C. Carnes and John A. Garraty, from *The American Nation: A History of the United States*, 11/e, p. 267. New York: Longman, 2003.
20: Edward F. Bergman and William H. Renwick, from *Introduction to Geography: People, Places, and Environment*, 2/e, p. 263. Copyright © 2002. Adapted by permission of Pearson Education, Inc., Upper Saddle River, NJ.
24: William J. Germann and Cindy L. Stanfield, *Principles of Human Physiology*, 1/e, p. 174. San Francisco: Benjamin Cummings, 2002.
26: Jeffrey Bennett, Megan Donahue, Nicholas Schneider, and Mark Voit, *The Cosmic Perspective*, 2/e, p. 218. San Francisco: Addison-Wesley, 2002.
30: Teresa Audesirk, Gerald Audesirk, and Bruce E. Byers, from *Life on Earth*, 3/e, p. 237. Copyright © 2003. Adapted by permission of Pearson Education, Inc., Upper Saddle River, NJ.

Chapter 3

33: Leon Baradat, from *Understanding American Democracy*, p. 163. Copyright © 1992. Reprinted by permission of Pearson Education, Inc., Upper Saddle River, NJ.
33: Josh R. Gerow, from *Psychology: An Introduction*, 5/e, p. 553. Copyright © 1997. Reprinted by permission of Pearson Education, Inc., Upper Saddle River, NJ.
34: Joseph A. DeVito, from *The Interpersonal Communication Book*, 9/e, p. 182. Published by Allyn and Bacon, Boston, MA. Copyright © 2001 by Pearson Education. Reprinted by permission of the publisher.
34: Josh R. Gerow, from *Psychology: An Introduction*, 5/e, p. 700. Copyright © 1997. Reprinted by permission of Pearson Education, Inc., Upper Saddle River, NJ.
34: Robert A. Wallace, from *Biology: The World of Life*, 6/e, p. 283. Copyright © 1992 HarperCollins College Publishers. Reprinted by permission of Pearson Education, Inc.
35: James Coleman and Donald Cressey, *Social Problems*, 6/e, p. 277. New York: HarperCollins College Publishers, 1996.
35: William Keefe, et al., *American Democracy*, 3/e, p. 178. New York: Harper & Row, 1990.
35: Josh R. Gerow, from *Psychology: An Introduction*, 5/e, p. 250. Copyright © 1997. Reprinted by permission of Pearson Education, Inc., Upper Saddle River, NJ.
35: Karen Timberlake, *Chemistry: An Introduction to General, Organic, and Biological Chemistry*, 6/e, p. 30. New York: HarperCollins College Publishers, 1996.
36: Mix, et al., from *Biology: The Network of Life*, 2/e, p. 532. Copyright © 1992 Michael Mix, Paul Farber, and Keith I. King. Reprinted by permission of Pearson Education, Inc.
36: William Keefe, et al., *American Democracy*, 3/e, p. 186. New York: Harper & Row, 1990.
36: William E. Thompson and Joseph V. Hickey, from *Society in Focus*, 4/e, p. 198. Published by Allyn and Bacon, Boston, MA. Copyright © 2002 by Pearson Education, Inc. Reprinted by permission of the publisher.
36: Joseph A. DeVito, *Human Communication: The Basic Course*, 9/e, p. 217. Boston: Allyn and Bacon, 2003.
36: Ebert and Griffin, from *Business Essentials*, 4/e, p. 64. Copyright © 2003. Reprinted by permission of Pearson Education, Inc., Upper Saddle River, NJ.
36: Barbara Miller, from *Cultural Anthropology*, 2/e, pp. 145–146. Boston: Allyn and Bacon, 2004.
37: Paul G. Hewitt, from *Conceptual Physics*, 9/e, p. 39. San Francisco: Addison Wesley, 2002.
37: Michael R. Solomon and Elnora W. Stuart, from *Marketing: Real People, Real Choices*, 3/e, p. 108. Copyright © 2003. Reprinted by permission of Pearson Education, Inc., Upper Saddle River, NJ.
37: Rebecca Donatelle, from *Health: The Basics*, 5/e, p. 105. Copyright © 2003 by Pearson Education, publishing as Benjamin Cummings. Reprinted by permission.
39: Nora Newcombe, from *Child Development: Change Over Time*, p. 354. New York: HarperCollins College Publishers, 1996.
39: Michael R. Solomon, 1 par. "The average American . . ." from *Consumer Behavior: Buying, Having, and Being*, 5/e, p. 184. Upper Saddle River, NJ: Prentice Hall, 2002.

39: Jeffrey Bennett, Megan Donahue, Nicholas Schneider, and Mark Voit, *The Cosmic Perspective*, Brief Edition, p. 28. New York: Longman, 2000.

40: Nandy Bandyo-Padhyay, from *Computing for Non-Specialists*, 1/e, p. 4. New York: Addison-Wesley, 2000.

41: William E. Thompson and Joseph V. Hickey, from *Society in Focus*, 3/e, p. 162. New York: Longman, 1999.

41: Roger LeRoy Miller, *Economics Today*, 8/e, p. 185. New York: HarperCollins College Publishers, 1994.

42: Roger LeRoy Miller, *Economics Today*, 8/e, p. 513. New York: HarperCollins College Publishers, 1994.

42: Josh R. Gerow, from *Psychology: An Introduction*, 5/e, p. 319. Copyright © 1997. Reprinted by permission of Pearson Education, Inc., Upper Saddle River, NJ.

42: George C. Edwards III, Martin P. Wattenberg, and Robert L. Lineberry, *Government in America: People, Politics, and Policy*, 10/e, p. 422; New York: Longman, 2002.

43: Roy A. Cook, Laura J. Yale, and Joseph J. Marqua, *Tourism: The Business of Travel*, 2/e, p. 370. Upper Saddle River, NJ: Prentice Hall, 2002.

43: Elaine Marieb, from *Human Anatomy and Physiology*, 5/e, p. 9. Copyright © 2001 The Benjamin Cummings Publishing Company. Reprinted by permission of Pearson Education, Inc.

44: Joseph A. DeVito, *Messages: Building Interpersonal Communication Skills*, 5/e, p. 161. Boston, MA: Allyn and Bacon, 2002.

47: James Geiwitz, from *Psychology: Looking at Ourselves*, 2/e, p. 512. Boston: Little, Brown, 1980.

47: James Geiwitz, from *Psychology: Looking at Ourselves*, 2/e, p. 513. Boston: Little, Brown, 1980.

47: James Geiwitz, from *Psychology: Looking at Ourselves*, 2/e, p. 229. Boston: Little, Brown, 1980.

48: Richard George, *The New Consumer Survival Kit*, p. 14. Boston: Little, Brown, 1978.

48: "ABC's of How a President is Chosen," *U.S. News & World Report*, February 18, 1980.

48: Edward H. Reiley and Carroll Shry, from *Introductory Horticulture*, p. 114. Albany, NY: Delmar Publishers, 1979.

Chapter 4

53: Michael Mix, Paul Farber, and Keith I. King, from *Biology: The Network of Life*, 2/e, p. 262. Copyright © 1992 Michael Mix, Paul Farber, and Keith I. King. Reprinted by permission of Pearson Education, Inc.

53: Barbara Miller, from *Cultural Anthropology*, 2/e, pp. 308–309. Boston: Allyn and Bacon, 2004.

54: Elaine Marieb, from *Essentials of Human Anatomy and Physiology*, 6/e, p. 3. San Francisco: Benjamin Cummings, 2000.

54: Gerard Tortora, *Introduction to the Human Body: The Essentials of Anatomy and Physiology*, 2/e, p. 56. New York: HarperCollins College Publishers, 1991.

55: Edward Tarbuck and Frederick Lutgens, from *Earth Science*, 9/e, p. 309. Copyright © 2000. Reprinted by permission of Pearson Education, Inc., Upper Saddle River, NJ.

56: Edward Tarbuck and Frederick Lutgens, from *Earth Science*, 9/e, pp. 620–621. Copyright © 2000. Reprinted by permission of Pearson Education, Inc., Upper Saddle River, NJ.

57: Gary B. Nash et al., from *The American People: Creating a Nation and Society*, p. 1099. Copyright © 2004 by Pearson Education, Inc. Reprinted by permission.

57: Gary B. Nash et al., from *The American People: Creating a Nation and Society*, pp. 611–613. Copyright © 2004 by Pearson Education, Inc. Reprinted by permission.

58: Jackson R. Wilson et al., *The Pursuit of Liberty: A History of the American People*, 3/e, p. 493. New York: HarperCollins College Publishers, 1996.

59: Philip Zimbardo and Richard Gerrig, from *Psychology and Life*, 14/e, p. 115. New York: HarperCollins College Publishers, 1996.

59: Bishop, from *Introduction to Chemistry*, 1/e, p. 749. San Francisco: Benjamin Cummings, 2002.

60: Rebecca Donatelle, from *Access to Health*, 7/e, p. 264. Copyright © 2002, Pearson Education, Inc., publishing as Benjamin Cummings. Reprinted by permission.

60: Alex Thio, from *Sociology*, 4/e, p. 255. New York: HarperCollins College Publishers, 1996.

61: Wilson Dizard, from *Old Media, New Media*, 3/e, p. 179. New York: Longman, 2000.

61: Michael Mix, Paul Farber, and Keith I. King, from *Biology: The Network of Life*, 2/e, pp. 663–664. Copyright © 1992 Michael Mix, Paul Farber, and Keith I. King. Reprinted by permission of Pearson Education, Inc.

62: Gerard Tortora, from *Introduction to the Human Body: The Essentials of Anatomy and Physiology*, 2/e, p. 77. New York: HarperCollins College Publishers, 1991.

63: Alex Thio, from *Sociology*, 4/e, p. 534. New York: HarperCollins College Publishers, 1996.

64: Paul G. Hewitt, from *Conceptual Physics*, 9/e, p. 272. San Francisco: Addison Wesley, 2002.

64: Rebecca Donatelle, from *Access to Health*, 7/e, p. 516. Copyright © 2002, Pearson Education, Inc., publishing as Benjamin Cummings. Reprinted by permission.

65: Thomas C. Kinnear, Thomas C. Bernhardt, and Kathleen Krentler, from *Principles of Marketing*, 4/e, p. 218. Copyright © 1995. Reprinted by permission of Pearson Education, Inc., Upper Saddle River, NJ.

66: Leon Baradat, from *Understanding American Democracy*, p. 300. Copyright © 1992. Reprinted by permission of Pearson Education, Inc., Upper Saddle River, NJ.

66: James M. Henslin, from *Social Problems*, 5/e, p. 154. Copyright © 2000. Reprinted by permission of Pearson Education, Inc., Upper Saddle River, NJ.

67: William Pride, Robert Hughes, and Jack Kapoor, from *Business*, 5/e, p. 189. Boston: Houghton Mifflin, 1996.

68: James M. Henslin, from *Social Problems*, 5/e, p. 252. Copyright © 2000. Reprinted by permission of Pearson Education, Inc., Upper Saddle River, NJ.

68: George C. Edwards III, Martin P. Wattenberg, and Robert L. Lineberry, *Government in America: People, Politics, and Policy*, 9/e, p. 330. New York: Longman, 2000.

70: Edward S. Greenberg, and Benjamin I. Page, from *The Struggle for Democracy*, Brief 2/e, p. 71. New York: Longman, 1999.

70: Gerard Tortora, from *Introduction to the Human Body: The Essentials of Anatomy and Physiology*, 2/e, p. 77. New York: HarperCollins College Publishers, 1991.

70: William J. Germann and Cindy L. Stanfield, from *Principles of Human Physiology*, 1/e, pp. 606–607. San Francisco: Benjamin Cummings, 2002.

70: Leon Baradat, from *Understanding American Democracy*, p. 202. Copyright © 1992. Reprinted by permission of Pearson Education, Inc., Upper Saddle River, NJ.

71: Rebecca Donatelle, adapted excerpt from *Health: The Basics*, 5/e. Copyright © 2003 Pearson Education Inc. Reproduced by permission of Pearson Education, Inc.

71: Edward F. Bergman and William H. Renwick, from *Introduction to Geography: People, Places, and Environment*, 2/e, p. 185. Copyright © 2002. Adapted by permission of Pearson Education, Inc., Upper Saddle River, NJ.

72: Wilson Dizard, from *Old Media, New Media*, 3/e, p. 169. New York: Longman, 2000.

72: Stephen F. Davis and Joseph J. Palladino, from *Psychology*, 3/e, p. 210. Upper Saddle River, NJ: Prentice Hall 2000.

72: Edward F. Bergman and William H. Renwick, from *Introduction to Geography: People, Places, and Environment*, 2/e, p. 182. Copyright © 2002. Adapted by permission of Pearson Education, Inc., Upper Saddle River, NJ.

73: Rebecca Donatelle, from *Access to Health*, 7/e, p. 81. Copyright © 2002, Pearson Education, Inc., publishing as Benjamin Cummings. Reprinted by permission.

74: Henslin, James M., from *Social Problems*, 5/e, p. 93. Copyright © 2000. Reprinted by permission of Pearson Education, Inc., Upper Saddle River, NJ.

74: James M. Henslin, from *Social Problems*, 5/e, p. 91. Copyright © 2000. Reprinted by permission of Pearson Education, Inc., Upper Saddle River, NJ.

74: Edward F. Bergman and William H. Renwick, from *Introduction to Geography: People, Places, and Environment*, 2/e, p. 197. Copyright © 2002. Adapted by permission of Pearson Education, Inc., Upper Saddle River, NJ.

74: Joseph A. DeVito, from *Human Communication: The Basic Course*, 7/e, p. 103. New York: Longman, 1997.

Chapter 5

78: Thomas C. Kinnear, Thomas C. Bernhardt, and Kathleen Krentler, from *Principles of Marketing*, 4/e, p. 301. Copyright © 1995. Reprinted by permission of Pearson Education, Inc., Upper Saddle River, NJ.

81: William E. Thompson and Joseph V. Hickey, from *Society in Focus*, 4/e, p. 544. Published by Allyn and Bacon, Boston, MA. Copyright © 2002 by Pearson Education, Inc. Reprinted by permission of the publisher.

81: William J. Germann, and Cindy L. Stanfield, from *Principles of Human Physiology*, 1/e, p. 185. San Francisco: Benjamin Cummings, 2002.

82: Joseph A. DeVito, from *Essentials of Human Communication*, 4/e, pp. 36–37. Boston: Allyn and Bacon, 2002.

82: Gini Stephens Frings, from *Fashion: From Concepts to Consumer*, 6/e, p. 11. Upper Saddle River, NJ: Prentice Hall, 1999.

82: Duane Preble and Sarah Preble, from *Artforms: An Introduction to the Visual Arts*, 7/e, p. 34. Upper Saddle River, NJ: Prentice Hall, 2002.

83: James A. Fagin, from *Criminal Justice*, 1/e, p. 195. Published by Allyn and Bacon, Boston, MA. Copyright © 2003 by Pearson Education. Reprinted by permission of the publisher.

Chapter 6

85: Arlene Skolnick, from *The Intimate Environment: Exploring Marriage and the Family*, 6/e, p. 96. New York: HarperCollins College Publishers, 1996.

85: Robert L. Lineberry and George C. Edwards III, from *Government in America: People, Politics, and Policy*, 4/e, p. 540. Glenview, IL: Scott, Foresman, 1989.

86: Rebecca Donatelle, from *Health: The Basics*, 5/e, p. 215. Copyright © 2003 by Pearson Education, publishing as Benjamin Cummings. Reprinted by permission.

86: Rebecca Donatelle, from *Access to Health*, 8/e, pp. 372–373. Copyright © 2004 by Pearson Education, publishing as Benjamin Cummings. Reprinted by permission.

86: B.E. Pruitt, and Jane J. Stein, from *Health Styles: Decisions for Living Well*, 2/e, pp. 572–573. Boston: Allyn and Bacon, 1999.

87: William E. Thompson and Joseph V. Hickey, Joseph V., from *Society in Focus*, 4/e, p. 364. Published by Allyn and Bacon, Boston, MA. Copyright © 2002 by Pearson Education, Inc. Reprinted by permission of the publisher.

91: Bess Armstrong, from essay in *The Choices We Made*, edited by Angela Bonavoglia, p. 165. New York: Random House, 1991.

92: Robert A. Wallace, from *Biology: The World of Life*, 6/e, p. 518. Copyright © 1992 HarperCollins College Publishers. Reprinted by permission of Pearson Education, Inc.

93: Marie Winn, from *The Plug-In-Drug*. New York: Viking Press, 1977.

96: Jane Kenyon, excerpt from "The Suitor." Copyright 2005 by the Estate of Jane Kenyon. Reprinted from *Collected Poems* with the permission of Graywolf Press, Saint Paul, Minnesota.

96: Shelley, Percy Bysshe, "Adonais," 1821.

96: Emily Dickinson, from "My Life Had Stood a Loaded Gun." Reprinted by permission of the publishers and the Trustees of Amherst College from *The Poems of Emily Dickinson*, Johnson, Thomas H., ed., J754, Cambridge, Mass.: The Belknap Press of Harvard University Press, Copyright © 1951, 1955, 1979, 1983 by the President and Fellows of Harvard College.

96: Gustave Flaubert, *The Legend of Saint Julian the Hospitaller*, 1838.

Chapter 7

99: Robert A. Wallace, from *Biology: The World of Life*, 6/e, pp. 708, 710. Copyright © 1992 HarperCollins College Publishers. Reprinted by permission of Pearson Education, Inc.

100: Robert A. Wallace, from *Biology: The World of Life*, 6/e, pp. 712–713. Copyright © 1992 HarperCollins College Publishers. Reprinted by permission of Pearson Education, Inc.

100: James A. Fagin, from *Criminal Justice*, 1/e, p. 89. Published by Allyn and Bacon, Boston, MA. Copyright © 2003 by Pearson Education. Reprinted by permission of the publisher.
101: Ronald J. Ebert and Ricky W. Griffin, *Business Essentials*, 4/e, p. 71. Upper Saddle River, NJ: Prentice Hall, 2003.
101: "How Commercial Jingles Work" by Tim Faulkner from HowStuffWorks.com. Reprinted courtesy of HowStuffWorks.com.
107: Miller, Barbara, from *Cultural Anthropology*, 2/e, p. 302. Boston: Allyn and Bacon, 2004.
108: William E. Thompson and Joseph V. Hickey, from *Society in Focus*, 4/e, p. 355. Published by Allyn and Bacon, Boston, MA. Copyright © 2002 by Pearson Education, Inc. Reprinted by permission of the publisher.
110: William E. Thompson and Joseph V. Hickey, from *Society in Focus*, 4/e, p. 285. Published by Allyn and Bacon, Boston, MA. Copyright © 2002 by Pearson Education, Inc. Reprinted by permission of the publisher.
111: Alex Thio, from *Sociology: A Brief Introduction*, 5/e, pp. 35–36. Boston: Allyn and Bacon, 2003.
113: James A. Fagin, from *Criminal Justice*, 1/e, p. 107. Published by Allyn and Bacon, Boston, MA. Copyright © 2003 by Pearson Education. Reprinted by permission of the publisher.
114: Rebecca Donatelle, from *Health: The Basics*, 5/e, p. 179. Copyright © 2003 by Pearson Education, publishing as Benjamin Cummings. Reprinted by permission.
114: Robert Divine et al., from *America Past and Present*, 4/e, pp. 890–891. Copyright © 1996 by HarperCollins College Publishers. Reprinted by permission of Pearson Education, Inc.
116: Louis Berman and J.C. Evans, from *Exploring the Cosmos*, 5/e, p. 145. Boston: Little, Brown, 1986.

Chapter 9

122: United Nations Foundation home page from http://www.unfoundation.org. © 2006 UN Foundation. All Rights Reserved. Reprinted by permission.

Chapter 10

137: Samuel E. Wood, Ellen Green Wood, and Denise Boyd, "Mastering the World of Psychology," pp. 145–146. © 2008 Pearson Education, Inc. Reproduced by permission of Pearson Education, Inc.
144: Deborah A. Lott, from "The New Flirting Game," *Psychology Today*, January 1999. Reprinted with permission from Psychology Today, Copyright © 2006. www.psychologytoday.com.
152: Dr. Benjamin Carson, "Coming Into My Own." Taken from *Gifted Hands: The Ben Carson Story* by Dr. Benjamin Carson, pp. 115–117. Copyright 1990 by Review and Herald ® Publishing Association. Used by permission of the Zondervan Corporation.

Chapter 11

159: Bonnie Schiedel, "Use It and Lose It," *Chatelaine*, July 2000, Vol. 73, No. 7. © Rogers Publishing Ltd. Reprinted by permission.
169: Tamar Nordenberg "Make No Mistake: Medical Errors Can Be Deadly Serious," *FDA Consumer*, October 16, 2000. www.fda.gov.
179: Elaine Marieb, "Athletes Looking Good and Doing Better with Anabolic Steroids?" from *Human Anatomy and Physiology*, 5/e. Copyright © 2001 by The Benjamin Cummings Publishing Company. Reprinted by permission of Pearson Education, Inc.

Photo Credits

34: Michael S. Wirtz/Phladelphia Inquirer/Newscom; **122:** Bob Deammrich/The Image Works; **123:** Associated Press; **127:** The New Yorker Collection 2008 David Borchart from cartoonbank.com. All Rights Reserved.; **102:** Tim Boyle/Getty Images; **103:** Business Wire/Getty Images; **104:** Justin Sullivan/Getty Images. **138:** Marilynn K. Yee/The New York Times; **144:** Raffaele Celentano/laif/Redux; **152:** The Baltimore Sun; **179:** Mark Allen Johnson/ZUMA/Corbis;

Index

Psychology Now: Modern Perspectives

12.4   What are the basic ideas behind the seven modern perspectives, as well as the important contributions of Skinner, Maslow, and Rogers?

Even today, there isn't one single perspective that is used to explain all human behavior and mental processes. There are actually seven modern perspectives, with two of those being holdovers from the early days of the field.

PSYCHODYNAMIC PERSPECTIVE

Freud's theory is still with us today in use by many professionals in therapy situations. It is far less common today than it was a few decades ago, however, and even those who use his techniques modify them for modern use. In the more modern **psychodynamic perspective,** the focus is still on the unconscious mind and its influence over conscious behavior and on early childhood experiences, but with less of an emphasis on sex and sexual motivations and more emphasis on the development of a sense of self and the discovery of other motivations behind a person's behavior.

Freud had a number of followers who took his original ideas and modified them to their own perspectives. Their students continued to modify those theories until today we have a kind of neo-Freudianism (Freud et al., 1990; Meadow & Clevans, 1978). Therapists often speak of Freudian complexes and use much of his terminology in their work with clients. Part of the reason that Freudian concepts are so

psychodynamic perspective modern version of psychoanalysis that is more focused on the development of a sense of self and the discovery of other motivations behind a person's behavior than sexual motivations.

enduring is the lack of any scientific way to test them and, therefore, show them to be either useful or useless. Nevertheless, despite the lack of testability, Freud's theory continues to appeal to many modern theorists.

BEHAVIORAL PERSPECTIVE

Like psychoanalysis, behaviorism is still also very influential. When its primary supporter, John B. Watson, moved on to greener pastures in the world of advertising, B. F. Skinner became the new leader of the field.

Skinner not only continued research in classical conditioning, but he also developed a theory of how voluntary behavior is learned called *operant conditioning* (Skinner, 1938). In this theory, behavioral responses that are followed by pleasurable consequences are strengthened, or *reinforced*. For example, a child who cries and is rewarded by getting his mother's attention will cry again in the future. In addition to the psychodynamic and behavioral perspectives, there are five newer perspectives that have developed within the last 50 years.

HUMANISTIC PERSPECTIVE

One of the newer perspectives, often called the "third force" in psychology, was really a reaction to both psychodynamic theory and behaviorism. In the early to mid-1900s, if you were a psychologist you were either a psychoanalyst or a behaviorist—there weren't any other major viewpoints to rival those two. Behaviorism was seen as a very "mechanical" theory—stimulus goes in, response comes out, and what happens in the middle is of no interest. The environment determines behavior and the individual has little input into his or her development. Psychoanalysis wasn't mechanistic, but in that theory the workings of the physical body (in the form of sexual and aggressive instincts) determine behavior, and the individual, once again, has little to do with his or her own destiny.

Some professionals began to develop a perspective that would allow them to focus on people's ability to direct their own lives. These theorists wanted to shift the focus to the aspects of human nature that make us uniquely human—our appreciation for beauty, for example. In a very real sense, then, this approach owes far more to the early roots of psychology in the field of philosophy rather than the more scientific fields of medicine and physiology. Humanists held the view that people have *free will*, the freedom to choose their own destiny. Two of the earliest and most famous founders of this view were Abraham Maslow (1908–1970) and Carl Rogers (1902–1987).

Both Maslow and Rogers emphasized the human potential, the ability of each person to become the best person he or she could be (Maslow, 1968; Rogers, 1961). They believed that studying animals in laboratories (as the behaviorists did) or people with nervous disorders (as the psychoanalysts did) could not lead to a better understanding of this human potential for *self-actualization*, as Maslow termed it—achieving one's full potential or ideal self. Today, humanism is still very influential in psychotherapy.

COGNITIVE PERSPECTIVE

Cognitive psychology, which focuses on how people think, remember, store, and use information, became a major force in the field in the 1960s. It wasn't a new idea, as

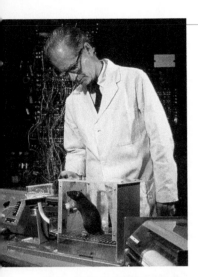

Behaviorist B. F. Skinner puts a rat through its paces. What challenges might arise from applying information gained from studies with animals to human behavior?

the Gestalt psychologists had themselves supported the study of mental processes of learning. The development of computers (which just happened to make great models of human thinking), the work of Piaget with children, Chomsky's analysis of Skinner's views of language, and discoveries in biological psychology all stimulated an interest in studying the processes of thought. The **cognitive perspective** with its focus on memory, intelligence, perception, thought processes, problem solving, language, and learning has become a major force in psychology.

Within the cognitive perspective, the relatively new field of **cognitive neuroscience** includes the study of the physical workings of the brain and nervous system when engaged in memory, thinking, and other cognitive processes. Cognitive neuroscientists use tools for imaging the brain and watching the workings of a living brain, such as magnetic resonance imaging (MRI) and positron emission tomography (PET). The emerging field of brain imaging is an important one in the study of cognitive processes.

SOCIOCULTURAL PERSPECTIVE

Another modern perspective in psychology is the **sociocultural perspective,** which actually combines two areas of study: *social psychology*, which is the study of groups, social roles, and rules of social actions and relationships; and *cultural psychology*, which is the study of cultural norms,* values, and expectations. These two areas are related in that they are both about the effect that people have on one another, either individually or in a larger group, such as a culture (Peplau & Taylor, 1997). Russian psychologist Lev Vygotsky (1978) also used sociocultural concepts in forming his sociocultural theory of children's cognitive development.

The sociocultural perspective is important because it reminds people that how they and others behave (or even think) is influenced not only by whether they are alone, with friends, in a crowd, or part of a group, but also by the social norms, fads, class differences, and ethnic identity concerns of the particular culture in which they live. *Cross-cultural research* also fits within this perspective. In cross-cultural research, the contrasts and comparisons of a behavior or issue are studied in at least two or more cultures. This type of research can help illustrate the different influences of environment (culture and training) when compared to the influence of heredity (genetics, or the influence of genes on behavior).

For example, in a classic study, researchers Darley and Latané (1968) found that the presence of other people actually *lessened* the chances that a person in trouble would receive help. The phenomenon is called the bystander effect and it is believed to be the result of *diffusion of responsibility*, which is the tendency to feel that someone else is responsible for taking action when others are present. But would this effect appear in other cultures? Shorey (2001), in his discussion of the brutal beating death of a Somali prisoner in a Canadian military facility while bystanders looked on without acting, suggests that it just might. But is Canadian culture too similar to our own to lead us to this conclusion? Would another culture very different from Western culture show the same effect? This is exactly the kind of question that the sociocultural perspective, using cross-cultural research, asks and attempts to answer.

cognitive perspective
modern perspective that focuses on memory, intelligence, perception, problem solving, and learning.

cognitive neuroscience
study of the physical changes in the brain and nervous system during thinking.

sociocultural perspective
perspective that focuses on the relationship between social behavior and culture.

---

*Norms: standards or expected behavior.

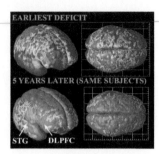

These brain scans show the increasing malfunction of the brains of schizophrenics over a five-year period, highlighting the focus of the biological perspective.

That explains why people don't like bitter stuff, like the white part of an orange peel, but that's really a physical thing. How would the evolutionary perspective help us ▶ understand something psychological like relationships?

biopsychological perspective perspective that attributes human and animal behavior to biological events occurring in the body, such as genetic influences, hormones, and the activity of the nervous system.

evolutionary perspective perspective that focuses on the biological bases of universal mental characteristics that all humans share.

BIOPSYCHOLOGICAL PERSPECTIVE

Biopsychology, or the study of the biological bases of behavior and mental processes, isn't really as new a perspective as one might think.

In the **biopsychological perspective,** human and animal behavior is seen as a direct result of events in the body. Hormones, heredity, brain chemicals, tumors, and diseases are some of the biological causes of behavior and mental events. ⓛⓘⓝⓚ *to Chapter Thirteen: The Biological Perspective, pp. 251–261.*

For example, evidence is mounting for a biological cause (perhaps even genetic) for *schizophrenia*, a mental disorder involving delusions (false beliefs), hallucinations (false sensory impressions), and extremely distorted thinking (Brzustowicz et al., 2004; Maziade et al., 1997).

EVOLUTIONARY PERSPECTIVE

The **evolutionary perspective** focuses on the biological bases for universal mental characteristics that all humans share. It seeks to explain general mental strategies and traits, such as why we lie, how attractiveness influences mate selection, why fear of snakes is so universal, and why people like music and dancing, among many others.

In this perspective, the mind is seen as a set of information-processing machines, designed by the same process of natural selection that Darwin (1859) first theorized, allowing human beings to solve the problems faced in the early days of human evolution—the problems of the early hunters and gatherers. For example, *evolutionary psychologists* (psychologists who study the evolutionary origins of human behavior) would view the human behavior of not eating substances that have a bitter taste (such as poisonous plants) as an adaptive* behavior that evolved as early humans came into contact with such bitter plants. Those who ate the bitter plants would die, while those who spit them out survived to pass their "I don't like this taste" genes on to their offspring, who would pass the genes on to their offspring, and so on, until after a long period of time there is an entire population of humans that naturally avoid bitter-tasting substances.

That explains why people don't like bitter stuff, like the white part of an orange peel, but that's really a physical thing. How would the evolutionary perspective help us understand something psychological like relationships?

Relationships between men and women are one of the many areas in which evolutionary psychologists conduct research. For example, in one study researchers surveyed young adults about their relationships with the opposite sex, asking the participants how likely they would be to forgive either a sexual infidelity or an emotional one (Shackelford et al., 2002). Evolutionary theory would predict that men would find it more difficult to forgive a woman who had sex with someone else than a woman who was only emotionally involved with someone because the man wants to be sure that the children the woman bears are his (Geary, 2000). Why put all that effort into providing for children who could be another man's offspring? Women, on the other hand, should find it harder to forgive an emotional infidelity, as they are always sure that their children are their own, but (in evolutionary terms, mind you) they need the emotional loyalty of the men to provide for those children (Buss et al., 1992; Daly et al., 1982). The results of the study bore out the prediction: Men found it harder to forgive a partner's sexual straying and were more likely to break up

---

*Adaptive: having the quality of adjusting to the circumstances or need; in the sense used here, a behavior that aids in survival.

with the woman than if the infidelity were purely emotional; for women, the opposite results were found. Another study concerning mating found that women seem to use a man's kissing ability to determine his worthiness as a potential mate (Hughes et al., 2007).

Psychological Professionals and Areas of Specialization

There are a number of professionals who work in the field of psychology. These professionals have different training, different focuses, and may have different goals from the typical psychologist.

12.5 How does a psychiatrist differ from a psychologist, and what are the other types of professionals who work in the various areas of psychology?

A **psychiatrist** has a medical (M.D. or D.O.) degree and is a medical doctor who has specialized in the diagnosis and treatment of psychological disorders. Psychiatrists can prescribe medicine in addition to providing therapy and counseling, and they typically work in private practice or hospital settings.

A **psychoanalyst** is usually either a psychiatrist (M.D.) or a psychologist (Ph.D., Psy.D., or Ed.D.) who has special training in the theories of Sigmund Freud and his method of psychoanalysis. Psychoanalysts, like psychiatrists, usually work in private practice or hospital settings. (Like the term *therapist*, the label of *psychoanalyst* is not protected by federal or state law and anyone—trained or not—may use this label. If you are looking for a therapist of any type, always ask to see the person's credentials.)

A **psychiatric social worker** is trained in the area of social work and usually possesses a Master of Social Work (M.S.W.) degree, and often has obtained a professional license, such as a Licensed Clinical Social Worker (L.C.S.W.). These professionals focus more on the environmental conditions that can have an impact on mental disorders, such as poverty, overcrowding, stress, and drug abuse. They work out of clinics, hospitals, and social service organizations.

Psychologists with an evolutionary perspective would be interested in how this couple selected each other as partners.

Psychiatric social workers use many tools to help children deal with problems such as divorce or abuse. How might using hand puppets help this young girl to talk about the problems in her life?

psychiatrist a medical doctor who has specialized in the diagnosis and treatment of psychological disorders.

psychoanalyst either a psychiatrist or a psychologist who has special training in the theories of Sigmund Freud and his method of psychoanalysis.

psychiatric social worker a social worker with some training in therapy methods who focuses on the environmental conditions that can have an impact on mental disorders, such as poverty, overcrowding, stress, and drug abuse.

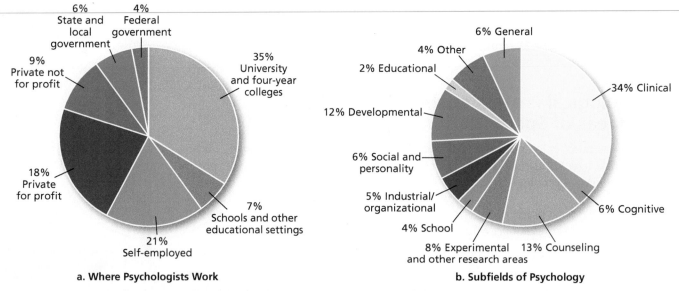

a. Where Psychologists Work

b. Subfields of Psychology

Figure 12.2 **Work Settings and Subfields of Psychology**

(a) There are many different work settings for psychologists. Although not obvious from the chart, many psychologists work in more than one setting. For example, a clinical psychologist may work in a hospital setting as well as teach at a university or college. (J. Tsapogas et al., 2006)

(b) This pie chart shows the specialty areas of psychologists who recently received their doctorates. (T. B. Hoffer et al., 2007)

Note: Due to rounding, percentages may not total to 100 percent.

A **psychologist** has no medical training but has a doctorate degree. (A person with a master's degree might be a counselor, therapist, or researcher but is typically not referred to as a psychologist.) Psychologists undergo intense academic training, learning about many different areas of psychology before choosing an area in which to specialize. Because the focus of their careers can vary so widely, psychologists work in many different vocational* settings. Figure 12.2a shows the types of settings in which psychologists work. Although typically psychologists cannot prescribe medications, in some states psychologists can go through special training in the prescription of drugs for certain psychological disorders. Psychologists in the counseling profession must be licensed to practice in their states.

AREAS OF SPECIALIZATION

▶ You said not all psychologists do counseling. But I thought that was all that psychologists do—what else is there?

You said not all psychologists do counseling. But I thought that was all that psychologists do—what else is there?

Although many psychologists do participate in delivering therapy to people who need help, there is a nearly equal number of psychologists who do other tasks: researching, teaching, designing equipment and workplaces, and developing educational methods, for example. Also, not every psychologist is interested in the same area of human—or animal—behavior and most psychologists work in several different areas of interest, as shown in Figure 12.2b, Subfields of Psychology.

There are many other areas as well, as psychology can be used in fields such as health, sports performance, legal issues, business concerns, and even in the design of equipment, tools, and furniture.

psychologist a professional with an academic degree and specialized training in one or more areas of psychology.

_____

*Vocational: having to do with a job or career.

● **Psychodynamic** ——— focuses on the role of the unconscious mind and its influence on conscious behavior,
based on Freud's theory   early childhood experiences, development of sense of self, and other motivations

● **Behavioral** ——— focuses on how behavioral responses are learned through classical or operant conditioning
based on early work
of Watson and later B.F. Skinner

● **Humanistic** ——— focuses on human potential, free will, and possibility of self-actualization
two pioneers are Carl Rogers
and Abraham Maslow

● **Cognitive** ——— focuses on memory, intelligence, perception, thought processes,
has roots in   problem solving, language, and learning
Gestalt psychology

Psychology Now: Modern Perspectives
(No one single perspective is used to explain all human behavior and processes)

● **Sociocultural** ——— focuses on the behavior of individuals as the result of the presence (real or
imagined) of other individuals, as part of groups, or as part of a larger culture

● **Biopsychological** ——— focuses on influences of hormones, brain structures and chemicals, disease, etc.;
human and animal behavior is seen as a direct result of events in the body

● **Evolutionary** ——— focuses on the biological bases for universal mental characteristics, such as why we lie, how attractiveness
influences mate selection, the universality of fear, and why we enjoy things like music and dance

Types of Psychological Professionals
(people working in the field of psychology have a variety of training experiences and different focuses)

● **psychiatrist**

• medical doctor
(M.D. or D.O.) that
specializes in diag-
nosis and treatment
of psychological
disorders; can
prescribe medication

● **psychoanalyst**

• usually a psychiatrist
or psychologist
who has special
training in theories
of Freud

● **psychiatric
social worker**

• has training in area of
social work (M.S.W.)
and often has
a professional license
to practice (L.C.S.W.)

● **psychologist**

• has a doctorate degree (Ph.D., Psy.D., or Ed.D.)
and works with either humans or animals in a
variety of settings based on the area of specialization

• must be licensed to practice independently; typically
does not prescribe medications but can go through
specialized training to do so in some states

PRACTICE **QUIZ:** HOW MUCH DO YOU REMEMBER?

Pick the best answer.

1. Which of the following pairs represents the two psychology perspectives that were also part of the historical beginnings of psychology?
 a. humanism and behaviorism
 b. behaviorism and psychodynamics
 c. psychodynamics and humanism
 d. cognitive psychology and psychodynamics

2. Which perspective is known as the "third force" in psychology?
 a. psychoanalysis   **c.** cognitive psychology
 b. behaviorism   **d.** humanism

3. Elsie suffered a stroke and had to be hospitalized. While in the hospital, she talked in funny, garbled words and seemed to think that she was being held against her will. Which of the following perspectives BEST explains Elsie's odd behavior?
 a. psychodynamics   **c.** behaviorism
 b. cognitive psychology   **d.** biopsychology

4. Which perspective would a researcher be taking if she were studying the way children store and retrieve information?
 a. psychoanalysis   **c.** cognitive psychology
 b. behaviorism   **d.** evolutionary perspective

(continued)

5. Which of the following professionals in psychology focuses more on the environmental conditions that affect mental disorders?

    a. psychiatrist   **c.** psychiatric social worker

    b. psychoanalyst   **d.** psychologist

6. Dr. Roaden works in a school system, dealing directly with children who have emotional, academic, and behavioral problems. Dr. Roaden is most likely which type of psychologist?

    a. personality   **c.** school

    b. developmental   **d.** comparative

Brainstorming: Do you believe that violence is a part of human nature? Is violent behavior something that can someday be removed from human behavior or, at the very least, controlled? Think about this question from each of the perspectives discussed in this chapter.

Psychology: The Science

WHY PSYCHOLOGISTS USE THE SCIENTIFIC METHOD

Have you ever played the "airport game"? You sit at the airport (bus terminal, doctor's office, or any other place where people come and go and you have a long wait) and try to guess what people do for a living based only on their appearance. Although it's a fun game, the guesses are rarely correct. People's guesses also sometimes reveal the biases that they may have about certain physical appearances: men with long hair are musicians, people wearing suits are executives, and so on. On the other hand, psychology is about trying to determine facts and reduce uncertainty.

12.6   Why is psychology considered a science, and what are the steps in using the scientific method?

The scientific method can be used to determine if children who watch violence on television are more likely to be aggressive than those who do not.

In psychology, researchers want to see only what is really there, not what their biases might want them to see. The way to do that is by using the **scientific method,** a system for reducing bias and error in the measurement of data.

    The first step in any investigation is to have a question to investigate, right? So the first step in the scientific method is this:

1. **Perceiving the Question:** You notice something interesting happening in your surroundings for which you would like to have an explanation. An example might be that you've noticed that your children seem to get a little more aggressive with each other after watching a particularly violent children's cartoon program on Saturday morning. You wonder if the violence in the cartoon could be creating the aggressive behavior in your children. This step is derived from the goal of description: What is happening here?

    Once you have a question, you want an answer. The next logical step is to form a tentative* answer or explanation for the behavior you have seen. This tentative explanation is known as a **hypothesis.**

2. **Forming a Hypothesis:** Based on your initial observations about what's going on in your surroundings, you form an educated guess about the explanation for your observations, putting it into the form of a statement that can be tested in some way. Going back to the previous example, you might say, "Children who watch violent cartoons will become more aggressive."

scientific method   system of gathering data so that bias and error in measurement are reduced.

hypothesis   tentative explanation of a phenomenon based on observations.

_____

*Tentative: something that is not fully worked out or completed as yet.

The next step is testing the hypothesis. People have a tendency to notice only things that agree with their view of the world, a kind of selective perception called *confirmation bias*. For example, if a person is convinced that all men with long hair smoke cigarettes, that person will tend to notice only those long-haired men who are smoking and ignore all the long-haired men who don't smoke. The scientific method is designed to overcome the tendency to look at only the information that confirms people's biases by forcing them to actively seek out information that might *contradict* their biases (or hypotheses). So when you test your hypothesis, you are trying to determine if the factor you suspect has an effect and that the results weren't due to luck or chance. That's why psychologists keep doing research over and over—to get more evidence that hypotheses are "supported."

3. **Testing the Hypothesis:**   The method you use to test your hypothesis will depend on exactly what kind of answer you think you might get. You might make more detailed observations or do a survey in which you ask questions of a large number of people, or you might design an experiment in which you would deliberately change one thing to see if it causes changes in the behavior you are observing. In the example, the best method would probably be an experiment in which you select a group of children, show half of them a cartoon with violence and half of them a cartoon with no violence, and then find some way of measuring aggressive behavior in the two groups.

What do you do with the results of your testing? Of course, testing the hypothesis is all about the goal of getting an explanation for behavior, which leads to the next step.

4. **Drawing Conclusions:**   Once you know the results of your hypothesis testing, you will find that either your hypothesis was supported—which means that your little experiment worked, or your measurements supported your initial observations—or it wasn't supported, which means that you need to go back to square one and think of another possible explanation for what you have observed. (Could it be that Saturday mornings make children a little more aggressive? Or Saturday breakfasts?)

The results of any method of hypothesis testing won't be just the raw numbers or measurements. Any data that come from your testing procedure will be analyzed with some kind of statistical method that helps to organize and refine the data. You have come to some conclusion about your investigation's success or failure, and you want to let other researchers know what you have found.

Why tell anyone what happened if it failed?

Just because one experiment or other study did not find support for the hypothesis does not necessarily mean that the hypothesis is incorrect. Your study might have been poorly designed, or there might have been factors not under your control that interfered with the study. But other researchers are asking the same kinds of questions that you might have asked. They need to know what has already been found out about the answers to those questions so that they can continue investigating and adding more knowledge about the answers to those questions. Even if your own investigation didn't go as planned, that tells other researchers what *not* to do in the future. So the final step in any scientific investigation is reporting the results.

5. **Report Your Results:**   At this point, you would want to write up exactly what you did, why you did it, how you did it, and what you found, so that others can learn from what you have already accomplished—or failed to accomplish.

◄ Why tell anyone what happened if it failed?

replicate in research, repeating a study or experiment to see if the same results will be obtained in an effort to demonstrate reliability of results.

observer effect tendency of people or animals to behave differently from normal when they know they are being observed.

Another reason for reporting your results is that even if your research gave you the answer you expected, your investigation might have been done incorrectly, or the results might have been a fluke or due to chance alone. So if others can **replicate** your research (do exactly the same study over again and get the same results), it gives much more support to your findings. This allows others to predict behavior based on your findings as well as use the results of those findings to modify or control behavior, the last two goals in psychology.

This might be a good place to make a distinction between questions that can be scientifically or empirically studied and those that cannot. For example, "What is the meaning of life?" is not a question that can be studied using the scientific or empirical method. Empirical questions are those that can be tested through direct observation or experience. For example, "Has life ever existed on Mars?" is a question that scientists are trying to answer through measurements, experimentation, soil samples, and other methods. Eventually they will be able to say with some degree of confidence that life could have existed or could not have existed. That is an empirical question, because it can be supported or disproved by gathering real evidence. The meaning of life, however, is a question of belief for each person. One does not need proof to *believe*, but scientists need proof (in the form of objectively gathered evidence) to *know*.

In psychology, researchers try to find the answers to empirical questions. Questions that involve beliefs and values are best left to philosophy and religion.

DESCRIPTIVE METHODS

12.7 How are naturalistic and laboratory settings used to describe behavior, and what are some of the advantages and disadvantages associated with these settings?

There are a number of different ways to investigate the answers to research questions, and which one researchers use depends on the kind of question they want to answer. If they want to simply gather information about what has happened or what is happening, they would want a method that gives them a detailed description.

Researcher Jane Goodall watches chimpanzees behave in their natural environment. How might her presence have affected the behavior of the chimpanzees?

Naturalistic Observation Sometimes all researchers need to know is what is happening to a group of animals or people. The best way to look at the behavior of animals or people is to watch them behave in their normal environment. That's why animal researchers like Jane Goodall went to the areas where chimpanzees lived and watched them eat, play, mate, and sleep in their own natural surroundings. With people, researchers might want to observe them in their workplaces, homes, or on playgrounds. For example, if someone wanted to know how adolescents behave with members of the opposite sex in a social setting, that researcher might go to the mall on a weekend night.

What is the advantage of naturalistic observation? It allows researchers to get a realistic picture of how behavior occurs because they are actually watching that behavior. In a more artificial setting, like a laboratory, they might get behavior that is contrived or artificial rather than genuine. Of course, there are precautions that must be taken. In many cases, animals or people who know they are being watched will not behave normally anyway, in a process called the **observer effect,** so often the observer needs to remain hidden from view. When researching humans, this is often a difficult thing to do. In the mall setting with the teenagers, a researcher might find that pretending to read a book is a good disguise, especially if one wears glasses to hide the movement of the eyes. Then the researchers would be able to look up at what goes on between the teens without them knowing that they were being watched. In other cases, researchers might use one-way mirrors, or they might actually become participants in a group, a technique called **participant observation.**

Are there disadvantages? Unfortunately, yes. One of the disadvantages of naturalistic observation is the possibility of **observer bias.** That happens when the person doing the observing has a particular opinion about what he or she is going to see or expects to see. If that is the case, sometimes that person sees only those actions that support that expectation and ignores actions that don't fit. A way around that is to have *blind observers*: people who do not know what the research question is and, therefore, have no preconceived notions about what they "should" see. It's also a good idea to have more than one observer, so that the various observations can be compared.

Another disadvantage is that each naturalistic setting is unique and unlike any other. Observations that are made at one time in one setting may not hold true for another time, even if the setting is similar, because the conditions are not going to be exactly the same time after time—researchers don't have that kind of control over the natural world. For example, famed gorilla researcher Diane Fossey had to battle poachers who set traps for the animals in the area of her observations (Mowat, 1988). The presence and activities of the poachers affected the normal behavior of the gorillas she was trying to observe.

Laboratory Observation   Sometimes observing behavior in animals or people is just not practical in a natural setting. For example, a researcher might want to observe the reactions of infants to a mirror image of themselves and record the reactions with a camera mounted behind the one-way mirror. That kind of equipment might be difficult to set up in a natural setting. In a laboratory observation, the researcher would bring the infant to the equipment, controlling the number of infants and their ages as well as everything else that goes on in the laboratory.

As mentioned previously, laboratory settings have the disadvantage of being an artificial situation that might result in artificial behavior—both animals and people often react differently in the laboratory than they would in the real world. The main advantage of this method is the degree of control that it gives to the observer.

Both naturalistic and laboratory observations can lead to the formation of hypotheses that can later be tested.

12.8   How are case studies and surveys used to describe behavior, and what are some drawbacks to each of these methods?

Case Studies   Another descriptive technique is called the **case study,** in which one individual is studied in great detail. In a case study, researchers try to learn everything they can about that individual. For example, Sigmund Freud based his entire theory of psychoanalysis on his numerous case studies of his patients in which he gathered information about their childhoods and relationships with others from the very beginning of their lives to the present.

The advantage of the case study is the tremendous amount of detail it provides. It may also be the only way to get certain kinds of information. For example, one famous case study was the story of Phineas Gage, who had a large metal rod driven through his head and suffered a major personality change as a result (Damasio et al., 1994). Researchers couldn't study that with naturalistic observation and an experiment is out of the question. Imagine anyone responding to an ad in the newspaper that read:

Wanted: 50 people willing to suffer nonfatal brain damage for scientific study of the brain. Will pay all medical expenses.

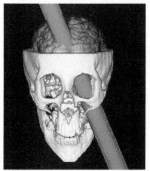

At the top is a computer-generated reconstruction of the damaged skull of Phineas Gage. The red area shows the path taken by the steel rod driven through his skull by an explosion in 1848. At the bottom is a model of his head and next to it the actual skull.

participant observation a naturalistic observation in which the observer becomes a participant in the group being observed.

observer bias tendency of observers to see what they expect to see.

case study study of one individual in great detail.

It's pretty certain that anyone who actually answered that ad might already be suffering from some rather extensive brain damage. Case studies are also good ways to study things that are rare, such as multiple personality (now called *dissociative identity disorder).*

The disadvantage of the case study is that researchers can't really apply the results to other similar people. In other words, they can't assume that if another person had the same kind of experiences growing up that he or she would turn out just like the person in their case study. People are unique and have too many complicating factors in their lives to be that predictable. So what researchers find in one case won't necessarily apply or generalize to others. Another weakness of this method is that case studies are a form of detailed observation and are vulnerable to bias on the part of the person conducting the case study, just as observer bias can occur in naturalistic or laboratory observation. ❋⸤Learn more on MPL

Surveys   Sometimes what psychologists want to know about is pretty personal—like what people do in their sexual relationships, for example. The only way to find out about very private (covert) behavior is to ask questions.

In the survey method, researchers will ask a series of questions about the topic they are studying. Surveys can be conducted in person in the form of interviews or on the telephone, the Internet, or with a questionnaire. The questions in interviews or on the telephone can vary, but usually the questions in a survey are all the same for everyone answering the survey. In this way, researchers can ask lots of questions and survey literally hundreds of people.

That is the big advantage of surveys, aside from their ability to get at private information. Researchers can get a tremendous amount of data on a very large group of people. Of course, there are disadvantages. One disadvantage is researchers have to be very careful about the group of people they survey. If they want to find out what college freshmen think about politics, for example, they can't really ask every single college freshman in the entire United States. But they can select a **representative sample** from that group. They could randomly* select a certain number of college freshmen from several different colleges across the United States, for example. Why randomly? Because the sample has to be *representative* of the **population,** which is the entire group in which the researcher is interested. If researchers selected only freshmen from Ivy League schools, for example, they would certainly get different opinions on politics than they might get from small community colleges. But if they take a lot of colleges and select their *participants* (people who are part of the study) randomly, they will be more certain of getting answers that a broad selection of college students would typically give.

That brings up the other major disadvantage of the survey technique: People aren't always going to give researchers accurate answers. The fact is, people tend to misremember things, distort the truth, and may lie outright—even if the survey is an anonymous** questionnaire. Remembering is not a very accurate process sometimes, especially when people think that they might not come off sounding very desirable or socially appropriate. Some people deliberately give the answer they think is more socially correct rather than their true opinion, so that no one gets offended,

"Next question: I believe that life is a constant striving for balance, requiring frequent tradeoffs between morality and necessity, within a cyclic pattern of joy and sadness, forging a trail of bittersweet memories until one slips, inevitably, into the jaws of death. Agree or disagree?"

representative sample randomly selected sample of subjects from a larger population of subjects.

population   the entire group of people or animals in which the researcher is interested.

---

*Randomly: in this sense, selected so that each member of the group has an equal chance of being chosen.
**Anonymous: not named or identified.

in a process called *courtesy bias*. Researchers must take their survey results with a big grain of salt*—they may not be as accurate as they would like them to be.

Both the wording of survey questions and the order in which they appear on the survey can affect the outcome. It is difficult to find a wording that will be understood in exactly the same way by all those who read the question. For example, questions can be worded in a way that the desired answer becomes obvious (often resulting in courtesy bias–type answers), or a question that appears at the end of a survey might be answered quite differently than if it had appeared at the beginning. Explore more on MPL

Explore more with a simulation on observational studies, the scientific method.
www.mypsychlab.com

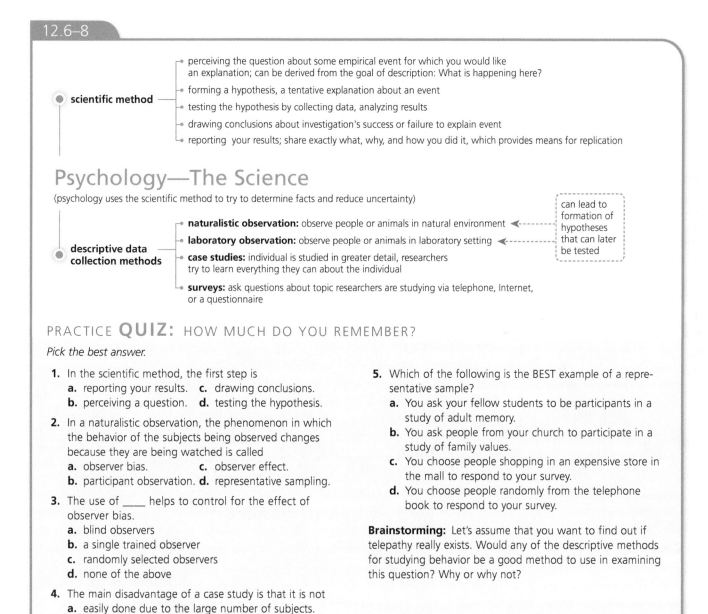

12.6–8

scientific method
- perceiving the question about some empirical event for which you would like an explanation; can be derived from the goal of description: What is happening here?
- forming a hypothesis, a tentative explanation about an event
- testing the hypothesis by collecting data, analyzing results
- drawing conclusions about investigation's success or failure to explain event
- reporting your results; share exactly what, why, and how you did it, which provides means for replication

Psychology—The Science
(psychology uses the scientific method to try to determine facts and reduce uncertainty)

descriptive data collection methods
- **naturalistic observation:** observe people or animals in natural environment ◄------
- **laboratory observation:** observe people or animals in laboratory setting ◄------
- **case studies:** individual is studied in greater detail, researchers try to learn everything they can about the individual
- **surveys:** ask questions about topic researchers are studying via telephone, Internet, or a questionnaire

can lead to formation of hypotheses that can later be tested

PRACTICE **QUIZ:** HOW MUCH DO YOU REMEMBER?

Pick the best answer.

1. In the scientific method, the first step is
   a. reporting your results. c. drawing conclusions.
   b. perceiving a question. d. testing the hypothesis.

2. In a naturalistic observation, the phenomenon in which the behavior of the subjects being observed changes because they are being watched is called
   a. observer bias. c. observer effect.
   b. participant observation. d. representative sampling.

3. The use of ____ helps to control for the effect of observer bias.
   a. blind observers
   b. a single trained observer
   c. randomly selected observers
   d. none of the above

4. The main disadvantage of a case study is that it is not
   a. easily done due to the large number of subjects.
   b. detailed enough for most research questions.
   c. generalizable to other similar conditions.
   d. biased.

5. Which of the following is the BEST example of a representative sample?
   a. You ask your fellow students to be participants in a study of adult memory.
   b. You ask people from your church to participate in a study of family values.
   c. You choose people shopping in an expensive store in the mall to respond to your survey.
   d. You choose people randomly from the telephone book to respond to your survey.

Brainstorming: Let's assume that you want to find out if telepathy really exists. Would any of the descriptive methods for studying behavior be a good method to use in examining this question? Why or why not?

---

*Big grain of salt: a phrase meaning to be skeptical; to doubt the truth or accuracy of something.

FINDING RELATIONSHIPS

The methods discussed so far only provide descriptions of behavior. There are really only two methods that allow researchers to know more than just a description of what has happened: correlations and experiments. Correlation is actually a statistical technique, a particular way of organizing numerical information so that it is easier to look for patterns in the information. This method will be discussed here rather than in the statistics appendix found at the back of this text because correlation, like the experiment, is about finding relationships. In fact, the data from the descriptive methods just discussed are often analyzed using the correlational technique.

12.9   What is the correlational technique, and what does it tell researchers about relationships?

Correlations   A **correlation** is a measure of the relationship between two or more variables. A *variable* is anything that can change or vary—scores on a test, temperature in a room, gender, and so on. For example, researchers might be curious to know whether or not cigarette smoking is connected to life expectancy—the number of years a person can be expected to live. Obviously, the scientists can't hang around people who smoke and wait to see when those people die. The only way (short of performing a really unethical and lengthy experiment) to find out if smoking behavior and life expectancy are related to each other is to use the medical records of people who have already died. (For privacy's sake, the personal information such as names and social security numbers would be removed, with only the facts such as age, gender, weight, and so on available to researchers.) Researchers would look for two facts from each record: the number of cigarettes the person smoked per day and the age of the person at death.

Now the researcher has two sets of numbers for each person in the study that go into a mathematical formula to produce a number called the **correlation coefficient**. The correlation coefficient represents two things: the direction of the relationship and its strength.

Direction? How can a mathematical relationship have a direction?

Whenever researchers talk about two variables being related to each other, what they really mean is that knowing the value of one variable allows them to predict the value of the other variable. For example, if researchers found that smoking and life expectancy are indeed related, they should be able to predict how long someone might live if they know how many cigarettes a person smokes in a day. But which way does that prediction work? If a person smokes a lot of cigarettes, does that mean that

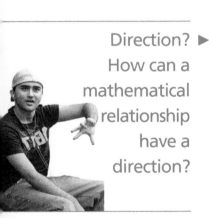

Direction? ▶ How can a mathematical relationship have a direction?

correlation   a measure of the relationship between two variables.

correlation coefficient   a number derived from the formula for measuring a correlation and indicating the strength and direction of a correlation.

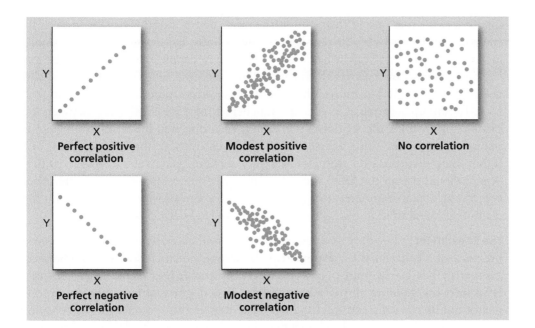

Figure 12.3
Five scatterplots showing direction and strength of correlation. It should be noted that perfect correlations, whether positive or negative, rarely occur in the real world.

he or she will live a longer life or a shorter one? Does life expectancy go up or down as smoking increases? That's what is meant by the *direction* of the relationship.

In terms of the correlation coefficient (represented by the small letter r), the number researchers get from the formula will either be a positive number or a negative number. If positive, the two variables increase in the same direction—as one goes up, the other goes up; as one decreases, the other also decreases. If negative, the two variables have an inverse* relationship. As one increases, the other decreases. If researchers find that the more cigarettes a person smoked, the younger that person was when he or she died, that would mean that the correlation between the two variables is negative. (As smoking goes up, life expectancy goes down—an inverse relationship.)

The strength of the relationship between the variables will be determined by the actual number itself. That number will always range between +1.00 and −1.00. The reason that it cannot be greater than +1.00 or less than −1.00 has to do with the formula and an imaginary line on a graph around which the data points gather, a graph called a scatterplot (see Figure 12.3). If the relationship is a strong one, the number will be closer to +1.00 or to −1.00. A correlation of +.89 for example, would be a very strong positive correlation. That might represent the relationship between scores on the SAT and an IQ test, for example. A correlation of −.89 would be equally strong but negative. That would be more like the correlation researchers would probably find between smoking cigarettes and the age at which a person dies.

Notice that the closer the number is to zero, the weaker the relationship becomes. Researchers would probably find that the correlation coefficient for the relationship between people's weight and the number of freckles they have is pretty close to zero, for example.

Go back to the cigarette thing—if we found that the correlation between cigarette smoking and life expectancy was high, does that mean that smoking causes your life expectancy to be shortened?

Not exactly. The biggest error that people make concerning correlation is to assume that it means one variable is the cause of the other. Remember that *correlation does not prove causation.* Just because two variables are related to each other, researchers

◄ Go back to the cigarette thing—if we found that the correlation between cigarette smoking and life expectancy was high, does that mean that smoking causes your life expectancy to be shortened?

*Inverse: opposite in order.

cannot assume that one of them causes the other one to occur. They could both be related to some other variable that is the cause of both. For example, cigarette smoking and life expectancy might be linked only because people who smoke may be less likely to take care of their health by eating right and exercising, whereas people who don't smoke may tend to eat healthier foods and exercise more than smokers do.

To sum up, a correlation will tell researchers if there is a relationship between the variables, how strong the relationship is, and in what direction the relationship goes. If researchers know the value of one variable, they can predict the value of the other. If they know someone's IQ score, for example, they can predict about what score that person should get on the SAT—not the exact score, just a reasonable estimate. Also, even though correlation does not prove causation, it can provide a starting point for examining causal relationships with another type of study, the experiment.

The Experiment　The only research method that will allow researchers to determine the cause of a behavior is the **experiment.** In an experiment, researchers deliberately manipulate (change in some purposeful way) the variable they think is causing some behavior while holding all the other variables that might interfere with the experiment's results constant and unchanging. That way, if they get changes in behavior (an effect, in other words), they know that those changes must be due to the manipulated variable. For example, remember the discussion of the steps in the scientific method. It talked about how to study the effects of watching violent cartoons on children's aggressive behavior. The most logical way to study that particular relationship is by an experiment.

First, researchers might start by selecting the children they want to use in the experiment. The best method to do that is through random selection of a sample of children from a "population" determined by the researchers—just as a sample would be selected for a survey. Ideally, researchers would decide on the age of child they wanted to study—say, children who are 3 to 4 years old. Then researchers would go to various day care centers and randomly select a certain number of children of that age. Of course, that wouldn't include the children who don't go to a day care center. Another way to get a sample in the age range might be to ask several pediatricians to send out letters to parents of children of that age and then randomly select the sample from those children whose parents responded positively.

12.10　How are operational definitions, independent and dependent variables, experimental and control groups, and random assignment used in designing an experiment?

The Variables　Another important step is to decide on the variable the researchers want to manipulate (which would be the one they think causes changes in behavior) and the variable they want to measure to see if there are any changes (this would be the effect on behavior of the manipulation). Often deciding on the variables in the experiment comes before selection of the participants or subjects. ◄○ Explore more on MPL

In the example of aggression and children's cartoons, the variable that researchers think causes changes in aggressive behavior is the violence in the cartoons. Researchers would want to manipulate that in some way, and in order to do that they have to define the term *violent cartoon.* They would have to find a cartoon that contains violence or make one. Then they would show that cartoon to the participants and try to measure their aggressive behavior afterwards. In measuring the aggressive behavior, they would have to define exactly what they mean by "aggressive behavior" so that it can be measured. This definition is called an **operational definition** because it specifically names the operations (steps or procedures) that the experimenter must use to

◄○ **Explore more** with a simulation on distinguishing independent and dependent variables.
www.mypsychlab.com

experiment　a deliberate manipulation of a variable to see if corresponding changes in behavior result, allowing the determination of cause-and-effect relationships.

operational definition definition of a variable of interest that allows it to be directly measured.

control or measure the variables in the experiment. An operational definition of aggressive behavior might be a checklist of very specific actions such as hitting, pushing, and so on that an observer can mark off as the children do the items on the list. If the observers were just told to look for "aggressive behavior," the researchers would probably get half a dozen or more different interpretations of what aggressive behavior is.

The name for the variable that is manipulated in any experiment is the **independent variable** because it is *independent* of anything the participants do. The participants in the study do not get to choose or vary the independent variable, and their behavior does not affect this variable at all. In the preceding example, the independent variable would be the presence or absence of violence in the cartoons.

The response of the participants to the manipulation of the independent variable *is* a dependent relationship, so the response of the participants that is measured is known as the **dependent variable.** Their behavior, if the hypothesis is correct, should *depend* on whether or not they were exposed to the independent variable, and in the example, the dependent variable would be the measure of aggressive behavior in the children. The dependent variable is always the thing (response of subjects or result of some action) that is measured to see just how the independent variable may have affected it.

The Groups *If researchers do all of this and find that the children's behavior is aggressive, can they say that the aggressive behavior was caused by the violence in the cartoon?* No, what has been described so far is not enough. The researchers may find that the children who watch the violent cartoon are aggressive, but how would they know if their aggressive behavior was caused by the cartoon or was just the natural aggressive level of those particular children or the result of the particular time of day they were observed? Those sorts of *confounding variables* (variables that interfere with each other and their possible effects on some other variable of interest) are the kind researchers have to control for in some way. For example, if most children in this experiment just happened to be from a pretty aggressive family background, any effects the violent cartoon in the experiment might have had on the children's behavior could be confused (confounded) with the possible effects of the family background. The researchers wouldn't know if the children were being aggressive because they watched the cartoon or because they liked to play aggressively anyway.

The best way to control for confounding variables is to have two groups of participants: those who watch the violent cartoon, and those who watch a nonviolent cartoon for the same length of time. Then the researchers would measure the aggressive behavior in both groups. If the aggressive behavior is significantly greater in the group that watched the violent cartoon (statistically speaking), then researchers can say that in this experiment, violent cartoon watching caused greater aggressive behavior.

The group that is exposed to the independent variable (the violent cartoon in the example) is called the **experimental group,** because it is the group that receives the experimental manipulation. The other group that gets either no treatment or some kind of treatment that should have no effect (like the group that watches the nonviolent cartoon in the example) is called the **control group** because it is used to *control* for the possibility that other factors might be causing the effect that is being examined. If researchers were to find that both the group that watched the violent cartoon and the

The act of hitting each other with toy swords could be part of an operational definition of aggressive behavior.

If researchers do all of this and find that the children's behavior is ◄ aggressive, can they say that the aggressive behavior was caused by the violence in the cartoon?

independent variable variable in an experiment that is manipulated by the experimenter.

dependent variable variable in an experiment that represents the measurable response or behavior of the subjects in the experiment.

experimental group subjects in an experiment who are subjected to the independent variable.

control group subjects in an experiment who are not subjected to the independent variable and who may receive a placebo treatment.

group that watched the nonviolent cartoon were equally aggressive, they would have to assume that the violent content did not influence their behavior at all.

The Importance of Randomization   As mentioned previously, random selection is the best way to choose the participants for any study. Participants must then be assigned to either the experimental group or the control group. Not surprisingly, **random assignment** of participants to one or the other condition is the best way to ensure control over other interfering, or *extraneous*, variables. Random assignment means that each participant has an equal chance of being assigned to each condition. If researchers simply looked at the children and put all of the children from one day care center or one pediatrician's recommendations into the experimental group and the same for the control group, they would run the risk of biasing their research. Some day care centers may have more naturally aggressive children, for example, or some pediatricians may have a particular client base in which the children are very passive. So researchers want to take the entire participant group and assign each person randomly to one or the other of the groups in the study. Sometimes this is as simple as picking names out of a hat. ⊙ See more on **MPL**

● See more video classic footage on Konrad Lorenz on controlling an experiment. www.mypsychlab.com

12.11   How do the placebo and experimenter effects cause problems in an experiment, and how can single-blind and double-blind studies control for these effects?

Experimental Hazards: The Placebo Effect and the Experimenter Effect   There are a few other problems that might arise in any experiment, even with the use of control groups and random assignment. These problems are especially likely when studying people instead of animals, because people are often influenced by their own thoughts or biases about what's going on in an experiment. For example, say there is a new drug that is supposed to improve memory in people who are in the very early stages of *Alzheimer's disease* (a form of mental deterioration that occurs in some people as they grow old). Researchers would want to test the drug to see if it really is effective in helping to improve memory, so they would get a sample of people who are in the early stages of the disease, divide them into two groups, give one group the drug, and then test for improvement. They would probably have to do a test of memory both before and after the administration of the drug to be able to measure improvement.

Let me see if I've got this straight. The group that gets the drug would be the experimental group, and the one that doesn't is the control group, right?

Right, and getting or not getting the drug is the independent variable, whereas the measure of memory improvement is the dependent variable. But there's still a problem with doing it this way. What if the researchers do find that the drug group had greater memory improvement than the group that received nothing? Can they really say that the drug itself caused the improvement? Or is it possible that the participants who received the drug *knew* that they were supposed to improve in memory and, therefore, made a major effort to do so? The improvement may have had more to do with participants' *belief* in the drug than the drug itself, a phenomenon* known as the **placebo effect**: The expectations and biases of the participants in a study can influence their behavior. In medical research, the control group is often given a harmless substitute for the real drug, such as a sugar pill or an injection of salt water, and this substitute (which has no medical effect) is called the *placebo*. If there is a placebo effect, the control group will show changes in the dependent variable even though the participants in that group received only a placebo.

Let me see if I've got this straight. The group that gets the drug would be the experimental group, and the one that ▶ doesn't is the control group, right?

random assignment process of assigning subjects to the experimental or control groups randomly, so that each subject has an equal chance of being in either group.

placebo effect   the phenomenon in which the expectations of the participants in a study can influence their behavior.

_____

*Phenomenon: an observable fact or event.

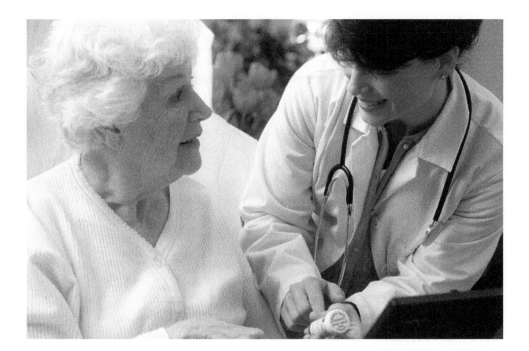

This elderly woman has Alzheimer's disease, which causes a severe loss of recent memory. If she were given a drug to improve her memory, the researcher could not be certain that any improvement shown was caused by the drug rather than by the elderly woman's belief that the drug would work. The expectations of any person in an experimental study can affect the outcome of the study, a phenomenon known as the placebo effect.

Another way that expectations about the outcome of the experiment can influence the results, even when the participants are animals rather than people is called the **experimenter effect**. It has to do with the expectations of the experimenter, not the participants. As discussed earlier in the section about naturalistic observations, sometimes observers are biased—they see what they expect to see. Observer bias can also happen in an experiment. When the researcher is measuring the dependent variable, it's possible that he or she could give the participants clues about how they are supposed to respond—with body language, tone of voice, or even eye contact. Although not deliberate, it does happen. It could go something like this in the example: You, the Alzheimer's patient, are in the experimenter's office to take your second memory test after trying the drug. The experimenter seems to pay a lot of attention to you and to every answer that you give in the test, so you get the feeling that you are supposed to have improved a lot. So you try harder, and any improvement you show may be caused only by your own increased effort, not by the drug. That's the experimenter effect: The behavior of the experimenter caused the participant to change his or her response pattern.

Single-Blind and Double-Blind Studies Fortunately, there are ways to control for these effects. The classic way to control for the placebo effect is to give the control group an actual placebo—some kind of treatment that doesn't affect behavior at all. In the drug experiment, the placebo would have to be some kind of sugar pill or saline (salt) solution that looks like and is administered just like the actual drug. The participants in both the experimental and the control groups would not know whether or not they got the real drug or the placebo. That way, if their expectations have any effect at all on the outcome of the experiment, the experimenter will be able to tell by looking at the results for the control group and comparing them to the experimental group. Even if the control group improves a little, the drug group should improve significantly more if the drug is working. This is called a **single-blind study** because the participants are "blind" to the treatment they receive.

experimenter effect
tendency of the experimenter's expectations for a study to unintentionally influence the results of the study.

single-blind study study in which the subjects do not know if they are in the experimental or the control group.

For a long time, that was the only type of experiment researchers did in psychology. But researchers Robert Rosenthal and Lenore Jacobson reported in their 1968 book, *Pygmalion in the Classroom*, that when teachers were told that some students had a high potential for success and others a low potential, the students showed significant gains or decreases in their performance on standardized tests depending on which "potential" they were supposed to have (Rosenthal & Jacobson, 1968). Actually, the students had been selected randomly and randomly assigned to one of the two groups, "high" or "low." Their performances on the tests were affected by the attitudes of the teachers concerning their potential. This study and similar studies after it highlighted the need to have the experimenter be "blind" as well as the participants in research. So in a **double-blind study** neither the participants nor the person or persons measuring the dependent variable know who got what. That's why everything in a double-blind experiment gets coded in some way, so that only after all the measurements have been taken can anyone determine who was in the experimental group and who was in the control group.

Other Experimental Designs In the field of developmental psychology, researchers are always looking for the ways in which a person's age influences his or her behavior. The problem is that age is a variable that cannot be randomly controlled. In a regular experiment, for example, participants can be randomly assigned to the various conditions: drug or placebo, special instructions or no special instructions, and so on. But participants cannot be randomly assigned to different age groups. It would be like saying, "Okay, these people are now going to be 20, and these others will be 30."

To get around this problem, researchers use alternative designs (called *quasi-experimental designs*) that are not considered true experiments because of the inability to randomly assign participants to the experimental and control groups (Gribbons & Herman, 1997).

For a good example of a typical experiment, read the following section about Dr. Teresa Amabile's experiment in creativity and rewards.

Classic Studies in Psychology

Teresa Amabile and the Effect of Extrinsic Reward on Creativity

12.12 What are the basic elements of Amabile's creativity experiment?

A very good example of an experiment is a classic study by famed Harvard Business College professor, Dr. Teresa Amabile. Amabile (1982) has made great strides in the study of creativity in both children and adults. In her 1982 study, she randomly selected a group of girls from a local public school. The girls ranged in age from 7 to 11. Dr. Amabile randomly divided them into two groups, an experimental group and a control group. She arranged to have an "art party" at the school after regular class hours and set up an empty classroom as her "laboratory." In this classroom she placed all the materials the children would need to make collages—poster board, paste, and numerous shapes and

double-blind study study in which neither the experimenter nor the subjects know if the subjects are in the experimental or control group.

colors of construction paper. (A collage is just bits of paper or pictures glued onto a poster or paper—no drawing skills are necessary.)

Her hypothesis was that the girls who created art for an *extrinsic* (external) reward, such as toys, would be significantly less creative than the girls who created art for its own sake, or who have *intrinsic* (internal) motivation. On the day of the art party for the experimental group, she showed the children all the materials they would be using and *told them that the best three collages would win prizes*. This instruction was actually one part of her independent variable because she wanted to manipulate the children into believing that they were creating art for an extrinsic reward.

On a different day, she brought the girls in her control group into the same classroom with the same materials, but she told these children that the prizes she showed them at the beginning would be raffled off by drawing names out of a hat at the end of the party. So these children had the same materials, the same amount of time, and the same prizes—but they were making their collages purely for the fun of it, or because of intrinsic motivation.

At the end of the party for *both* groups, she actually raffled off the prizes. It wasn't important that the children in the experimental group actually *win* the prizes with their art, only that they *believed that they would*.

This girl is putting together a collage, using materials very similar to those used in Amabile's classic experiment.

Now all the basic elements of an experiment were in place: the hypothesis (the prediction), the independent variable (the two different sets of instructions), the experimental group (the ones who were told they could win prizes), and the control group (the ones just having fun). From her hypothesis, Amabile's dependent variable has to be how creative the artwork of the children in both groups actually was, but how could she measure something as subjective as creativity?

This is where cleverness comes in. Amabile got several local artists, art critics, and art teachers to come in after the children were gone. She had taped all of the collages (with all the identifying information on the back and, therefore, invisible) to the walls of the school corridors. Each "judge" rated each piece of artwork for its creativity, and then Amabile collected the ratings for each collage, averaged them, and came up with a "creativity score" that she could analyze with statistics.

Amabile's hypothesis was indeed supported by the results of her study. The judges' scores for the experimental group (who all believed they were competing for prizes) were consistently and significantly lower than the scores for the control group (Amabile, 1982). She concluded that creativity is decreased when reward is in the picture in the form of prizes or money (as her studies with adults have shown).

Questions for Further Discussion

1. In thinking about how researchers control for biases in experiments, why did Dr. Amabile ask several local artists and art critics to judge the collages after the children had gone? (Hint: There are two important effects being controlled by Dr. Amabile's decision.)

2. How might the particular school from which Dr. Amabile selected her participants have been an interfering factor in the experiment?

3. How can parents and educators encourage creativity without the use of external rewards?

12.9–12

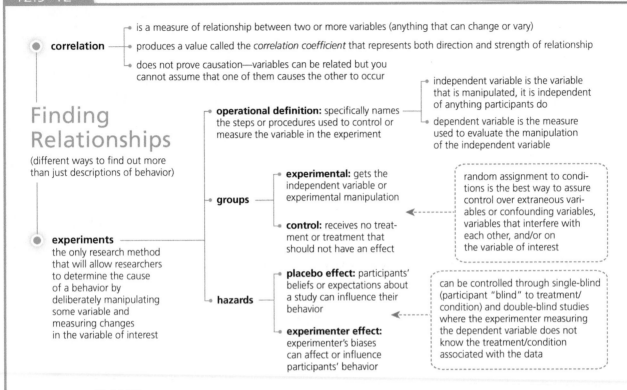

correlation ─── is a measure of relationship between two or more variables (anything that can change or vary)

produces a value called the *correlation coefficient* that represents both direction and strength of relationship

does not prove causation—variables can be related but you cannot assume that one of them causes the other to occur

Finding Relationships

(different ways to find out more than just descriptions of behavior)

operational definition: specifically names the steps or procedures used to control or measure the variable in the experiment

independent variable is the variable that is manipulated, it is independent of anything participants do

dependent variable is the measure used to evaluate the manipulation of the independent variable

groups

experimental: gets the independent variable or experimental manipulation

control: receives no treatment or treatment that should not have an effect

random assignment to conditions is the best way to assure control over extraneous variables or confounding variables, variables that interfere with each other, and/or on the variable of interest

experiments
the only research method that will allow researchers to determine the cause of a behavior by deliberately manipulating some variable and measuring changes in the variable of interest

hazards

placebo effect: participants' beliefs or expectations about a study can influence their behavior

experimenter effect: experimenter's biases can affect or influence participants' behavior

can be controlled through single-blind (participant "blind" to treatment/ condition) and double-blind studies where the experimenter measuring the dependent variable does not know the treatment/condition associated with the data

PRACTICE **QUIZ:** HOW MUCH DO YOU REMEMBER?

Pick the best answer.

1. It's common knowledge that the more you study, the higher your grade will be. What kind of correlation is this relationship?
   a. positive
   b. negative
   c. zero
   d. causal

2. Which of the following would indicate the strongest relationship between two variables?
   a. +1.04
   b. −0.89
   c. +0.75
   d. +0.54

3. In an experiment to test the effects of alcohol on memory, the experimenter gives vodka mixed in orange juice to one group of subjects and orange juice with no vodka to the other group. She then measures the memory skills of both groups by means of a memory test. In this study, the independent variable would be
   a. scores on the memory test.
   b. the presence or absence of vodka in the orange juice.
   c. intelligence.
   d. a placebo.

4. In that same experiment, the control group is the one that gets
   a. only one drink of orange juice with vodka.
   b. a fake test of memory.
   c. only something to eat.
   d. the orange juice without vodka.

5. In a _____ study, neither the experimenter nor the participants know who is in the control group and who is in the experimental group.
   a. placebo
   b. single-blind
   c. double-blind
   d. triple-blind

6. In Dr. Amabile's classic experiment of the effects of reward on creativity, what was the dependent variable?
   a. the special instructions to each group
   b. the collage party
   c. the ratings of creativity from the experts for each child's collage
   d. the size of the collages

Ethics of Psychological Research

The study that Dr. Watson did with "Little Albert" and the white rat seems pretty cruel, when you think about it. Do researchers today do that kind of study?

Actually, as psychology began to grow and more research with people was being done, psychologists began to realize that some protections had to be put in place. No one wanted to be thought of as a "mad scientist," and if studies were permitted that could actually harm people, the field of psychology might die out pretty quickly. Scientists in other areas of research were also realizing that ethical treatment of the participants in studies had to be ensured in some way. Ethical treatment, of course, means that people who volunteer for a study will be able to expect that no physical or psychological harm should come to them.

12.13   What are some ethical concerns that can occur when conducting research with people and animals?

Universities and colleges (where most psychological research is carried out) usually have *institutional review boards*, groups of psychologists or other professionals who look over each proposed research study and judge it according to its safety and consideration for the participants in the study. These review boards look at all aspects of the proposed research, from the written materials that explain the research to the potential subjects to the equipment that may be used in the study itself.

THE GUIDELINES FOR DOING RESEARCH WITH PEOPLE

There are quite a few ethical concerns when dealing with human subjects in an experiment or other type of study. Here is a list of the most common ethical guidelines:

1. **Rights and well-being of participants must be weighed against the study's value to science.** In other words, people come first, research second.

2. **Participants must be allowed to make an informed decision about participation.** This means that researchers have to explain the study to the people they want to include before they do anything to them or with them—even children—and it has to be in terms that the participants can understand. If researchers are using infants or children, their parents have to be informed and give their consent. This is known as *informed consent*. Even in single- or double-blind studies, it is necessary to tell the participants that they may be members of either the experimental or the control group—they just won't find out which group they were actually in until after the experiment is concluded.

3. **Deception must be justified.** In some cases, it is necessary to deceive the participants because the study wouldn't work any other way. The participants have to be told after the study exactly why the deception was important. This is called *debriefing.*

4. **Participants may withdraw from the study at any time.** The participants must be allowed to drop out for any reason. Sometimes people get bored with the study, decide they don't have the time, or don't like what they have to do, for example. Children are particularly likely to decide not to play. Researchers have to let them go, even if it means having to get more participants.

"He says he wants a lawyer."

5. **Participants must be protected from risks or told explicitly of risks.** For example, if researchers are using any kind of electrical equipment, care must be taken to ensure that no participant will experience a physical shock from faulty electrical equipment.

6. **Investigators must debrief participants, telling the true nature of the study and expectations of results.** This is important in all types of studies but particularly in those involving a deception.

7. **Data must remain confidential.** Freud recognized the importance of confidentiality, referring to his patients in his books and articles with false names. Likewise, psychologists and other researchers today tend to report only group results rather than results for a single individual, so that no one could possibly be recognized (American Psychological Association, 1992).

Psychologists also study animals to find out about behavior, often drawing comparisons between what the animals do and what people might do under similar conditions.

But why not ▶ just study people in the first place?

But why not just study people in the first place?

Some research questions are extremely important but difficult or impossible to answer by using human participants. Animals live shorter lives, so looking at long-term effects becomes much easier. Animals are also easier to control—the scientist can control diet, living arrangements, and even genetic relatedness. The white laboratory rat has become a recognized species different from ordinary rats, bred with its own kind for many decades until each white rat is essentially a little genetic "twin" of all the others. Animals also engage in much simpler behavior than humans do, making it easier to see the effects of manipulations. But the biggest reason that researchers use animals in some research is that animals can be used in ways that researchers could never use people. For example, it took a long time for scientists to prove that the tars and other harmful substances in tobacco cause cancer because they had to do correlational studies with people and experiments only with animals. There's the catch—researchers can do many things to animals that they can't do to people. That might seem cruel at first, but when you think that without animal research there would be no vaccines for deadly diseases, no insulin treatments for diabetics, no transplants, and so on, then the value of the research and its benefits to humankind far outweigh the hazards to which the research animals are exposed.

There are also ethical considerations when dealing with animals in research, just as there are with humans. With animals, though, the focus is on avoiding exposing them to any *unnecessary* pain or suffering. So if surgery is part of the study, it is done under anesthesia. If the research animal must die in order for the effects of some drug or other treatment to be examined in an autopsy, the death must be accomplished humanely. Animals are used in only about 7 percent of all psychological studies (Committee on Animal Research and Ethics, 2004).

Critical Thinking

What good is all this focus on science and research going to ▶ do for me? I live in the real world, not a laboratory.

What good is all this focus on science and research going to do for me? I live in the real world, not a laboratory.

The real world is full of opportunities for scientific thinking. Think about all the commercials on television for miracle weight loss, hair restoration, or herbal remedies for arthritis, depression, and a whole host of physical and mental problems. Wouldn't it be nice to know how many of these claims people should believe?

Wouldn't you like to know how to evaluate claims like these and possibly save yourself some time, effort, and money? That's exactly the kind of "real-world" problem that critical thinking can help sort out. ((•─[**Hear** more on **MPL**

((•● **Hear more** with the Psychology in the News podcast. www.mypsychlab.com

THE CRITERIA FOR CRITICAL THINKING

12.14 What are the basic principles of critical thinking, and how can critical thinking be useful in everyday life?

According to Beyer (1995), **critical thinking** means making reasoned judgments. The word *reasoned* means that people's judgments should be logical and well thought out. There are four basic criteria* for critical thinking that people should remember when faced with statements about the world around them (Gill, 1991; Shore, 1990):

1. **There are very few "truths" that do not need to be subjected to testing.** Although people may accept religious beliefs and personal values on "faith," everything else in life needs to have supporting evidence. Questions that can be investigated empirically should be examined using established scientific methods. One shouldn't accept anything at face value but should always ask, "How do you know that? What is the evidence?"

2. **All evidence is not equal in quality.** One of the most important steps in critical thinking and one that is often overlooked is evaluating how evidence is gathered before deciding that it provides good support for some idea. For example, there are poorly done experiments, incorrect assumptions based on correlations rather than experiments, and studies in which there was either no control group or no attempt made to control for placebo effects or experimenter effects.

3. **Just because someone is considered to be an authority or to have a lot of expertise does not make everything that person claims automatically true.** One should always ask to see the evidence rather than just take some expert's word for anything. How good is the evidence? Are there other alternative explanations? For example, Linus Pauling, a famous and respected scientist, made claims about the benefits of vitamin C for curing the common cold. Although research is beginning to support the idea that vitamin C may help fight cancer, research has also found that even larger doses of this vitamin don't cure the common cold (Padayatty & Levine, 2001).

4. **Critical thinking requires an open mind.** Although it is good to be a little skeptical, people should not close their minds to things that are truly possible. At the same time, it's good for people to have open minds but not so open that they are gullible** and apt to "swallow anything." Critical thinking requires a delicate balance between skepticism and willingness to consider possibilities—even possibilities that disagree with previous judgments or beliefs. For example, scientists have yet to find any convincing evidence that there was once life on Mars. That doesn't mean that scientists totally dismiss the idea of life on Mars, just that there is no convincing evidence *yet*. I don't believe that there are Martians on Mars, but if I were shown convincing evidence, I would have to be willing to change my thinking—as difficult as that might be.

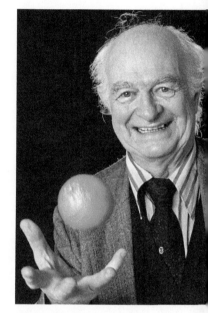

Linus Pauling is a two-time winner of the Nobel Prize. He proposed the use of vitamin C supplements to prevent the common cold, but scientific evidence has repeatedly failed to find support for his belief.

---

*Criteria: standards on which a judgment or decision may be based.
**Gullible: easily fooled or cheated.

critical thinking making reasoned judgments about claims.

PSEUDOPSYCHOLOGIES: WHY DO PEOPLE FALL FOR FAKERY?

> I guess I understand about the importance of critical thinking—there seems to be a lot of people out there who will fall for anything.

I guess I understand about the importance of critical thinking—there seems to be a lot of people out there who will fall for anything.

Actually, the kind of people who fall for the dumbest-sounding scams is rather surprising. Many very intelligent people fall prey to the same kinds of faulty reasoning that less "sophisticated" persons do. Con artists and scammers know the flaws in human nature pretty well, and that's how they survive.

Some of the easiest things to fall for are the **pseudopsychologies,** systems of explaining human behavior that are not based on scientific evidence and that have no real value other than being entertaining (Bunge, 1984). Because people like to try to understand themselves, they often participate in these activities.

One false system is *palmistry*, or the reading of palms. There is overwhelming evidence that the lines of the palm have absolutely no relationship to personality and cannot predict the future (Ben-Shakhar et al., 1986; Dean et al., 1992), yet many people still believe that palm readers are for real. What about handwriting? Surely one's personality would be revealed in handwriting? The pseudopsychology called *graphology*, or the analysis of personality through handwriting, even has respectable companies using handwriting analysis to select prospective employees, yet graphologists score close to zero on tests of accuracy in personality measurement (Ben-Shakhar et al., 1986).

Astrology is another popular pseudopsychology that attempts to predict the future and explain personality by using the positions of the stars and planets at the moment of birth. But does it work? Here's an example of critical thinking applied to astrology:

1. **Are astrologers' charts up-to-date?** The basic astrological charts were designed over 3,000 years ago. The stars, planets, and constellations are no longer in the same positions in the sky, due to changes in the rotation of the Earth's axis over long periods of time—over 24 degrees in just the last 2,000 years (Dean & Kelly, 2000; Kelly, 1980). So a Gemini is really a Cancer and will be a Leo in another 2,000 years.

2. **What exactly is so important about the moment of birth?** Why not the moment of conception? What happens if a baby is born by cesarean section and not at the time it would have been born naturally? Is that person's whole life screwed up?

3. **Why would the stars and planets have any effect on a person? Is it gravity?** The body mass of the doctor who delivers the baby has a far greater gravitational pull on the infant's body than the moon does. (Maybe people should use skinny obstetricians?)

Research also shows no connection between astrological signs and personality, careers, skills, marriage rates, divorce rates, or even physical characteristics (Dean & Kelly, 2000; Kelly, 1980). Studies of thousands of predictions by astrologers showed that only a very small percentage of those predictions actually came true (Dean & Kelly, 2000), and the ones that did come true were very vague or easily guessed from current events ("I predict that a famous star will have plastic surgery this year.") ✳ Learn more on **MPL**

pseudopsychologies
systems of explaining human behavior that are not based on or consistent with scientific evidence.

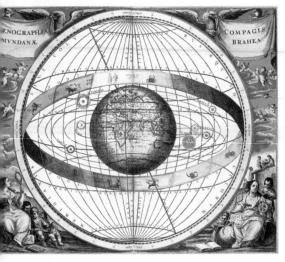

This is a map of sixteenth-century astrologer Tycho Brahe's earth-centered universe. He rejected Copernicus's notion that the planets, including the earth, revolved around the sun, preferring his own theory that the earth was the center of the universe.

✳ **Learn more** about phrenology. Can your skull explain certain personality traits?
www.mypsychlab.com

12.13   12.14

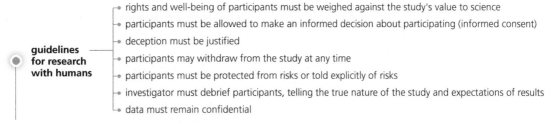

guidelines
for research
with humans
- rights and well-being of participants must be weighed against the study's value to science
- participants must be allowed to make an informed decision about participating (informed consent)
- deception must be justified
- participants may withdraw from the study at any time
- participants must be protected from risks or told explicitly of risks
- investigator must debrief participants, telling the true nature of the study and expectations of results
- data must remain confidential

Ethics of Psychological Research

(psychological scientists have a primary goal of protecting the health and welfare of their animal or human participants)

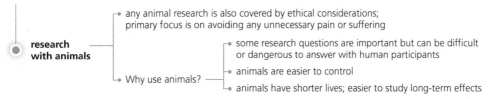

research
with animals
- any animal research is also covered by ethical considerations; primary focus is on avoiding any unnecessary pain or suffering

Why use animals?
- some research questions are important but can be difficult or dangerous to answer with human participants
- animals are easier to control
- animals have shorter lives; easier to study long-term effects

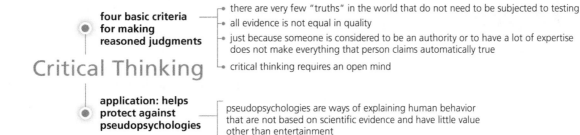

four basic criteria
for making
reasoned judgments
- there are very few "truths" in the world that do not need to be subjected to testing
- all evidence is not equal in quality
- just because someone is considered to be an authority or to have a lot of expertise does not make everything that person claims automatically true
- critical thinking requires an open mind

Critical Thinking

application: helps
protect against
pseudopsychologies
pseudopsychologies are ways of explaining human behavior that are not based on scientific evidence and have little value other than entertainment

PRACTICE QUIZ: HOW MUCH DO YOU REMEMBER?

Pick the best answer.

1. Which of the following is NOT one of the common ethical rules?
   a. Participants have to give informed consent.
   b. Deception cannot be used in any studies with human beings.
   c. The rights and well-being of the participants must come first.
   d. Data must remain confidential.

2. We use animals in research because
   a. animals have simple behavior that makes it easy to see changes.
   b. animals don't live as long as humans and are easier to control.
   c. we can do things to animals that we can't do to people.
   d. all of the above are true.

3. A famous newscaster advertises a new magnetic mattress for controlling pain. If Nathaniel decides to order the mattress because he believes that such a well-known personality should know if it works or not, he has made an error in which of the following?
   a. Few "truths" do not need to be tested.
   b. All evidence is not equal in quality.
   c. Authority or expertise does not make the claims of the authority or expert true.
   d. Critical thinking requires an open mind.

4. Critical thinking means making judgments based on
   a. emotional issues.
   b. keeping a closed mind.
   c. reason and logical evaluation.
   d. authority and expertise.

5. Which pseudopsychology claims to understand personality through a study of the bumps on one's skull?
   a. phrenology   c. graphology
   b. palmistry   d. astrology

Applying Psychology to Everyday Life: Stereotypes, Athletes, and College Test Performance

It seems that many people have a negative stereotype of college athletes—that they are graded and promoted on the basis of their ability on the athletic field and not on the basis of classroom performance. Evidence does exist for poorer performance on academic tests of athletes when compared to nonathletes in college (National Collegiate Athletic Association, 2002; Purdy et al., 1982; Upthegrove et al., 1999). If you are an athlete, can that negative stereotype actually have a negative impact on your test performance? Wesleyan University researchers Matthew Jameson, Robert Diehl, and Henry Danso have some evidence that such stereotypes can have just that kind of negative impact (Jameson et al., 2007).

In their experiment, 72 male college athletes from the sports teams of the university were given an intellectual test. Half of the athletes answered a brief questionnaire before taking the test, whereas the other half received the same questionnaire after taking the test. The questionnaire asked three questions, with the third question being, "Rate your likelihood of being accepted to the university without the aid of athletic recruiting." This item was designed to bring the negative stereotype of athletes ("dumb jocks") to the forefront of students' minds, creating a "high threat" for that stereotype.

Could knowing that other people might think your success in school is due to your athletic ability and not to your intelligence make you perform poorly on an academic test?

The results? Those students who answered the "high threat" question *before* the intellectual test scored significantly lower on that test than those who answered the question *after* the test. The researchers also found a correlation between the students' exposure to the "high threat" stereotype condition and accuracy on the intellectual test: The more students believed that they got into college primarily because of their ability in sports (based on their rating of that third question), the worse they performed on the subsequent test. Jameson and colleagues concluded that obvious negative stereotypes in higher education may be an important cause of the tendency of college athletes to underperform in academics.

Questions for Further Discussion

1. In this experiment, which group was the experimental group and which was the control? What was the independent variable? The dependent variable?

2. What might educators do to try to prevent the effect of the "dumb jock" negative stereotype on college athletes?

12

CHAPTER SUMMARY ((•—[Hear more on **MPL** Listen to an audio file of your chapter. **www.mypsychlab.com**

What Is Psychology?

12.1 What defines psychology as a field of study and what are psychology's four primary goals?

- Psychology is the scientific study of behavior and mental processes.
- The four goals of psychology are description, explanation, prediction, and control.

Psychology Then: The History of Psychology

12.2 How did structuralism and functionalism differ, and who were the important people in those early fields?

- In 1879 psychology began as a science of its own in Germany with the establishment of Wundt's psychology laboratory. He developed the technique of objective introspection.
- Titchener, a student of Wundt, brought psychology in the form of structuralism to America. Structuralism died out in the early twentieth century. Margaret F. Washburn, Titchener's student, was the first woman to receive a Ph.D. in psychology in 1894 and published *The Animal Mind*.
- William James proposed a countering point of view called functionalism, that stressed the way the mind allows us to adapt.

- Functionalism influenced the modern fields of educational psychology, evolutionary psychology, and industrial/organizational psychology.

12.3 What were the basic ideas and who were the important people behind the early approaches known as Gestalt, psychoanalysis, and behaviorism?

- Wertheimer and others studied sensation and perception, calling the new perspective Gestalt (an organized whole) psychology.
- Freud proposed that the unconscious mind controls much of our conscious behavior in his theory of psychoanalysis.
- Watson proposed a science of behavior called behaviorism, which focused only on the study of observable stimuli and responses.
- Watson and Rayner demonstrated that a phobia could be learned by conditioning a baby to be afraid of a white rat.

Classic Studies in Psychology: Psychologist Mary Cover Jones and "Little Peter"

- Mary Cover Jones later demonstrated that a learned phobia could be counterconditioned.

Psychology Now: Modern Perspectives

12.4 What are the basic ideas behind the seven modern perspectives, as well as the important contributions of Skinner, Maslow, and Rogers?

- Modern Freudians such as Anna Freud, Jung, and Adler changed the emphasis in Freud's original theory into a kind of neo-Freudianism.
- Skinner's operant conditioning of voluntary behavior became a major force in the twentieth century. He introduced the concept of reinforcement to behaviorism.
- Humanism, which focuses on free will and the human potential for growth, was developed by Maslow and Rogers, among others, as a reaction to the deterministic nature of behaviorism and psychoanalysis.
- Cognitive psychology is the study of learning, memory, language, and problem solving.
- Biopsychology emerged as the study of the biological bases of behavior.
- The principles of evolution and the knowledge we currently have about evolution are used in this perspective to look at the way the mind works and why it works as it does. Behavior is seen as having an adaptive or survival value.

Psychological Professionals and Areas of Specialization

12.5 How does a psychiatrist differ from a psychologist, and what are the other types of professionals who work in the various areas of psychology?

- Psychiatrists are medical doctors who provide diagnosis and therapy for persons with mental disorders, whereas psychoanalysts are psychiatrists or psychologists with special training in the theory of psychoanalysis.
- Psychiatric social workers are social workers with special training in the influences of the environment on mental illness.
- Psychologists have academic degrees and can do counseling, teaching, and research and may specialize in any one of a large number of areas within psychology.

- There are many different areas of specialization in psychology, including clinical, counseling, developmental, social, and personality as areas of work or study.

Psychology: The Science

12.6 Why is psychology considered a science, and what are the steps in using the scientific method?

- The scientific method is a way to determine facts and control the possibilities of error and bias when observing behavior. The five steps are perceiving the question, forming a hypothesis, testing the hypothesis, drawing conclusions, and reporting the results.

12.7 How are naturalistic and laboratory settings used to describe behavior, and what are some of the advantages and disadvantages associated with these settings?

- Naturalistic observations involve watching animals or people in their natural environments but have the disadvantage of lack of control.
- Laboratory observations involve watching animals or people in an artificial but controlled situation, such as a laboratory.

12.8 How are case studies and surveys used to describe behavior, and what are some drawbacks to each of these methods?

- Case studies are detailed investigations of one subject, whereas surveys involve asking standardized questions of large groups of people that represent a sample of the population of interest.
- Information gained from case studies cannot be applied to other cases. People responding to surveys may not always tell the truth or remember information correctly.

12.9 What is the correlational technique, and what does it tell researchers about relationships?

- Correlation is a statistical technique that allows researchers to discover and predict relationships between variables of interest.
- Positive correlations exist when increases in one variable are matched by increases in the other variable, whereas negative correlations exist when increases in one variable are matched by decreases in the other variable.
- Correlations cannot be used to prove cause-and-effect relationships.

12.10 How are operational definitions, independent and dependent variables, experimental and control groups, and random assignment used in designing an experiment?

- Experiments are tightly controlled manipulations of variables that allow researchers to determine cause-and-effect relationships.
- The independent variable in an experiment is the variable that is deliberately manipulated by the experimenter to see if related changes occur in the behavior or responses of the participants and is given to the experimental group.
- The dependent variable in an experiment is the measured behavior or responses of the participants.
- The control group receives either a placebo treatment or nothing.
- Random assignment of participants to experimental groups helps to control for individual differences both within and between the groups that might otherwise interfere with the experiment's outcome.

12.11 How do the placebo and experimenter effects cause problems in an experiment, and how can single-blind and double-blind studies control for these effects?

* Experiments in which the subjects do not know if they are in the experimental or control groups are single-blind studies, whereas experiments in which neither the experimenters nor the subjects know this information are called double-blind studies.

Classic Studies in Psychology: Teresa Amabile and the Effect of Extrinsic Reward on Creativity

12.12 What are some basic elements of Amabile's creativity experiment?

* Dr. Teresa Amabile's experiment explored the relationship of rewards and creativity by promising a reward to one group of children for being creative (the experimental group) and not to a second group of children, who were being creative for fun (the control group).

* Her conclusion was that external rewards have a negative effect on creativity.

Ethics of Psychological Research

12.13 What are some ethical concerns that can occur when conducting research with people and animals?

* Ethical guidelines for doing research with human beings include the protection of rights and well-being of participants, informed consent, justification when deception is used, the right of participants to withdraw at any time, protection of participants from physical or psychological harm, confidentiality, and debriefing of participants at the end of the study.

* Animals in psychological research make useful models because they are easier to control than humans, they have simpler behavior, and they can be used in ways that are not permissible with humans.

Critical Thinking

12.14 What are the basic principles of critical thinking, and how can critical thinking be useful in everyday life?

* Critical thinking is the ability to make reasoned judgments. The four basic criteria of critical thinking are that there are few concepts that do not need to be tested, evidence can vary in quality, claims by experts and authorities do not automatically make something true, and keeping an open mind is important.

* Faulty reasoning and a failure to use critical thinking can lead to belief in false systems such as palmistry and graphology.

Applying Psychology to Everyday Life: Stereotypes, Athletes, and College Test Performance

* Athletes were given an intellectual test either before or after being exposed to a stereotyping question designed to increase their awareness of negative stereotypes toward college athletes. Those exposed to the stereotyping question before taking the intellectual test scored much lower than those who were exposed to the question after taking the test, implying that obvious negative stereotypes in higher education may be an important cause of the tendency of college athletes to underperform in academics.

TEST YOURSELF

✓● **Practice** more on **MPL** **Ready for your test?** More quizzes and a customized study plan. **www.mypsychlab.com**

Study Help Note: These longer quizzes appear at the end of every chapter and cover all the major learning objectives that you should know after reading the chapter. These quizzes also provide practice for exams.

Pick the best answer.

1. In the definition of psychology, the term *mental processes* means
   a. internal, covert processes.   c. overt actions and reactions.
   b. outward behavior.   d. only animal behavior.

2. A psychologist is interested in finding out why identical twins have different personalities. This psychologist is most interested in the goal of
   a. description.   c. prediction.
   b. explanation.   d. control.

3. Psychologists who give potential employees tests that determine what kind of job those employees might best fit are interested in the goal of
   a. description.   c. prediction.
   b. explanation.   d. control.

4. Which early theorist developed his perspective on psychology by basing it on Darwin's "survival of the fittest" doctrine?
   a. Wilhelm Wundt   c. John Watson
   b. William James   d. Sigmund Freud

5. "The whole is greater than the sum of the parts" is a statement associated with the perspective of
   a. introspectionism.   c. psychoanalysis.
   b. functionalism.   d. Gestalt psychology.

6. _____ was (were) the focus of Watson's behaviorism.
   a. Conscious experiences   c. The unconscious mind
   b. Gestalt perceptions   d. Observable experiences

7. Who is most associated with the technique of introspection?
   a. Wundt   c. Watson
   b. James   d. Wertheimer

8. Who was denied a Ph.D. despite completing all the requirements for earning the degree?
   a. Mary Whiton Calkins   c. Margaret Washburn
   b. Mary Cover Jones   d. Eleanor Gibson

9. Which perspective focuses on free will and self-actualization?
   a. psychoanalysis   c. cognitive psychology
   b. behaviorism   d. humanism

10. Jenna suffers from a nervous tic of washing her hands repeatedly and being unable to resist washing them again and again. Which perspective would explain Jenna's hand-washing behavior as a result of repressed conflicts?
    a. psychodynamic perspective c. behaviorism
    b. cognitive psychology   d. biopsychology

11. Which perspective looks at perception, learning, and memory?
    a. psychoanalysis
    c. cognitive psychology
    b. behaviorism
    d. evolutionary perspective

12. Which perspective assumes that human behavior may have developed in certain directions because it served a useful function in preserving the species?
    a. psychoanalysis
    c. cognitive psychology
    b. behaviorism
    d. evolutionary perspective

13. Which of the following professionals in psychology has the broadest area of interests and functions?
    a. psychiatrist
    c. psychiatric social worker
    b. psychoanalyst
    d. psychologist

14. A person who has suffered a major stroke and is now experiencing severe personality problems because of the damage would best be advised to see a
    a. psychiatrist.
    c. psychiatric social worker.
    b. psychoanalyst.
    d. psychologist.

15. Which of the following specialties in psychology provides diagnosis and treatment for less serious mental problems such as adjustment disorders?
    a. developmental
    c. personality
    b. counseling
    d. experimental

16. In the scientific method, forming an educated guess is called
    a. reporting your results.
    c. drawing conclusions.
    b. perceiving a question.
    d. forming a hypothesis.

17. The main advantage of laboratory observation is
    a. the degree of control it allows the observer.
    b. the degree of participation it allows the observer.
    c. the observer effect.
    d. the opportunity for representative sampling.

18. Harlan wanted to write realistically about street gangs, so he pretended to be a teenager and joined a real gang. This is most similar to the method of
    a. laboratory observation.
    c. the case study.
    b. the observer effect.
    d. participant observation.

19. The main advantage of a case study is
    a. the ease of generalizing the results to others.
    b. being able to determine cause and effect.
    c. the amount of detail it provides about an individual.
    d. the large number of people that can be studied at one time.

20. The entire group that a researcher is interested in is called a
    a. sample.
    c. subject pool.
    b. population.
    d. survey.

21. Professor Jones surveyed her six classes and found that students who slept less than five hours the night before the exam received lower exam scores than those students who slept seven hours or more. What kind of correlation is this relationship between hours of sleep and scores?
    a. positive
    c. zero
    b. negative
    d. causal

22. Drinking orange juice is negatively correlated with the risk of cancer. Based on this information, which of the following statements is TRUE?
    a. The more orange juice you drink, the higher your risk of cancer.
    b. The more orange juice you drink, the lower your risk of cancer.
    c. The less orange juice you drink, the lower your risk of cancer.
    d. Drinking orange juice causes people to be cancer free.

23. A researcher designs an experiment to test the effects of playing video games on memory. What would be the dependent variable?
    a. scores on a memory test
    b. playing video games
    c. number of hours spent playing video games
    d. the type of video game played

24. In that same experiment, the experimental group would
    a. not play the video games.
    b. take the memory test while the control group would not.
    c. not take the memory test while the control group would.
    d. play the video games.

25. In Dr. Amabile's experiment on creativity and reward, what was the independent variable?
    a. the creativity scores for the collages
    b. the judgments of the art experts
    c. the raffles held at the end of the parties
    d. the special instructions to each group

26. In a _____ study, only the experimenter knows who is in the control group and who is in the experimental group.
    a. placebo
    c. double-blind
    b. single-blind
    d. triple-blind

27. Double-blind studies control for
    a. the placebo effect.
    b. the experimenter effect.
    c. the placebo effect and the experimenter effect.
    d. extrinsic motivation.

28. Dr. Silverberg conducted a study in which she tests infants for memory ability. Before she can begin her study, she must obtain
    a. permission from the infants.
    b. permission from the parents.
    c. informed consent from the parents.
    d. confidential information from the parents.

29. Several years ago two scientists announced that they had achieved "cold fusion" in the laboratory, but further studies failed to replicate their findings and later other scientists found that the original two scientists had used sloppy methods. This highlights which of the following critical thinking principles?
    a. Few "truths" do not need to be tested.
    b. All evidence is not equal in quality.
    c. Authority or expertise does not make the claims of the authority or expert true.
    d. Critical thinking requires an open mind.

30. Which pseudopsychology claims to understand personality through a study of the positions of heavenly bodies?
    a. phrenology
    b. palmistry
    c. astrology
    d. graphology

12.1

Psychology
(is the scientific study of behavior and mental processes)

- **has methods for studying phenomena**
- **has four primary goals**
  - describe
  - explain
  - predict
  - control

12.2–3   p. 210

Psychology Then: The History of Psychology
(has roots in several disciplines, including philosophy, medicine, and physiology, and has developed through several perspectives)

- A relatively new science that formally began in 1879 when Wilhelm Wundt ("father of psychology") established the first psychological laboratory in Leipzig, Germany

  was a student of Wundt's

  - **Structuralism**
    founded by Edward Titchener
  - **Functionalism**
    founded by William James
  - **Gestalt psychology**
    founded by Max Wertheimer
  - **Psychoanalysis**
    ideas put forth
    by Sigmund Freud
  - **Behaviorism**
    associated with work
    of John B. Watson,
    who was greatly influenced by
    Ivan Pavlov's work
    in conditioning/learning

12.4   p. 217

- **Psychodynamic**
  based on Freud's theory
- **Behavioral**
  based on early work
  of Watson
  and later B.F. Skinner
- **Humanistic**
  two pioneers are
  Carl Rogers
  and Abraham Maslow
- **Cognitive**
  has roots in
  Gestalt psychology

Psychology Now:
Modern Perspectives
(No one single perspective is used to explain all human behavior and processes)

- **Sociocultural**
- **Biopsychological**
- **Evolutionary**

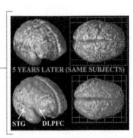

5 YEARS LATER (SAME SUBJECTS)

STG   DLPFC

12.5   p. 217

Types of
Psychological Professionals
(people working in the field of psychology have a variety
of training experiences and different focuses)

- **psychiatrist**
- **psychoanalyst**
- **psychiatric social worker**
- **psychologist**

12.6–8   p. 223

Psychology—The Science

(psychology uses the scientific method to try to determine facts and reduce uncertainty)

- **scientific method**
  - perceiving the question
  - forming a hypothesis
  - testing the hypothesis
  - drawing conclusions
  - reporting your results

- **descriptive data collection methods**
  - **naturalistic observation**
  - **laboratory observation**
  - **case studies**
  - **surveys**

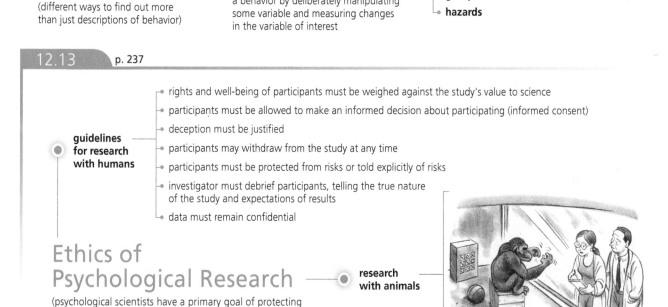

12.9–12   p. 232

- **correlation**
  - is a measure of relationship between two or more variables
  - produces a value called the *correlation coefficient*
  - does not prove causation

Finding relationships

(different ways to find out more than just descriptions of behavior)

- **experiments**
  the only research method that will allow researchers to determine the cause of a behavior by deliberately manipulating some variable and measuring changes in the variable of interest

- **operational definition** specifically names the steps or procedures used to control or measure the variable in the experiment
- **groups**
- **hazards**

12.13   p. 237

- **guidelines for research with humans**
  - rights and well-being of participants must be weighed against the study's value to science
  - participants must be allowed to make an informed decision about participating (informed consent)
  - deception must be justified
  - participants may withdraw from the study at any time
  - participants must be protected from risks or told explicitly of risks
  - investigator must debrief participants, telling the true nature of the study and expectations of results
  - data must remain confidential

Ethics of Psychological Research

(psychological scientists have a primary goal of protecting the health and welfare of their animal or human participants)

- **research with animals**

"He says he wants a lawyer."

12.14   p. 237

- **four basic criteria for making reasoned judgments**
  - there are very few "truths" in the world that do not need to be subjected to testing
  - all evidence is not equal in quality
  - just because someone is considered to be an authority or to have a lot of expertise does not make everything that person claims automatically true
  - critical thinking requires an open mind

Critical Thinking

- **application: helps protect against pseudopsychologies**
  - pseudopsychologies are ways of explaining human behavior that are not based on scientific evidence and have little value other than entertainment

13
The Biological Perspective

Half a Mind?

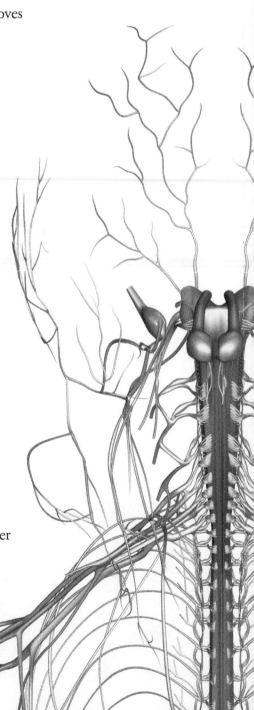

Michelle M. is a 29-year-old woman who holds a part-time job and loves to read, watch movies, and spend time with her family. She has the amazing ability to tell you exactly what day of the week on which any particular calendar date fell, and she's a whiz at playing solitaire. If you were to look at her, you would see that in addition to wearing glasses (like so many other people), Michelle's right wrist is a bit bent and slightly twisted. She can use this hand just fine, although she is actually left-handed. She wears a brace to support her right leg.

You might think that Michelle is very lucky to be so normal, since the weakness on her right side might indicate that she had suffered a moderate stroke at some time in her past, but you'd be wrong. Michelle is more than lucky—she's astonishing. The weakness in her right side comes from the fact that Michelle was born with only half a brain—the right half—and nothing but a fluid-filled cavity in the left side of her skull.

Michelle's case has fascinated doctors who study the brain. Her condition has existed since the womb, when some unknown accident caused the left side of her brain to fail to develop, while the right side grew normally. The left side of the brain, as you will see later in this chapter, normally controls skills such as speech, reading, analytical thinking, and understanding abstract concepts. Michelle, with no left brain, can do all of those things well with the exception of abstraction—she's a pretty detail-oriented, concrete person (Doidge, 2007).

How can Michelle function so normally when she's missing half of her brain? That's just one mystery that we will explore in the pages to come.

Why study the nervous system and the glands? How could we possibly understand any of our behavior, thoughts, or actions without knowing something about the incredible organs that allow us to act, think, and react? If we can understand how the brain, the nerves, and the glands interact to control feelings, thoughts, and behavior, we can begin to truly understand the complex organism called a human being.

An Overview of the Nervous System

13.1 What are the nervous system, neurons, and nerves, and how do they relate to one another?

This chapter will discuss a very complex system of cells, organs, and chemicals that work together to produce behavior, thoughts, and actions. The first part of this complex arrangement is the **nervous system**, a network of cells that carries information to and from all parts of the body. Before beginning the discussion on the cells that make up the nervous system, take a look at Figure 13.1. This figure shows the organization of the various parts of the nervous system and will help in understanding how all the different parts work together in controlling the way people and animals think, act, and feel.

nervous system an extensive network of specialized cells that carries information to and from all parts of the body.

Figure 13.1 **An Overview of the Nervous System**

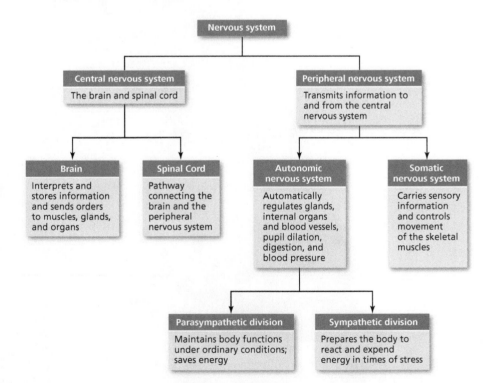

Nervous system

Central nervous system
The brain and spinal cord

Peripheral nervous system
Transmits information to and from the central nervous system

Brain
Interprets and stores information and sends orders to muscles, glands, and organs

Spinal Cord
Pathway connecting the brain and the peripheral nervous system

Autonomic nervous system
Automatically regulates glands, internal organs and blood vessels, pupil dilation, digestion, and blood pressure

Somatic nervous system
Carries sensory information and controls movement of the skeletal muscles

Parasympathetic division
Maintains body functions under ordinary conditions; saves energy

Sympathetic division
Prepares the body to react and expend energy in times of stress

Neurons and Nerves: Building the Network

The field of **neuroscience** is a branch of the life sciences that deals with the structure and functioning of the brain and the neurons, nerves, and nervous tissue that form the nervous system, especially focusing on their relationship to behavior and learning. It was Santiago Ramón y Cajal, a doctor studying slides of brain tissue, who in 1887 first theorized that the nervous system was made up of individual cells (Ramón y Cajal, translation, 1995). ✱ Learn more on MPL

STRUCTURE OF THE NEURON—THE NERVOUS SYSTEM'S BUILDING BLOCK

Although the entire body is composed of cells, each type of cell has a special purpose and function and, therefore, a special structure. Skin cells are flat, but muscle cells are long and stretchy. Most cells do have three things in common: a nucleus, a cell body, and a cell membrane holding it all together. The **neuron** is the specialized cell in the nervous system that receives and sends messages within that system. Neurons are one of the messengers of the body, and that means that they have a very special structure.

The parts of the neuron that receive messages from other cells are called the **dendrites**. The name *dendrite* means "branch," and this structure does indeed look like the branches of a tree. The dendrites are attached to the cell body, or **soma**, which is the part of the cell that contains the nucleus and keeps the entire cell alive and functioning. The **axon** (from the Greek for "axis") is a fiber attached to the soma, and its job is to carry messages out to other cells. (See Figure 13.2.)

✱ **Learn more** about Cajal's influence and discoveries.
www.mypsychlab.com

neuroscience a branch of the life sciences that deals with the structure and function of neurons, nerves, and nervous tissue, especially focusing on their relationship to behavior and learning.

neuron the basic cell that makes up the nervous system and that receives and sends messages within that system.

dendrites branchlike structures that receive messages from other neurons.

soma the cell body of the neuron responsible for maintaining the life of the cell.

axon tubelike structure that carries the neural message to other cells.

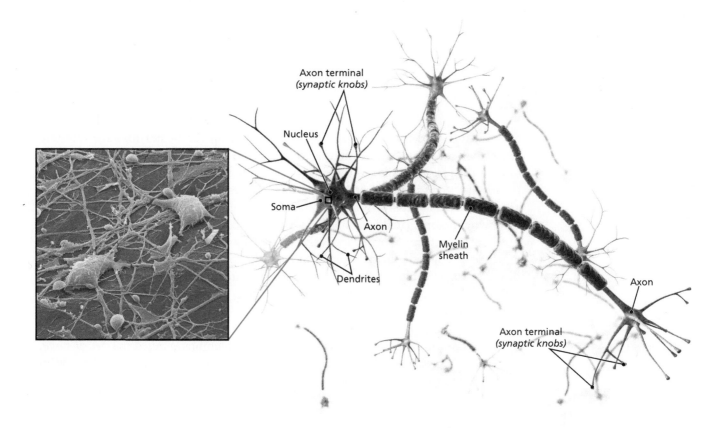

Figure 13.2 The Structure of the Neuron
The electron micrograph on the left shows neurons with axons and dendrites extending from them.

Most people think that the brain is made up entirely of neurons. They may also have heard the old saying that people use only 10 percent of their brains. Neither statement is true, however. People use every cell in the brain for *something*. The fact is that neurons make up only 10 percent of the cells in the brain. The other 90 percent of the brain is composed of **glial cells** that serve as a sort of structure on which the neurons develop and work and that hold the neurons in place. There are several different types of glial cells that perform various functions, such as getting nutrients to the neurons, cleaning up the remains of neurons that have died, communicating with neurons and other glial cells, and providing insulation for neurons. Recent research has found that some types of glial cells affect both the functioning of neurons and their structure and also "give birth" to new neurons during prenatal development (Breedlove et al., 2007; Bullock et al., 2005).

Why are the glial cells needed for structural support? Well, the neuron's message is going to travel through the cell, and within the cell the message is electrical. That means that if one neuron touches another one in the wrong area, they'll short each other out. So the glial cells act as insulation as well as support.

Neurons aren't found only in the brain. If they are spread all throughout the human body, how are they kept separated? The answer is simple. Two special types of glial cells, called *oligodendrocytes* and *Schwann cells*, generate a layer of fatty substances called **myelin**. (Oligodendrocytes produce myelin in the brain and spinal cord; Schwann cells produce myelin in the neurons of the body.) Myelin wraps around the shaft of the axons, forming a protective sheath. It's really the axons that do the bulk of the traveling through the body, with the somas clumped together near the spinal cord. So the axons of those various neurons can travel together throughout the body and never really touch each other directly. It's very similar to the concept of a telephone cable. Within the cable are lots of copper wires coated in plastic. The plastic serves the same insulating purpose for the wires as the myelin sheath does for the axons. Bundled all together, they form a cable that is much stronger and less vulnerable to breakage than any wire alone would be. It works the same way in the nervous system. Bundles of myelin-coated axons travel together in "cables" called **nerves**.

A few other facts about myelin: It not only insulates the neuron, but it also offers a little protection from damage and speeds up the neural message traveling down the axon. As shown in Figure 13.2, sections of myelin bump up next to each other on the axon, similar to the way sausages are linked together. The places where the myelin seems to bump are actually small spaces on the axon called nodes, which are not covered in myelin. When the electrical impulse that is the neural message travels down an axon coated with myelin, it "jumps" between the myelin sheath sections to the places where the axon is accessible at the nodes. That makes the message go much faster down the coated axon than it would down an uncoated axon of a neuron in the brain. This myelin sheath is a very important part of the neuron. The disease called *multiple sclerosis* damages the myelin sheath, which leads to a loss of function in those damaged cells (Allen, 1991).

In addition to the myelin sheath produced by the Schwann cells, axons of neurons found in the body are also coated with a thin membrane called the *neurilemma*, or Schwann's membrane. This membrane, which surrounds the axon and the myelin sheath, serves as a tunnel through which damaged nerve fibers can repair themselves. That's why a severed toe might actually regain some function and feeling if sewn back on in time. Unfortunately, axons of the neurons in the brain and spinal cord do not have this coating and are, therefore, more likely to be permanently damaged.

Exactly how does this "electrical message" work inside the cell?

glial cells grey fatty cells that provide support for the neurons to grow on and around, deliver nutrients to neurons, produce myelin to coat axons, clean up waste products and dead neurons, influence information processing, and, during prenatal development, influence the generation of new neurons.

myelin fatty substances produced by certain glial cells that coat the axons of neurons to insulate, protect, and speed up the neural impulse.

nerves bundles of axons coated in myelin that travel together through the body.

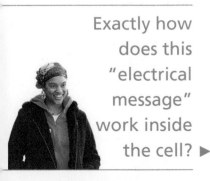

Exactly how does this "electrical message" work inside the cell? ▶

GENERATING THE MESSAGE WITHIN THE NEURON—
THE NEURAL IMPULSE

A neuron that's at rest—not currently firing a neural impulse or message—is actually electrically charged. The inside of the cell is really a semiliquid (jelly-like) solution in which there are charged particles, or *ions*. There is a semiliquid solution surrounding the outside of the cell as well that also contains ions. While there are both positive and negative ions inside and outside of the cell, the catch is that the ions inside the cell are mostly negatively charged, and the ions outside the cell are mostly positively charged. The cell membrane itself is *semipermeable*. This means some substances that are outside the cell can enter through tiny openings, or *gates*, in the membrane, while other substances in the cell can go outside. The negatively charged ions inside the cell, however, are so big that they can't get out, which leaves the inside of the cell primarily negative when at rest. Outside the cell are lots of positively charged sodium ions, but they are unable to enter the cell membrane when the cell is at rest—the ion gates that would allow them in are closed. But because the outside sodium ions are positive and the inside ions are negative, and because opposite electrical charges attract each other, the sodium ions will cluster around the membrane. This difference in charges is an electrical potential. ◄●⊢[Explore more on **MPL**

Think of the ions inside the cell as a baseball game inside a stadium (the cell walls). The sodium ions outside the cell are all the fans in the area, and they want to get inside to see the game. When the cell is resting (a state called the **resting potential**, because the cell is at rest), the fans are stuck outside. The sodium ions cannot enter when the cell is at rest, because even though the cell membrane has all these gates, the *particular* gates for the big sodium ions aren't open yet. But when the cell receives a strong enough stimulation from another cell (meaning that the dendrites are activated), the cell membrane opens up those *particular* gates, one after the other, all down its surface, allowing the sodium ions (the "fans") to rush into the cell. That causes the inside of the cell to become mostly positive and the outside of the cell to become mostly negative, because many of the positive sodium ions are now inside the cell—at the point where the first gate opened. This electrical charge reversal will start at the part of the axon closest to the soma (the first gate) and then proceed down the axon in a kind of chain reaction. (Picture a long hallway with many doors in which the first door opens, then the second, and so on all the way down the hall.) This electrical charge reversal is known as the **action potential** because the electrical potential is now in action rather than at rest. Each action potential sequence takes about one-thousandth of a second, so the neural message travels very fast—from 2 miles per hour in the slowest, shortest neurons to 270 miles per hour in other neurons. (See Figure 13.3.)

Now the action potential is traveling down the axon. When it gets to the end of the axon, something else happens—the message will get transmitted to another cell—that will be discussed momentarily. Meanwhile, what is happening to the parts of the cell that the action potential has already left behind? How does the cell get the "fans" back outside? Remember, the action potential means that the cell is now positive inside and negative outside at the point where the gate opened. Several things happen to return the cell to its resting state. First, the sodium ion gates close immediately after the action potential has passed, allowing no more "fans" (sodium ions) to enter. The cell membrane also literally pumps the positive sodium ions back outside the cell, kicking the "fans" out until the next action potential opens the gates again. This pumping process is a little slow, so another type of ion gets into the act. Small, positively charged potassium ions inside the neuron move rapidly out of the cell after the action potential passes, helping to more quickly restore the inside of the cell to a negative charge. Now the cell becomes negative inside and positive outside, and the neuron is capable of "firing off" another message.

◄●─ **Explore more** with a simulation of neurons and neurotransmitters.
www.mypsychlab.com

resting potential the state of the neuron when not firing a neural impulse.

action potential the release of the neural impulse consisting of a reversal of the electrical charge within the axon.

Figure 13.3 The Neural Impulse Action Potential

In the graph below, voltage readings are shown at a given place on the neuron over a period of 20 or 30 milliseconds (thousandths of a second). At first the cell is resting; it then reaches threshold and an action potential is triggered. After a brief refractory period, the cell returns to its resting potential.

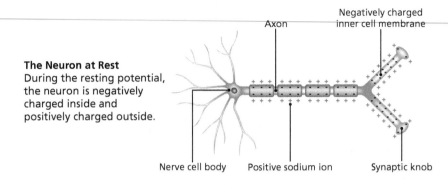

The Neuron at Rest
During the resting potential, the neuron is negatively charged inside and positively charged outside.

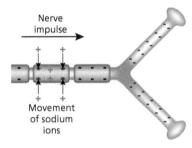

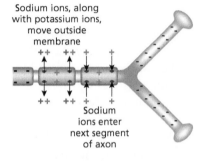

The Neural Impulse
The action potential occurs when positive sodium ions enter into the cell, causing a reversal of the electrical charge from negative to positive.

The Neural Impulse Continues
As the action potential moves down the axon toward the axon terminals, the cell areas behind the action potential return to their resting state of a negative charge as the positive sodium ions are pumped to the outside of the cell, and the positive potassium ions rapidly leave.

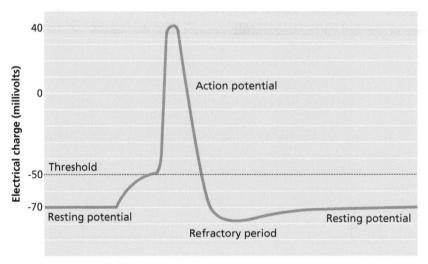

Once the sodium pumps finish pumping out the sodium ions, the neuron can be said to have returned to its full resting potential.

To sum all that up, when the cell is stimulated, the first gate opens and the electrical charge *at that gate* is reversed. Then the next gate opens and *that* charge is reversed, but in the meantime the *first* gate has been closed and the charge is returning to what it was when it was at rest. The action potential is the *sequence* of gates opening all down the length of the cell.

So if the stimulus that originally causes the neuron to fire is very strong, will the neuron fire more strongly than it would if the stimulus were weak?

Neurons actually have a threshold for firing, and all it takes is a stimulus that is just strong enough to get past that threshold to make the neuron fire. Here's a simple version of how this works: Each neuron is receiving many signals from other neurons. Some of these signals are meant to cause the neuron to fire, whereas others are meant to prevent the neuron from firing. The neuron constantly adds together the effects of the "fire" messages and subtracts the "don't fire" messages, and if the "fire" messages are great enough, the threshold is crossed and the neuron fires. When a neuron does fire, it fires in an **all-or-none** fashion. Neurons are either firing at full strength or not firing at all—there's no such thing as "partial" firing of a neuron. It would be like turning on a light switch—it's either on or it's off. Once the switch is turned to the on position, the light will come on. When it's turned to the off position, the light is off.

So what's the difference between strong stimulation and weak stimulation? A strong message will cause the neuron to fire more quickly (as if someone flicked the light switch on and off as quickly as possible), and it will also cause more neurons to fire (as if there were a lot of lights going on and off instead of just one). The latter point can be demonstrated quite easily. Just touch lightly on the palm of your hand. You feel a very light pressure sensation. Now push hard in the same spot. You will feel a much stronger pressure sensation, and you can see with your own eyes that more of the skin on the palm of your hand is pushed in by your touch—more skin involved means more neurons firing.

Now that we know how the message travels within the axon of the cell, what is that "something else" that happens when the action potential reaches the end of the axon?

SENDING THE MESSAGE TO OTHER CELLS: THE SYNAPSE

13.2   How do neurons use neurotransmitters to communicate with each other and with the body?

Look once again at Figure 13.2 on page 247. The end of the axon actually fans out into several shorter fibers called **axon terminals**. The tip of each axon terminal has a little knob on it. Figure 13.4 shows this knob blown up to giant size. Notice that the knob (called the **synaptic knob** or sometimes the *terminal button*) is not empty. It has a number of little saclike structures in it called **synaptic vesicles**. The word *vesicle* is Latin and means a "little blister" or "fluid-filled sac."

Inside the synaptic vesicles are chemicals suspended in fluid, which are molecules of substances called **neurotransmitters**. The name is simple enough—they are inside a neuron and they are going to transmit a message. Next to the synaptic knob is the dendrite of another neuron (see Figure 13.4). Between them is a fluid-filled space called the **synapse** or the **synaptic gap**. Instead of an electrical charge, the vesicles at the end of the axon contain the molecules of neurotransmitters, whereas the surface of the dendrite right next to the axon contains special little locks called **receptor sites**. These locks have a special shape that allows only a particular molecule of neurotransmitter to fit into it, just as only a particular key will fit into a keyhole. (The end of the axon containing the neurotransmitters is also called the presynaptic membrane and the surface of the receiving neuron is called the postsynaptic membrane.)

How do the neurotransmitters get across the gap? Recall the action potential making its way down the axon after the neuron has been stimulated. When that action potential, or electrical charge, reaches the synaptic vesicles, the synaptic vesicles release their neurotransmitters into the synaptic gap. The molecules then float

◄ So if the stimulus that originally causes the neuron to fire is very strong, will the neuron fire more strongly than it would if the stimulus were weak?

Now that we know how the message travels ◄ within the axon of the cell, what is that "something else" that happens when the action potential reaches the end of the axon?

all-or-none   referring to the fact that a neuron either fires completely or does not fire at all.

axon terminals   branches at the end of the axon.

synaptic knob   rounded areas on the end of the axon terminals.

synaptic vesicles   saclike structures found inside the synaptic knob containing chemicals.

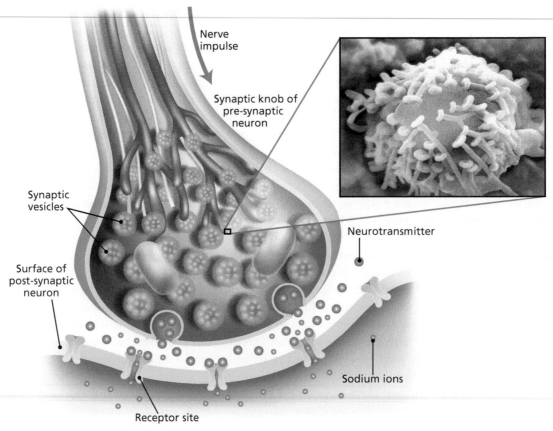

Nerve impulse

Synaptic knob of pre-synaptic neuron

Synaptic vesicles

Surface of post-synaptic neuron

Neurotransmitter

Sodium ions

Receptor site

Figure 13.4 **The Synapse**
The nerve impulse reaches the synaptic knobs, triggering the release of neurotransmitters from the synaptic vesicles. The molecules of neurotransmitter cross the synaptic gap to fit into the receptor sites that fit the shape of the molecule.

neurotransmitter
chemical found in the synaptic vesicles that, when released, has an effect on the next cell.

synapse (synaptic gap)
microscopic fluid-filled space between the synaptic knob of one cell and the dendrites or surface of the next cell.

receptor sites holes in the surface of the dendrites or certain cells of the muscles and glands, which are shaped to fit only certain neurotransmitters.

excitatory synapse
synapse at which a neurotransmitter causes the receiving cell to fire.

inhibitory synapse
synapse at which a neurotransmitter causes the receiving cell to stop firing.

across the synapse and many of them fit themselves into the receptor sites, activating the next cell. It is this very activation that stimulates, or releases, the action potential in that cell. It is important to understand that the "next cell" may be a neuron, but it may also be a cell on a muscle or a gland. Muscles and glands have special cells with receptor sites on them, just like on the dendrite of a neuron.

So far, we've been talking about the synapse as if neurotransmitters always cause the next cell to fire its action potential (or, in the case of a muscle or gland, to contract or start secreting its chemicals). But the neurons must have a way to be turned *off* as well as on. Otherwise, when a person burns a finger, the pain signals from those neurons would not stop until the burn was completely healed. Muscles are told to contract or relax, and glands are told to secrete or stop secreting their chemicals. The neurotransmitters found at various synapses around the nervous system (and there are at least 50 to 100 know neurotransmitters and theoretically several times that number exist) can either turn cells on (called an *excitatory* effect) or turn cells off (called an *inhibitory* effect), depending on exactly what synapse is being affected. Although some people refer to neurotransmitters that turn cells on as *excitatory* neurotransmitters and the ones that turn cells off as *inhibitory* neurotransmitters, it's really more correct to refer to **excitatory synapses** and **inhibitory synapses**. In other words, it's not the neurotransmitter itself that is excitatory or inhibitory, but rather it is the effect of that neurotransmitter that is either excitatory or inhibitory at the receptor sites of a particular synapse.

I think I understand the synapse now, but will knowing about neurotransmitters and synapses help me in the real world?

◄ I think I understand the synapse now, but will knowing about neuro-transmitters and synapses help me in the real world?

Most people have used drugs of some sort at some point in their lives. Knowing how and why drugs affect us can help us understand why a doctor might prescribe a particular drug or why certain drugs are dangerous and should be avoided. Because molecules of various drugs, if similar enough in shape to the neurotransmitters, can fit into the receptor sites on the receiving neurons just like the neurotransmitters do, drugs can affect what happens in the synapse in two ways. **Agonists** are chemical substances that can mimic or enhance the effects of neurotransmitters on the receptor sites of the next cell, which can result in an increase or decrease in the activity of the receiving cell, depending on what the effect of the original neurotransmitter (excitatory or inhibitory) was going to be. So if the original neurotransmitter was excitatory, the effect of the agonist will be to increase that excitation. If it was inhibitory, the effect of the agonist will be to increase that inhibition. For example, there are drugs that bind to receptors in the heart muscle (called *beta* receptors) that act as agonists by increasing the action of the neurotransmitter that stimulates the contractions of certain heart valves. Digoxin, which comes from the foxglove plant, is one example of this kind of agonist drug.

Other drugs act as **antagonists**, chemical substances that block or reduce a cell's response to the action of other chemicals or neurotransmitters. Although an antagonist might sound like it has only an inhibitory effect, it is important to remember that if the neurotransmitter that the antagonist affects is inhibitory itself, the result will actually be an *increase* in the activity of the cell that would normally have been inhibited; the agonist *blocks* the inhibitory effect.

Beta blockers are drugs that are used to control high blood pressure and (as the name suggests) serve as antagonists by blocking the effects of the neurotransmitters that stimulate the heart's contractions. This results in slower heart contractions and lowered blood pressure. Two examples of commonly prescribed beta blockers are propranolol (Inderal®) and metaprolol (Lopressor®). In the following discussion of specific types of neurotransmitters, there are more examples of agonists and antagonists and how they affect the nervous system.

NEUROTRANSMITTERS, MESSENGERS OF THE NETWORK

The first neurotransmitter to be identified was named *acetylcholine*. It is found at the synapses between neurons and muscle cells. Acetylcholine serves to stimulate the skeletal muscles to contract but actually slows contractions in the heart muscle. If acetylcholine receptor sites on the muscle cells are blocked in some way, then the acetylcholine can't get to the site and the muscle will be incapable of contracting—paralyzed, in other words. This is exactly what happens when *curare*, a drug used by South American Indians on their blow darts, gets into the nervous system. Curare's molecules are just similar enough to fit into the receptor site without actually stimulating the cell, making curare an antagonist for acetylcholine.

What would happen if the neurons released too much acetylcholine? The bite of a black widow spider does just that. Its venom stimulates the release of excessive amounts of acetylcholine and causes convulsions and possible death. Black widow spider venom is an agonist for acetylcholine. Acetylcholine is also found in the hippocampus, an area of the brain that is responsible for forming new memories, and low levels of acetylcholine have been associated with Alzheimer's disease, the most common type of dementia.

The venom of the black widow spider causes a flood of acetylcholine to be released into the body's muscle system, causing convulsions.

agonists chemical substances that mimic or enhance the effects of a neurotransmitter on the receptor sites of the next cell, increasing or decreasing the activity of that cell.

antagonists chemical substances that block or reduce a cell's response to the action of other chemicals or neurotransmitters.

The look on this young woman's face clearly indicates that she has experienced pain in her finger. Pain is a warning signal that something is wrong, in this case that touching the thorns on the stem of the rose was a bad idea. What might be some of the problems encountered by a person who could feel no pain at all?

Although acetylcholine was the first neurotransmitter found to have an excitatory effect at the synapse, the nervous system's major excitatory neurotransmitter is *glutamate*. Like acetylcholine, glutamate plays an important role in learning and memory, and may also be involved in the development of the nervous system.

Another neurotransmitter is *GABA*, or *γ-aminobatyric acid* (or said *gamma-aminobutyric acid*). Whereas glutamate is the major neurotransmitter with an excitatory effect, GABA is the most common neurotransmitter producing inhibition in the brain. GABA can help to calm anxiety, for example, by binding to the same receptor sites that are affected by tranquilizing drugs and alcohol. In fact, the effect of alcohol is to enhance the effect of GABA, which causes the general inhibition of the nervous system associated with getting drunk. This makes alcohol an agonist for GABA.

Serotonin is a neurotransmitter found in the lower part of the brain that can have either an excitatory or inhibitory effect, depending on the particular synapses being affected. It is associated with sleep, mood, and appetite. For example, low levels of serotonin activity have been linked to depression.

Dopamine is found in the brain and, like serotonin, can have different effects depending on the exact location of its activity. If too little dopamine is released in a certain area of the brain, the result is Parkinson's disease—the disease currently being battled by former boxing champ Muhammad Ali and actor Michael J. Fox (Ahlskog, 2003). If too much dopamine is released in another area, the result is a serious mental disorder called schizophrenia (Akil et al., 2003). (See Table 13.1 for a list of some neurotransmitters and their functions.)

Some neurotransmitters directly control the release of other neurotransmitters. These special neurotransmitters are called *neural regulators* or *neural peptides* (Agnati et al., 1992), and one that researchers know a little about is endorphin. *Endorphins* are pain-controlling chemicals in the body. When a person is hurt, a neurotransmitter that signals pain is released. When the brain gets this message, it triggers the release of endorphins. The endorphins bind to receptors that open the gates on the axon. This causes the cell to be unable to fire its pain signal and the

Table 13.1   Neurotransmitters and Their Functions

NEUROTRANSMITTERS	FUNCTIONS
Acetylcholine	Excitatory or inhibitory; involved in memory and controls muscle contractions.
Serotonin	Excitatory or inhibitory; involved in mood, sleep, and appetite.
GABA (gamma-aminobutyric acid)	Major inhibitory neurotransmitter; involved in sleep and inhibits movement.
Glutamate	Major excitatory neurotransmitter; involved in learning, memory formation, and nervous system development.
Norepinephrine	Mainly excitatory; involved in arousal and mood.
Dopamine	Excitatory or inhibitory; involved in control of movement and sensations of pleasure.
Endorphins	Inhibitory neural regulators; involved in pain relief.

pain sensations eventually lessen. For example, you might bump your elbow and experience a lot of pain right at first, but the pain will quickly subside to a much lower level. Endorphins! Sports players may injure themselves during an event and yet not feel the pain until after the event when the endorphin levels go down.

The name *endorphin* comes from the term *endogenous morphine*. (*Endogenous* means "native to the area"—in this case, native to the body.) Scientists studying the nervous system found receptor sites that fit morphine molecules perfectly and decided that there must be a natural substance in the body that has the same effect as morphine. Endorphins are the reason that heroin and the other drugs derived from opium are so addictive—when people take morphine or heroin, their bodies neglect to produce endorphins. When the drug wears off, they are left with no protection against pain at all, and *everything* hurts. Known as withdrawal, this pain is why most people want more heroin, creating an addictive cycle of abuse.

If the neurotransmitters are out there in the synaptic gap and in the receptor sites, what happens to them when they aren't needed anymore? ◄

> If the neuro-transmitters are out there in the synaptic gap and in the receptor sites, what happens to them when they aren't needed anymore?

CLEANING UP THE SYNAPSE: REUPTAKE AND ENZYMES

The neurotransmitters have to get out of the receptor sites before the next stimulation can occur. Most neurotransmitters will end up back in the synaptic vesicles in a process called **reuptake**. (Think of a little suction tube, sucking the chemicals back into the vesicles.) That way, the synapse is cleared for the next release of neurotransmitters. Some drugs, like cocaine, affect the nervous system by blocking the reuptake process. See Figure 13.5 for a visual representation of how dopamine is affected by cocaine.

There is one neurotransmitter that is not taken back into the vesicles, however. Because acetylcholine is responsible for muscle activity, and muscle activity needs to happen rapidly and continue happening, it's not possible to wait around for the "sucking up" process to occur. Instead, an enzyme* specifically designed to break apart acetylcholine clears the synaptic gap very quickly. There are enzymes that break down the other neurotransmitters as well.

The neurotransmitter serotonin helps regulate and adjust people's moods, but in some people the normal process of adjustment is not working properly. In some people, serotonin is either not produced or not released in great enough amounts, so it can't fully activate the receptors on the next neuron, leaving the person in a state of depression. Most of the drugs used to treat this condition are called SSRIs (selective serotonin reuptake inhibitors). SSRIs block the reuptake of serotonin, leaving more serotonin available in the synapse to bond with the receptor sites. Eventually, this elevates mood and lifts the depression. Although doctors used to "taper off" the use of antidepressants after the person's depression had lifted, new research has found that keeping a person on a maintenance dose of the drug helps prevent future episodes of depression (Geddes et al., 2003; Taylor et al., 2004).

This section covered the neuron and how neurons communicate. The next section looks at the bigger picture—the nervous system itself. Before reading on, try answering the following questions to test your memory.

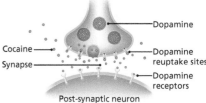

Figure 13.5 Reuptake of Dopamine

Dopamine is removed from the synapse by reuptake sites. Cocaine acts by blocking dopamine reuptake sites, allowing dopamine to remain active in the synapse longer.

reuptake process by which neurotransmitters are taken back into the synaptic vesicles.

---

*Enzyme: a complex protein that is manufactured by cells.

13.1–2

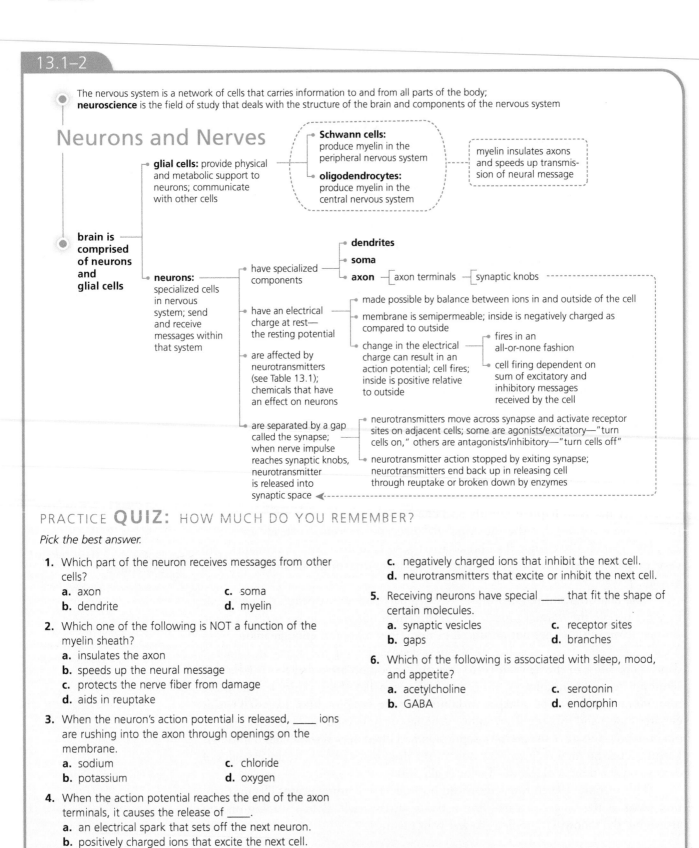

The nervous system is a network of cells that carries information to and from all parts of the body; **neuroscience** is the field of study that deals with the structure of the brain and components of the nervous system

Neurons and Nerves

glial cells: provide physical and metabolic support to neurons; communicate with other cells

Schwann cells: produce myelin in the peripheral nervous system

oligodendrocytes: produce myelin in the central nervous system

myelin insulates axons and speeds up transmission of neural message

brain is comprised of neurons and glial cells

neurons: specialized cells in nervous system; send and receive messages within that system

have specialized components

- **dendrites**
- **soma**
- **axon** — axon terminals — synaptic knobs

have an electrical charge at rest—the resting potential

- made possible by balance between ions in and outside of the cell
- membrane is semipermeable; inside is negatively charged as compared to outside
- change in the electrical charge can result in an action potential; cell fires; inside is positive relative to outside
  - fires in an all-or-none fashion
  - cell firing dependent on sum of excitatory and inhibitory messages received by the cell

are affected by neurotransmitters (see Table 13.1); chemicals that have an effect on neurons

are separated by a gap called the synapse; when nerve impulse reaches synaptic knobs, neurotransmitter is released into synaptic space

- neurotransmitters move across synapse and activate receptor sites on adjacent cells; some are agonists/excitatory—"turn cells on," others are antagonists/inhibitory—"turn cells off"
- neurotransmitter action stopped by exiting synapse; neurotransmitters end back up in releasing cell through reuptake or broken down by enzymes

PRACTICE **QUIZ:** HOW MUCH DO YOU REMEMBER?

Pick the best answer.

1. Which part of the neuron receives messages from other cells?
   a. axon
   b. dendrite
   c. soma
   d. myelin

2. Which one of the following is NOT a function of the myelin sheath?
   a. insulates the axon
   b. speeds up the neural message
   c. protects the nerve fiber from damage
   d. aids in reuptake

3. When the neuron's action potential is released, ____ ions are rushing into the axon through openings on the membrane.
   a. sodium
   b. potassium
   c. chloride
   d. oxygen

4. When the action potential reaches the end of the axon terminals, it causes the release of ____.
   a. an electrical spark that sets off the next neuron.
   b. positively charged ions that excite the next cell.
   c. negatively charged ions that inhibit the next cell.
   d. neurotransmitters that excite or inhibit the next cell.

5. Receiving neurons have special ____ that fit the shape of certain molecules.
   a. synaptic vesicles
   b. gaps
   c. receptor sites
   d. branches

6. Which of the following is associated with sleep, mood, and appetite?
   a. acetylcholine
   b. GABA
   c. serotonin
   d. endorphin

The Central Nervous System— The "Central Processing Unit"

The **central nervous system (CNS)** is composed of the brain and the spinal cord. Both the brain and the spinal cord are composed of neurons and glial cells that control the life-sustaining functions of the body as well as all thought, emotion, and behavior.

13.3 How do the brain and spinal cord interact?

THE BRAIN

The brain is the true core of the nervous system, the part that makes sense of the information received from the senses, makes decisions, and sends commands out to the muscles and the rest of the body. Later parts of this chapter will cover the brain in more detail. Without the spinal cord, however, the brain would be useless.

THE SPINAL CORD

The **spinal cord** is a long bundle of neurons that serves two vital functions for the nervous system. Look at the cross-sectional view of the spinal cord in Figure 13.6. Notice that it seems to be divided into two areas, one around the outside and one inside the cord. If it were a real spinal cord, the outer section would appear to be white and the inner section would seem gray. That's because the outer section is composed mainly of axons and nerves, which appear white, whereas the inner section is mainly composed of cell bodies of neurons, which appear gray. The purpose of the outer section is to carry messages from the body up to the brain and from the brain down to the body. It is simply a message "pipeline."

The Reflex ARC: Three Types of Neurons   The inside section, which is made up of cell bodies separated by glial cells, is actually a primitive sort of "brain." This part of the spinal cord is responsible for certain reflexes—very fast, lifesaving reflexes. To understand how the spinal cord reflexes work, it is important to know there are three basic types of neurons: **afferent (sensory) neurons** that carry messages from the senses to the spinal cord, **efferent (motor) neurons** that carry messages from the spinal cord to the muscles and glands, and **interneurons** that connect the afferent neurons to the motor neurons (and make up the inside of the spinal cord and the brain itself). (See Figure 13.6.) Touch a flame or a hot stove with your finger, for example, and an afferent neuron will send the pain message up to the spinal column where it enters into the central area of the spinal cord. The interneuron in that central area will then receive the message and send out a response along an efferent neuron, causing your finger to pull back. This all happens very quickly. If the pain message had to go all the way up to the brain before a response could be made, the

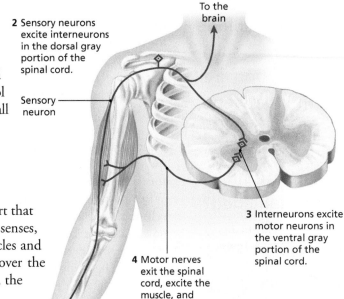

2 Sensory neurons excite interneurons in the dorsal gray portion of the spinal cord.

To the brain

Sensory neuron

3 Interneurons excite motor neurons in the ventral gray portion of the spinal cord.

4 Motor nerves exit the spinal cord, excite the muscle, and initiate a movement.

1 Flame stimulates pain receptors (sensory neurons).

Figure 13.6 The Spinal Cord Reflex

The pain from the burning heat of the candle flame stimulates the afferent nerve fibers, which carry the message up to the interneurons in the middle of the spinal cord. The interneurons then send a message out by means of the efferent nerve fibers, causing the hand to jerk away from the flame.

central nervous system (CNS)   part of the nervous system consisting of the brain and spinal cord.

spinal cord   a long bundle of neurons that carries messages between the body and the brain and is responsible for very fast, lifesaving reflexes.

afferent (sensory) neuron   a neuron that carries information from the senses to the central nervous system.

efferent (motor) neuron   a neuron that carries messages from the central nervous system to the muscles of the body.

If the spinal cord is such an important link between the body and ▶ the brain, what happens if it is damaged?

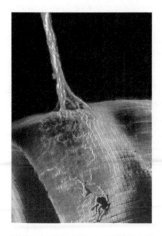

This electronmicrograph shows a motor neuron making contact with muscle fibers.

((•● Hear more with the Psychology in the News podcast. www.mypsychlab.com

interneuron a neuron found in the center of the spinal cord that receives information from the afferent neurons and sends commands to the muscles through the efferent neurons. Interneurons also make up the bulk of the neurons in the brain.

reflex arc the connection of the afferent neurons to the interneurons to the efferent neurons, resulting in a reflex action.

neuroplasticity the ability within the brain to constantly change both the structure and function of many cells in response to experience or trauma.

response time would be greatly increased and more damage would be done to your finger. So having this kind of **reflex arc** controlled by the spinal cord alone allows for very fast response times. (A good way to avoid mixing up the terms *afferent* and *efferent* is to remember "<u>a</u>fferent neurons <u>a</u>ccess the spinal cord, <u>e</u>fferent neurons <u>e</u>xit." The pain message does eventually get to the brain, where other motor responses may be triggered, like saying "Ouch!" and putting the finger in your mouth.

If the spinal cord is such an important link between the body and the brain, what happens if it is damaged?

Damage to the central nervous system was once thought to be permanent. Neurons in the brain and spinal cord were not seen as capable of repairing themselves. When people recovered from a stroke, for example, it was assumed that healthy brain cells took over the function of the damaged ones. Scientists have known for a while now that some forms of central nervous system damage can be repaired by the body's systems, and in recent years great strides have been made in repairing spinal cord damage. The brain actually exhibits a great deal of **neuroplasticity**, the ability to constantly change both the structure and function of many cells in the brain in response to experience and even trauma (Neville & Bavelier, 2000; Rossini et al., 2007; Sanders et al., in press). Scientists have been able to *implant* nerve fibers from outside the spinal cord onto a damaged area and then "coax" the damaged spinal nerves to grow through these "tunnels" of implanted fibers (Cheng et al., 1996). The first human trials have already begun (Blits & Bunge, 2006; Bunge & Pearse, 2003). It is also now known that the brain can change itself quite a bit by adapting neurons to serve new functions when old neurons die or are damaged. Dendrites grow and new synapses are formed in at least some areas of the brain, as people learn new things throughout life (Abraham & Williams, 2003). And as the case of Michelle M. from the opening story, it is actually possible to live a relatively normal life with a substantial amount of brain tissue missing.

Researchers are constantly looking for new ways to repair the brain. For a look at a new and promising treatment for people with diseases such as Parkinson's, Alzheimer's, and damage from strokes, read the following Psychology in the News section. ((•●─[Hear more on **MPL**

Psychology in the News

Stem Cells: New Hope for Damaged Brains?

Scientists have been researching the possibility of transplanting **stem cells** to repair damaged or diseased brain tissue. (See Figure 13.7.) Stem cells can create other cells, such as blood cells, nerve cells, and brain cells (National Institutes of Health, 2007). An ongoing controversy concerns the source of such stem cells, which can be obtained from human embryos, either from terminated pregnancies or fertilization clinics. Many people are opposed to the idea of putting embryos to this use, even if stem cell research promises cures for diseases, such as Parkinson's and Alzheimer's, or the repair of damaged spinal cords or brain tissue.

On August 9, 2001, President George W. Bush announced his decision to allow federal funding of stem cell research using human embryonic stem cells but only on cell lines already in existence. In 2004, House representatives proposed a bill called the Stem Cell Research Enhancement Act, which would have allowed researchers to use stem cells taken from donated embryos that came from fertilization clinics and would be discarded if not used. In the summer of 2006, President Bush vetoed this bill. On June 20, 2007, President Bush once again vetoed the bill (American Association for the Advancement of Science, 2007). With the stem cell lines that are already in existence dwindling in number, researchers are left with no choice but to seek out other sources of stem cells.

Stem cells are found in many of the organs of the body and also in the bone marrow. A study conducted by neurologist Alexander Storch of the University of Ulm in Germany and his colleagues may hold hope for the future of stem cell treatments without the controversial need to use human embryonic tissue (Hermann et al., 2006). In this study, the researchers were able to convert bone marrow stem cells from mice into cells resembling neural stem cells. The authors go on to describe the possibility of such conversion taking place in adult bone marrow stem cells.

Stem cells that are not embryonic tend not to be as "plastic"—they want to form into cells of the tissues in which they are found. Scientists are working to find ways to increase the plasticity of nonembryonic stem cells, such as those obtained from bone marrow, so that future generations may have hope that "permanent" brain damage may become a thing of the past (Croft & Przyborski, 2006; Maisel et al., 2007).

The Stem Cell
These cells develop into all other blood cells, including red, white, and platelets

Red Blood Cells
These cells supply oxygen to the organs and body tissues

White Blood Cells
These cells help the body fight off infections

Platelets
The platelets aid in blood clotting

Figure 13.7 The Stem Cell Stem cells are basic cells that differentiate into specific types of cells, such as these blood cells. Stem cells can also become other types of cells, such as brain cells and nerve cells.

stem cells special cells found in all the tissues of the body that are capable of manufacturing other cell types when those cells need to be replaced due to damage or wear and tear.

Questions for Further Discussion

1. If stem cells can be used to create tissues other than nerves and neurons, what other kinds of diseases might become treatable?

2. What ethical considerations might arise from doing bone marrow stem cell research with human volunteers?

3. How might understanding stem cell reproduction affect cancer research?

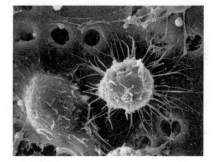

Microphotograph of a bone marrow stem cell.

The Peripheral Nervous System—Nerves on the Edge

Okay, that takes care of the central nervous system, except for the detail on the brain. How does the central nervous system communicate with the rest of the body?

The term *peripheral* refers to things that are not in the center or that are on the edges of the center. The **peripheral nervous system** or **PNS** (see Figure 13.8) is made up of all the nerves and neurons that are not contained in the brain and spinal cord. It is this system that allows the brain and spinal cord to communicate with the sensory systems of the eyes, ears, skin, and mouth and allows the brain and spinal cord to control the muscles and glands of the body. The PNS can be divided into two major systems, the **somatic nervous system** and the **autonomic nervous system (ANS).**

13.4 How do the somatic and autonomic nervous systems allow people and animals to interact with their surroundings and control the body's automatic functions?

THE SOMATIC NERVOUS SYSTEM

One of the parts of a neuron is the soma, or cell body (the word *soma* means "body"). The somatic nervous system is made up of the **sensory pathway**, which is all the nerves carrying messages from the senses to the central nervous system (those nerves containing

Okay, that takes care of the central nervous system,except for the detail on the brain. How does
◄ the central nervous system communicate with the rest of the body?

peripheral nervous system (PNS) all nerves and neurons that are not contained in the brain and spinal cord but that run through the body itself.

somatic nervous system division of the PNS consisting of nerves that carry information from the senses to the CNS and from the CNS to the voluntary muscles of the body.

afferent neurons), and the **motor pathway**, which is all of the nerves carrying messages from the central nervous system to the voluntary, or skeletal,* muscles of the body—muscles that allow people to move their bodies (those nerves composed of efferent neurons). When people are walking, raising their hands in class, smelling a flower, or seeing a pretty picture, they are using the somatic nervous system. (As seen in the discussion of spinal cord reflexes, although these muscles are called the voluntary muscles, they can move involuntarily when a reflex response occurs. They are called "voluntary" because they *can* be moved at will but are not limited to only that kind of movement.)

Involuntary** muscles, such as the heart, stomach, and intestines, together with glands such as the adrenal glands and the pancreas are all controlled by clumps of neurons located on or near the spinal column. (The words *on* or *near* are used quite deliberately here. The neurons *inside* the spinal column are part of the central nervous system, not the peripheral nervous system.) These large groups of neurons near the spinal column make up the *autonomic nervous system.*

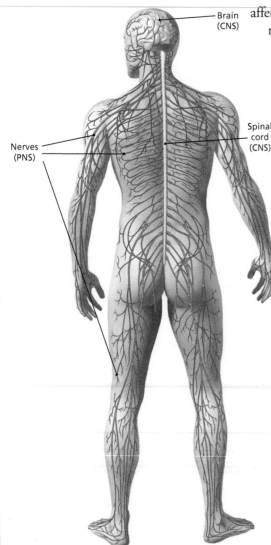

Figure 13.8 **The Peripheral Nervous System**

autonomic nervous system (ANS) division of the PNS consisting of nerves that control all of the involuntary muscles, organs, and glands.

sensory pathway nerves coming from the sensory organs to the CNS consisting of afferent neurons.

motor pathway nerves coming from the CNS to the voluntary muscles, consisting of efferent neurons.

sympathetic division (fight-or-flight system) part of the ANS that is responsible for reacting to stressful events and bodily arousal.

THE AUTONOMIC NERVOUS SYSTEM

The word *autonomic* suggests that the functions of this system are more or less automatic, which is basically correct. Whereas the somatic division of the peripheral nervous system controls the senses and voluntary muscles, the autonomic division controls everything else in the body—organs, glands, and involuntary muscles. The autonomic nervous system is divided into two systems, the **sympathetic division** and the **parasympathetic division**. (See Figure 13.9.) (For a visual representation of how all the various sections of the nervous system are organized, look back at Figure 13.1 on page 246.)

The Sympathetic Division   The sympathetic division of the autonomic nervous system is primarily located on the middle of the spinal column—running from near the top of the ribcage to the waist area. It may help to think of the name in these terms: The *sympathetic* division is in *sympathy* with one's emotions. In fact, the sympathetic division is usually called the *fight-or-flight system* because it is allows people and animals to deal with all kinds of stressful events. Emotions during these events might be anger (hence, the term *fight*) or fear (that's the *flight* part, obviously) or even extreme joy or excitement. Yes, even joy can be stressful. The sympathetic division's job is to get the body ready to deal with the stress.

What are the specific ways in which this division readies the body to react? (See Figure 13.9.) The pupils seem to get bigger, perhaps to let in more light and, therefore, more information. The heart starts pumping faster and harder, drawing blood away from nonessential organs such as the skin (so at first the person may turn pale) and sometimes even the brain itself (so the person might actually faint). Blood needs lots of oxygen before it goes to the muscles, so the lungs work overtime, too (the person may begin to breathe faster). One set of glands in particular receives special instructions.

---

*Skeletal: having to do with the bones of the body, or skeleton.
**Involuntary: not under deliberate control.

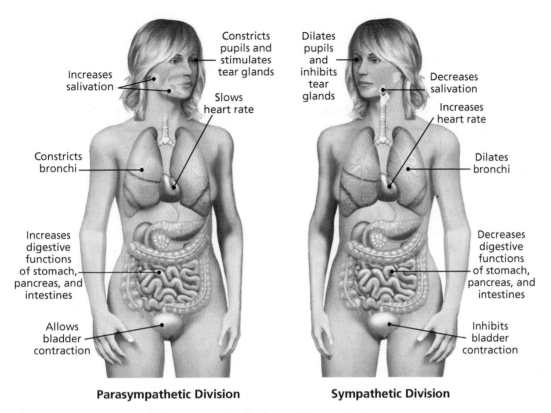

Parasympathetic Division

- Increases salivation
- Constricts pupils and stimulates tear glands
- Slows heart rate
- Constricts bronchi
- Increases digestive functions of stomach, pancreas, and intestines
- Allows bladder contraction

Sympathetic Division

- Dilates pupils and inhibits tear glands
- Decreases salivation
- Increases heart rate
- Dilates bronchi
- Decreases digestive functions of stomach, pancreas, and intestines
- Inhibits bladder contraction

Figure 13.9 Functions of the Parasympathetic and Sympathetic Divisions of the Nervous System

parasympathetic division part of the ANS that restores the body to normal functioning after arousal and is responsible for the day-to-day functioning of the organs and glands.

These young soccer players are using their senses and voluntary muscles controlled by the somatic division of the peripheral nervous system. What part of the autonomic nervous system are these girls also using at this time?

The adrenal glands will be stimulated to release certain stress-related chemicals (members of a class of chemicals released by glands called *hormones*) into the bloodstream. These stress hormones will travel to all parts of the body, but they will only affect certain target organs. Just as a neurotransmitter fits into a receptor site on a cell, the molecules of the stress hormones fit into receptor sites at the various target organs—notably, the heart, muscles, and lungs. This further stimulates these organs to work harder. (There are other hormones for other functions that have nothing to do with stress. For more about hormones and glands, see the last section in this chapter, The Chemical Connection: The Endocrine Glands.)

But not every organ or system will be stimulated by the activation of the sympathetic division. Digestion of food and excretion* of waste are not necessary functions when dealing with stressful situations, so these systems tend to be "shut down" or inhibited. Saliva, which is part of digestion, dries right up (ever try whistling when you're scared?). Food that was in the stomach sits there like a lump. Usually, the urge to go to the bathroom will be suppressed, but if the person is really scared the bladder or bowels may actually empty (this is why people who die under extreme stress, such as hanging or electrocution, will release their urine and waste). The sympathetic division is also going to demand that the body burn a tremendous amount of fuel, or blood sugar.

Now, all this bodily arousal is going on during a stressful situation. If the stress ends, the activity of the sympathetic division will be replaced by the activation of the parasympathetic division. If the stress goes on too long or is too intense, the person

---

*Excretion: in this sense, the act of eliminating waste products from the body.

British runner Kelly Holmes at the 2004 Summer Olympics in Athens, Greece. Her sympathetic nervous system is still in high gear in response to her emotional state.

might actually collapse (as a deer might do when being chased by another animal). This collapse occurs because the parasympathetic division overresponds in its inhibition of the sympathetic activity. The heart slows, blood vessels open up, blood pressure in the brain drops, and fainting can be the result.

The Parasympathetic Division   If the sympathetic division can be called the fight-or-flight system, the parasympathetic division might be called the eat-drink-and-rest system. The neurons of this division are located at the top and bottom of the spinal column, on either side of the sympathetic division neurons (*para* means "beyond" or "next to" and in this sense refers to the neurons located on either side of the sympathetic division neurons).

In looking at Figure 13.9, it might seem as if the parasympathetic division does pretty much the opposite of the sympathetic division, but it's a little more complex than that. The parasympathetic division's job is to restore the body to normal functioning after a stressful situation ends. It slows the heart and breathing, constricts the pupils, and reactivates digestion and excretion. Signals to the adrenal glands stop because the parasympathetic division isn't connected to the adrenal glands. In a sense, the parasympathetic division allows the body to put back all the energy it burned—which is why people are often very hungry *after* the stress is all over.

The parasympathetic division does more than just react to the activity of the sympathetic division. It is the parasympathetic division that is responsible for most of the ordinary, day-to-day bodily functioning, such as regular heartbeat and normal breathing and digestion. People spend the greater part of their 24-hour day eating, sleeping, digesting, and excreting. So it is the parasympathetic division that is normally active. At any given moment, then, one or the other of these divisions, sympathetic or parasympathetic, will determine whether people are aroused or relaxed.

13.3   13.4

The Central Nervous System — ● **brain** — true core of nervous system: takes information from senses, processes it, makes decisions, sends commands to rest of body

(comprised of the brain and spinal cord)

● **spinal cord** — long bundle of neurons that carries information to and away from the brain; helps control pain response

• spinal cord reflexes involve several different neurons (sensory neurons, interneurons, and motor neurons)

• spinal reflexes enable fast, often lifesaving, actions that do not require conscious thought

The Peripheral Nervous System — ● **somatic nervous system** controls the voluntary muscles of the body; involves the sensory pathway (sensory neurons carrying information to spinal cord and/or brain) and the motor pathway (nerves that carry information to voluntary skeletal muscles)

comprised of the nerves and neurons not contained in the brain and spinal cord; allows the brain and spinal cord to communicate with the sensory systems and to control the muscles and glands of the body; divided into somatic and autonomic nervous systems

● **autonomic nervous system** controls automatic functions of the body (organs, glands, involuntary muscles)

• **sympathetic division:** "fight-or-flight" functions— reacts to stressful events and bodily arousal

• **parasympathetic division:** "eat-drink-and-rest" functions— restores body to normal functioning after arousal and is responsible for day-to-day functioning of glands and organs

Pick the best answer.

1. If you burn your finger, your immediate reaction will probably involve all BUT which of the following?
   a. the brain
   b. the spinal cord
   c. afferent neurons
   d. efferent neurons

2. If you are typing on the computer keyboard, the motions of your fingers on the keys are probably being controlled by _____.
   a. the autonomic nervous system.
   b. sensory pathway neurons.
   c. motor pathway neurons.
   d. autonomic neurons.

3. The neurons of the motor pathway control _____.
   a. stress reactions.
   b. organs and glands.
   c. involuntary muscles.
   d. voluntary muscles.

4. What type of cell can create the other cells of the body?
   a. blood cells
   b. stem cells
   c. neurons
   d. basal cells

5. Which of the following is NOT a function of the sympathetic division?
   a. increasing digestive activity to supply fuel for the body
   b. dilating the pupils of the eyes
   c. increasing the heart rate
   d. increasing the activity of the lungs

6. Which of the following would be active if you are sleeping?
   a. sympathetic division
   b. parasympathetic division
   c. somatic division
   d. motor division

Peeking Inside the Brain

13.5 How do psychologists study the brain and how it works?

In ancient times, many early "scientists" would dissect the brains of those who had died—both animals and people—to try to see how the brain worked. The problem, of course, is that it is impossible tell what a structure in the brain is supposed to do if it's dead. A scientist can't even be sure what the brain tissue really looks like when it's inside the skull of a living person instead of sitting on a dissecting table. How can scientists find out what the various parts of the brain do? ◉ See more on **MPL**

CLINICAL STUDIES

One way to get some idea of what the various areas of the brain control is to study animals or people with damage to those areas. In animals, that may mean damaging a part of the brain deliberately. Then researchers test the animal to see what has happened to its abilities. Or they may electrically stimulate some particular area of the animal's brain and watch the result. Both the destruction and stimulation of brain tissue are accomplished by the same basic process. A thin wire insulated everywhere but the very tip is surgically inserted into the brain of the test animal. If brain tissue is to be destroyed, an electrical current strong enough to kill off the neurons at the tip of the wire is sent through it. This is called **deep lesioning**. (When cells are destroyed on the surface of the brain or just below, this process is sometimes called *shallow lesioning*.)

If researchers only want to stimulate that area of the brain, the electrical current will be much milder, causing the neurons to react as if they had received a message. This is called *electrical stimulation of the brain*, or *ESB*. Of course, animals aren't people even though some people treat them that way, and researchers can't be sure that a human brain is going to function exactly like the brain of a lower animal.

It should be obvious that researchers can't destroy areas of the brains of human beings. So how do researchers study human brain function? By finding people who already have brain damage and testing those people to see what they can or cannot do. It isn't an ideal way to study the brain, however, as no two case studies of human brain damage are likely to be in exactly the same area of the brain and involve exactly the same amount of damage.

◉ **See more** video classic on Wilder Penfield and electric brain stimulation. **www.mypsychlab.com**

This marathon runner collapsed where he stood after finishing the race. His parasympathetic nervous system is already slowing his breathing and heart rate as his bodily functions begin to return to normal.

deep lesioning insertion of a thin, insulated wire into the brain through which an electrical current is sent that destroys the brain cells at the tip of the wire.

THE EEG

A fairly harmless way to study the activity of the living brain is to record the electrical activity of the neurons just below the skull. This has been done for years, using a device called an **electroencephalograph (EEG)** machine. Small metal disks called electrodes are placed directly on the skin covering the skull, using a jelly-like substance to help conduct the electrical messages from the neurons just below. These electrodes are connected by wires to a computer. (Older machines connect to pens which move on graph paper.) The resulting electrical output forms waves that indicate many things, such as stages of sleep, seizures, and even the presence of tumors. The EEG can also be used to determine which areas of the brain are active during tasks such as reading, writing, and speaking. (See Figure 13.10.)

As can be seen in Figure 13.10a, very fast, irregular waves called *beta waves* indicate waking activity (third and sixth lines in Figure 13.10a). Slightly more regular and slower waves called *alpha waves* are a sign of relaxation, *theta waves* are associated with drowsiness and sleep, whereas much slower, larger waves called *delta waves* indicate a deep stage of sleep (first and fifth lines in Figure 13.10a).

Scientists have recently developed a new technique involving the way EEG recordings are interpreted (Makeig et al., 2004). The process allows identification of

electroencephalograph (EEG) machine designed to record the brain-wave patterns produced by electrical activity of the surface of the brain.

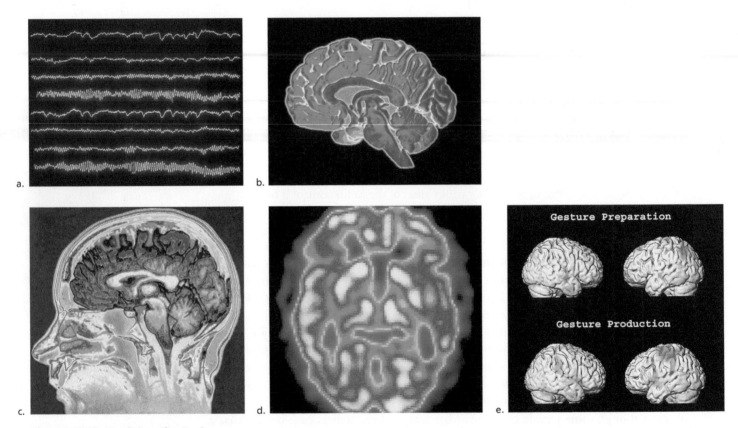

Figure 13.10 Studying the Brain

These are four methods researchers use to study the brain: EEGs, CT scans, MRIs, and PET scans. (a) An example of an EEG readout. (b) A CT scan (colored by a computer) showing the detail of a center cross section of the brain. (c) An MRI (colored by a computer) showing enhanced detail of the same view of the brain as in the CT scan. (d) A PET scan showing activity of the brain, using colors to indicate different levels of activity; areas that are very active are white, whereas areas that are inactive are dark blue. (e) An fMRI tracking the oxygen levels in the brain shows the difference between brain activity when preparing to make a gesture and brain activity when actually making the gesture.

individual signals coming from the different areas of the brain and is called *Independent Component Analysis (ICA)*. ICA allows a more detailed and precise interpretation of the signals coming from different areas of the brain's surface. Another technique using the EEG is called *event-related potential*, or *ERP*. In ERP, the results of multiple presentations of a stimulus are measured on an EEG and then averaged to remove the variations in random brain activity that occur in the background of any single EEG recording. The result is a measurement of the electrical potential of the brain related to the stimulus event itself or an event-related potential. ERP is being investigated for several different uses. For example, one study has looked at the possibility of using ERP to follow the progression of Alzheimer's disease (Katada et al., 2003), whereas another area of research involves using ERP as a method of lie detection (Mertens & Allen, 2007; Rosenfeld et al., 2004).

CT SCANS

The EEG only allows researchers to look at the activity of the surface of the brain. Scientists now have several ways to look inside the human brain without harm to the person. One way is to take a series of X-rays of the brain, aided by a computer. This is called a **CT scan** (CT stands for computed tomography, or mapping "slices" of the brain by computer). CT scans can show stroke damage, tumors, injuries, and abnormal brain structure. (See Figure 13.10b.)

MRI SCANS

As good as a CT scan can be, it still doesn't show very small details within the brain. A newer technique called **magnetic resonance imaging**, or **MRI**, provides much more detail, even allowing doctors to see the effects of very small strokes. (See Figure 13.10c.) The person getting an MRI scan will be placed inside a machine that generates a powerful magnetic field. There are even machines that take much less time, called—simply enough—fast MRIs. The magnetic field allows the computer to create a three-dimensional image of the brain and display "slices" of that image on a screen.

PET SCANS

While CT and MRI scans can show the structure of the brain, researchers who want to see the brain in action may use a **PET scan** (positron emission tomography). (See Figure 13.10d.) In this method, the person is injected with a radioactive glucose (a kind of sugar). The computer detects the activity of the brain cells by looking at which cells are using up the radioactive glucose and projecting the image of that activity onto a monitor. The computer uses colors to indicate different levels of activity. Areas that are very active usually show up as white or very light, whereas areas that are inactive are dark blue. With this method, researchers can actually have the person perform different tasks while the computer shows what his or her brain is doing during the task.

FUNCTIONAL MRI (fMRI)

Although traditional MRI scans only show structure, there is a technique called *functional MRI (fMRI)* in which the computer tracks changes in the oxygen levels of the blood (see Figure 13.10e). By placing this picture of where the oxygen goes in the brain on top of the picture of the brain's structure, researchers can tell what areas of

computed tomography (CT) brain-imaging method using computer-controlled X-rays of the brain.

magnetic resonance imaging (MRI) brain-imaging method using radio waves and magnetic fields of the body to produce detailed images of the brain.

positron emission tomography (PET) brain-imaging method in which a radioactive sugar is injected into the subject and a computer compiles a color-coded image of the activity of the brain with lighter colors indicating more activity.

the brain are active. By combining such images taken over a period of time, a sort of "movie" of the brain's functioning can be made (Lin et al., 2007). Functional MRIs can give more detail, tend to be clearer than PET scans, and are fast becoming an incredibly useful tool for research into the workings of the brain.

Okay, now I understand a little more about how we look inside the brain. What exactly IS inside the brain?

From the Bottom Up: The Structures of the Brain

Now it's time to look at the various structures of the brain, starting from the bottom and working up to the top. (A word of caution: This text won't be discussing every single part of the brain, only the parts interesting to psychologists as explorers of human behavior. Many parts of the brain also overlap in their functions, but a full understanding of the brain is not truly possible within one chapter of an introductory psychology text.)

13.6 What are the different structures of the bottom part of the brain and what do they do?

THE HINDBRAIN

Medulla The **medulla** (which, oddly enough, means "marrow" or "inner substance") is located at the top of the spinal column. In Figure 13.11, it is the first "swelling" at the top of the spinal cord, just at the very bottom of the brain. This is the part of the brain that a person would least want to have damaged, as it controls life-sustaining functions such as heartbeat, breathing, and swallowing. (Remember the actor Christopher Reeve, who played the lead in the original *Superman* movies and

medulla the first large swelling at the top of the spinal cord, forming the lowest part of the brain, which is responsible for life-sustaining functions such as breathing, swallowing, and heart rate.

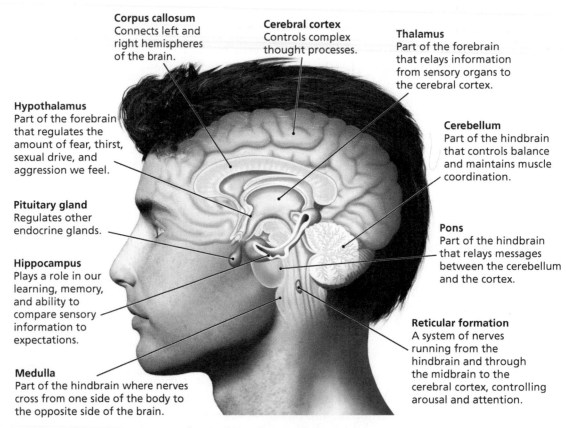

Corpus callosum Connects left and right hemispheres of the brain.

Cerebral cortex Controls complex thought processes.

Thalamus Part of the forebrain that relays information from sensory organs to the cerebral cortex.

Hypothalamus Part of the forebrain that regulates the amount of fear, thirst, sexual drive, and aggression we feel.

Cerebellum Part of the hindbrain that controls balance and maintains muscle coordination.

Pituitary gland Regulates other endocrine glands.

Pons Part of the hindbrain that relays messages between the cerebellum and the cortex.

Hippocampus Plays a role in our learning, memory, and ability to compare sensory information to expectations.

Reticular formation A system of nerves running from the hindbrain and through the midbrain to the cerebral cortex, controlling arousal and attention.

Medulla Part of the hindbrain where nerves cross from one side of the body to the opposite side of the brain.

Figure 13.11 **The Major Structures of the Human Brain**

Dr. Virgil Swann in the *Smallville* television series? After a fall from horse, his spinal cord was damaged. The damage was very serious because it was high enough to involve part of the medulla, leaving him paralyzed and unable to breath on his own [McDonald et al., 2002]. The upper part of the spinal cord and the lower part of the brain are highly interconnected.) It is in the medulla that the sensory nerves coming from the left and right sides of the body cross over, so that sensory information from the left side of the body goes to the right side of the brain and vice versa.

Pons The **pons** is the larger "swelling" just above the medulla. This term means "bridge," and the pons is indeed the bridge between the lower parts of the brain and the upper sections. As in the medulla, there is a crossover of nerves, but in this case it is the motor nerves carrying messages from the brain to the body. This allows the pons to coordinate the movements of the left and right sides of the body. (It will be useful to remember these nerve crossovers when reading about the functions of the left and right sides of the brain in a later part of this chapter.) The pons also influences sleep, dreaming, and arousal.

The Reticular Formation The **reticular formation (RF)** is an area of neurons running through the middle of the medulla and the pons and slightly beyond. These neurons are responsible for people's ability to selectively attend to certain kinds of information in their surroundings. Basically, the RF allows people to ignore constant, unchanging information (such as the noise of an air conditioner) and become alert to changes in information (for example, if the air conditioner stopped, most people would notice immediately).

The reticular formation is also the part of the brain that helps keep people alert and aroused. One part of the RF is called the *reticular activating system (RAS)*, and it stimulates the upper part of the brain, keeping people awake and alert. When a person is driving along and someone suddenly pulls out in front of the vehicle, it is the RAS that brings that driver to full attention. It is also the system that lets a mother hear her baby cry in the night, even though she might sleep through other noises. The RAS has also been suggested by brain-scanning studies as a possible area involved in attention-deficit hyperactivity disorder, in which children or adults have difficulty maintaining attention to a single task (Durston, 2003).

Studies have shown that when the RF of rats is electrically stimulated while they are sleeping, they immediately awaken. If the RF is destroyed (by deep lesioning, for example), they fall into a sleeplike coma from which they never awaken (Moruzzi & Magoun, 1949; Steriade & McCarley, 1990). The RF is also implicated in comas in humans (Plum & Posner, 1985).

Cerebellum At the base of the skull, behind the pons and below the main part of the brain, is a structure that looks like a small brain. (See Figure 13.11 on page 266.) This is the **cerebellum** (meaning "little brain"). The cerebellum is the part of the lower brain that controls all involuntary, rapid, fine motor movement. People can sit upright because the cerebellum controls all the little muscles needed to keep them from falling out of their chair. It also coordinates voluntary movements that have to happen in rapid succession, such as walking, diving, skating, gymnastics, dancing, typing (once it has been learned well), playing a musical instrument, and even the movements of speech. Learned reflexes, skills, and habits are also stored here, which allows them to become more or less automatic. Because of the cerebellum, people don't have to consciously think about their posture, muscle tone, and balance.

So if your cerebellum is damaged, you might be very uncoordinated? Yes. In fact, in a disease called *spinocerebellar degeneration* the first symptoms are tremors, an unsteady

This pitcher must count on his cerebellum to help him balance and coordinate the many fine muscle commands that allow him to pitch the baseball accurately and swiftly. What other kinds of professions depend heavily on the activity of the cerebellum?

pons the larger swelling above the medulla that connects the top of the brain to the bottom and that plays a part in sleep, dreaming, left–right body coordination, and arousal.

reticular formation (RF) an area of neurons running through the middle of the medulla and the pons and slightly beyond that is responsible for selective attention.

cerebellum part of the lower brain located behind the pons that controls and coordinates involuntary, rapid, fine motor movement.

So if your cerebellum is damaged, you might be very ◄ uncoordinated?

Explore more with a simulation on the lower brain structures.

www.mypsychlab.com

walk, slurred speech, dizziness, and muscle weakness. The person suffering from this disease will eventually be unable to walk, stand, or even get a spoon to his or her own mouth (Schöls et al., 1998). These symptoms are similar to what one might see in a person who is suffering from alcohol intoxication. **Explore** more on **MPL**

13.7 What are the structures of the brain that control emotion, learning, memory, and motivation?

STRUCTURES UNDER THE CORTEX

The cortex, which is discussed in detail later in this chapter, is the outer wrinkled covering of the brain. But there are a number of important structures located just under the cortex and above the brain stem. Each of these structures plays a part in our behavior. (See Figure 13.12.)

Limbic System   The **limbic system** (the word *limbic* means "marginal" and these structures are found in the inner margin of the upper brain) includes the thalamus, hypothalamus, hippocampus, and amygdala. In general, the limbic system is involved in emotions, motivation, and learning.

Thalamus   Have you ever had to go to the emergency room of a hospital? You may find yourself getting past the receptionist, but most of the time you will have to wait to see a triage nurse before you ever get to see the doctor—if you ever get to see the doctor. (The word *triage* refers to a process for sorting injured people into groups based on their need for or likely benefit from immediate medical treatment.) Triage nurses will ask people questions about their complaints. They may be able to partially treat minor complaints before the person sees a doctor. Then they will send the person to a treatment room with the equipment that might be needed for the ailment, and eventually the person will see a doctor.

limbic system a group of several brain structures located under the cortex and involved in learning, emotion, memory, and motivation.

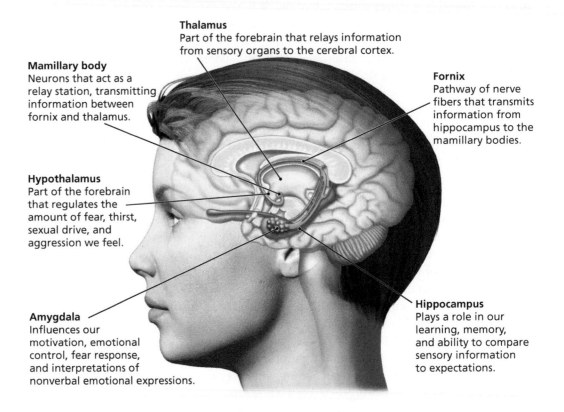

Figure 13.12 **The Limbic System**

The **thalamus** ("inner chamber") is in some ways similar to a triage nurse. This somewhat round structure in the center of the brain acts as a kind of relay station for incoming sensory information. Like a nurse, the thalamus might perform some processing of that sensory information before sending it on to the part of the cortex that deals with that kind of sensation—hearing, sight, touch, or taste. Damage to the thalamus might result in the loss or partial loss of any or all of those sensations.

The sense of smell is unique in that signals from the neurons in the sinus cavity go directly into special parts of the brain called **olfactory bulbs**, just under the front part of the brain. Smell is the only sense that cannot be affected by damage to the thalamus.

Hypothalamus A very small but extremely powerful part of the brain is located just below and in front of the thalamus (see Figure 13.12). The **hypothalamus** ("below the inner chamber") regulates body temperature, thirst, hunger, sleeping and waking, sexual activity, and emotions. It sits right above the *pituitary gland*, which is called the "master gland" because it controls the functions of all the other endocrine glands that will be discussed later in this chapter. The hypothalamus controls the pituitary, so the ultimate regulation of hormones lies with the hypothalamus.

Hippocampus The **hippocampus** is the Greek word for "seahorse" and it was given to this structure of the brain because the first scientists who dissected the brain thought it looked like a seahorse. Research has shown that the hippocampus is instrumental in forming long-term (permanent) memories that are then stored elsewhere in the brain (Bigler et al., 1996). As mentioned earlier, acetylcholine, the neurotransmitter involved in muscle control, is also involved in the memory function of the hippocampus. People who have Alzheimer's, for example, have much lower levels of acetylcholine in that structure than is normal and the drugs given to these people boost the levels of acetylcholine. The hippocampus is located within the temporal lobes on each side of the brain, and electrical stimulation of the temporal lobe may produce memory-like or dream-like experiences.

The hippocampus may be very close to the area of the brain where the memories for locations of objects are stored as well. Researchers have found that the right parahippocampal gyrus, located alongside the right hippocampus, is more active when a person is planning a travel route (Maguire et al., 1998), which might explain why elderly people who develop memory problems associated with deterioration of the hippocampus also tend to forget where they live, where they parked the car, and similar location problems. Deterioration in the hippocampal area may spread to or affect other nearby areas.

Amygdala The **amygdala** ("almond") is an area of the brain located near the hippocampus. These two structures seem to be responsible for fear responses and memory of fear. Information from the senses goes to the amygdala before the upper part of the brain is even involved, so that people can respond to danger very quickly, sometimes before they are consciously aware of what is happening. In 1939 researchers found that monkeys with large amounts of their temporal lobes removed—including the amygdala—were completely unafraid of snakes and humans, both normally fear-provoking stimuli (Klüver & Bucy, 1939). This effect came to be known as the *Klüver-Bucy syndrome*. Rats that have damaged amygdala structures will also show no fear when placed next to a cat (Maren & Fanselow, 1996). Case studies of human with damage to the amygdala also show a link to decreased fear response (Adophs et al., 2005).

What about Michelle M. from the story at the beginning? Was she missing any of these structures?

This young man's thirst is regulated by his hypothalamus.

thalamus part of the limbic system located in the center of the brain, this structure relays sensory information from the lower part of the brain to the proper areas of the cortex and processes some sensory information before sending it to its proper area.

olfactory bulbs two projections just under the front of the brain that receive information from the receptors in the nose located just below.

hypothalamus small structure in the brain located below the thalamus and directly above the pituitary gland, responsible for motivational behavior such as sleep, hunger, thirst, and sex.

hippocampus curved structure located within each temporal lobe, responsible for the formation of long-term memories and the storage of memory for location of objects.

What about Michelle M. from the story at the beginning? Was she missing any of these ◄ structures?

amygdala brain structure located near the hippocampus, responsible for fear responses and memory of fear.

Michelle M. did have some abnormalities in a few of these structures, but her greatest "missing piece" was one-half of a very important brain structure, the cortex. The next section explores the cortex and its functions.

THE CORTEX

👁 **See more** with a video podcast of a real human brain's surface anatomy. www.mypsychlab.com

As stated earlier, the **cortex** ("rind" or outer covering) is the outermost part of the brain, which is the part of the brain most people picture when they think of what the brain looks like. It is made up of tightly packed neurons and actually is only about one-tenth of an inch thick on average (Fischl et al., 2001; MacDonald et al., 2000; Zilles, 1990). The tissue appears grayish pink because the tightly packed neural bodies are gray and the small blood vessels appear pink. The cortex is very recognizable surface anatomy because it is full of wrinkles. 👁 See more on **MPL**

► Why is the cortex so wrinkled?

Why is the cortex so wrinkled?

The wrinkling of the cortex allows a much larger area of cortical cells to exist in the small space inside the skull. If the cortex were to be taken out, ironed flat, and measured, it would be about 2 to 3 square feet. (The owner of the cortex would also be dead, but that's fairly obvious, right?) As the brain develops before birth, it forms a smooth outer covering on all the other brain structures. This will be the cortex, which will get more and more wrinkled as the brain increases in size and complexity. This increase in wrinkling is called *corticalization* and is the real measure of human intelligence.

cortex outermost covering of the brain consisting of densely packed neurons, responsible for higher thought processes and interpretation of sensory input.

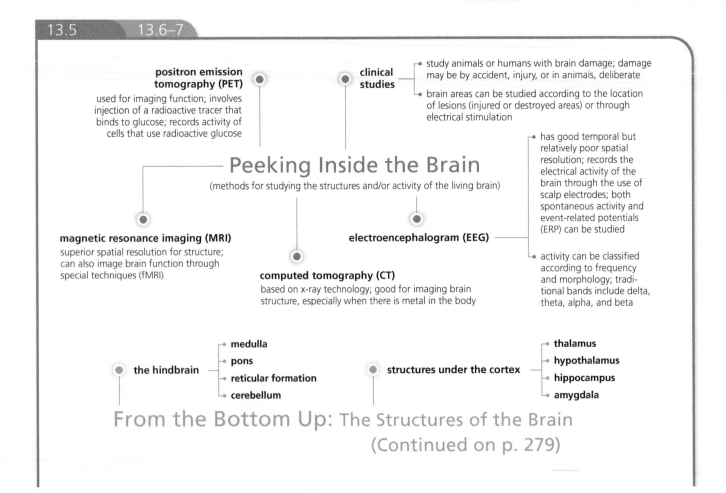

13.5   13.6–7

positron emission tomography (PET)
used for imaging function; involves injection of a radioactive tracer that binds to glucose; records activity of cells that use radioactive glucose

clinical studies
• study animals or humans with brain damage; damage may be by accident, injury, or in animals, deliberate
• brain areas can be studied according to the location of lesions (injured or destroyed areas) or through electrical stimulation

Peeking Inside the Brain
(methods for studying the structures and/or activity of the living brain)

• has good temporal but relatively poor spatial resolution; records the electrical activity of the brain through the use of scalp electrodes; both spontaneous activity and event-related potentials (ERP) can be studied

magnetic resonance imaging (MRI)
superior spatial resolution for structure; can also image brain function through special techniques (fMRI)

electroencephalogram (EEG)

computed tomography (CT)
based on x-ray technology; good for imaging brain structure, especially when there is metal in the body

• activity can be classified according to frequency and morphology; traditional bands include delta, theta, alpha, and beta

the hindbrain
• medulla
• pons
• reticular formation
• cerebellum

structures under the cortex
• thalamus
• hypothalamus
• hippocampus
• amygdala

From the Bottom Up: The Structures of the Brain
(Continued on p. 279)

Pick the best answer.

1. Which of the following techniques uses a radioactive sugar to look at the functioning of the brain?
   a. EEG   **c.** MRI
   b. CT   **d.** PET

2. Which brain structure is most responsible for our balance, posture, and muscle tone?
   a. medulla   **c.** reticular formation
   b. cerebellum   **d.** pons

3. Which brain structure would most likely result in death if damaged?
   a. medulla   **c.** reticular formation
   b. cerebellum   **d.** pons

4. If you were to develop a rare condition in which signals from your eyes were sent to the area of the brain that processes sound and signals from the ears were sent to the area of the brain that processes vision, which part of the brain would most likely be damaged?
   a. hippocampus   **c.** thalamus
   b. hypothalamus   **d.** amygdala

5. If you have problems storing away new memories, the damage is most likely in the _____ area of the brain.
   a. hippocampus
   b. hypothalamus
   c. cerebellum
   d. amygdala

13.8 What parts of the cortex control the different senses and the movement of the body?

The Lobes and Their Specialties   The cortex is divided into two sections called the **cerebral hemispheres**, which are connected by a thick, tough band of neural fibers (axons) called the **corpus callosum** (literally meaning "hard bodies," as calluses on the feet are hard). (See Figure 13.11 on page 266.) The corpus callosum allows the left and right hemispheres to communicate with each other. Each hemisphere can be roughly divided into four sections by looking at the deeper wrinkles, or fissures, in its surface (see Figure 13.13). (Remember, Michelle M.'s left hemisphere never developed—she had only the right hemisphere, and so only the right-side lobes.)

Occipital Lobes   At the base of the cortex, toward the back of the brain is an area called the **occipital lobe** (the term *occipital* refers to the rear of the head). This area processes visual information from the eyes in the *primary visual cortex*. The *visual association cortex*, also in this lobe, is the part of the brain that helps identify and make sense of the visual information from the eyes. The famed neurologist Oliver Sacks once had a patient who had a tumor in his right occipital lobe area. He could still see objects perfectly well and even describe them in physical terms, but he could not identify them by sight alone. For example, Sacks once gave him a rose to look at. The man turned it around and around and began to describe it as a "red inflorescence" of some type with a green tubular projection. Only when he held it under his nose (stimulating the sense of smell) did he recognize it as a rose (Sacks, 1990). Each area of the cortex has these association areas that help people make sense of sensory information.

Have you ever wondered why people "see stars" sometimes after being hit in the back of the head? Because the area of the brain at the back of the head processes vision, any stimulation to that area will be interpreted as vision—hence, the "stars."

Parietal Lobes   The **parietal lobes** (*parietal* means "wall") are at the top and back of the brain, just under the parietal bone in the skull. This area contains the **somatosensory cortex**, an area of neurons (see Figure 13.14) running down the front of the parietal lobes on either side of the brain. This area processes information from the skin and internal body receptors for touch, temperature, and body position. The somatosensory cortex is laid out in a rather interesting way—the cells at the top of the brain receive information from the bottom of the body, and as one moves down

cerebral hemispheres the two sections of the cortex on the left and right sides of the brain.

corpus callosum thick band of neurons that connects the right and left cerebral hemispheres.

occipital lobe section of the brain located at the rear and bottom of each cerebral hemisphere containing the visual centers of the brain.

parietal lobes sections of the brain located at the top and back of each cerebral hemisphere containing the centers for touch, taste, and temperature sensations.

somatosensory cortex area of neurons running down the front of the parietal lobes responsible for processing information from the skin and internal body receptors for touch, temperature, body position, and possibly taste.

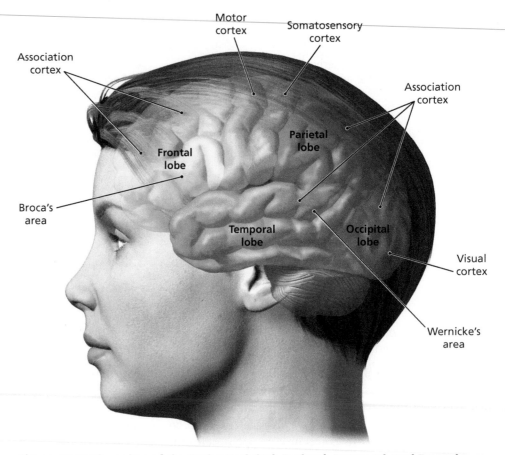

Figure 13.13 **The Lobes of the Brain: Occipital, Parietal, Temporal, and Frontal**

This boxer must rely on his parietal lobes to sense where his body is in relation to the floor of the ring and the other boxer, his occipital lobes to see his target, and his frontal lobes to guide his hand and arm into the punch.

temporal lobes areas of the cortex located just behind the temples containing the neurons responsible for the sense of hearing and meaningful speech.

frontal lobes areas of the cortex located in the front and top of the brain, responsible for higher mental processes and decision making as well as the production of fluent speech.

the area, the signals come from higher and higher in the body. It's almost as if a little upside-down person were laid out along this area of cells. (See Figure 13.14.)

Temporal Lobes The beginning of the **temporal lobes** (*temporal* means "of or near the temples") are found just behind the temples of the head. These lobes contain the *primary auditory cortex* and the *auditory association area*. If a person receives a blow to the side of the head, that person will probably "hear" a ringing sound. Also found in the left temporal lobe is an area that in most people is particularly involved with language. Oddly enough, the sense of taste also seems to be processed in the temporal lobe, deep inside a fold of the cortex, rather than anywhere in the parietal lobe (Fresquet et al., 2004).

Frontal Lobes These lobes are at the front of the brain, hence, the name **frontal lobes**. (It doesn't often get this easy in psychology; feel free to take a moment to appreciate it.) Here are found all the higher mental functions of the brain—planning, personality, memory storage, complex decision making, and (again in the left hemisphere in most people) areas devoted to language. The frontal lobe also helps in controlling emotions by means of its connection to the limbic system. Phineas Gage, who was mentioned in Chapter Twelve (p. 221), suffered damage to his frontal lobe. He lacked emotional control because of the damage to this lobe's connection with the limbic system structures, particularly the amygdala. People with damage to the frontal lobe may also experience problems with performing mental tasks, getting stuck on one step or one wrong answer and repeating it over and over again (Goel & Grafman, 1995).

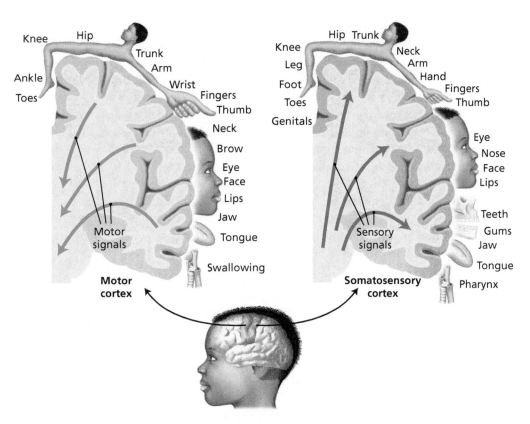

Figure 13.14 The Motor and Somatosensory Cortex
The motor cortex in the frontal lobe controls the voluntary muscles of the body. Cells at the top of the motor cortex control muscles at the bottom of the body, whereas cells at the bottom of the motor cortex control muscles at the top of the body. Body parts are drawn larger or smaller according to the number of cortical cells devoted to that body part. For example, the hand has many small muscles and requires a larger area of cortical cells to control it. The somatosensory cortex, located in the parietal lobe just behind the motor cortex, is organized in much the same manner and receives information about the sense of touch and body position.

The frontal lobes also contain the **motor cortex**, a band of neurons located at the back of each lobe. (See Figure 13.14.) These cells control the movements of the body's voluntary muscles by sending commands out to the somatic division of the peripheral nervous system. The motor cortex is laid out just like the somatosensory cortex, which is right next door in the parietal lobes.

You've mentioned association cortex a few times. Do the other lobes of the brain contain association cortex as well?

THE ASSOCIATION AREAS OF THE CORTEX

13.9 What parts of the cortex are responsible for higher forms of thought, such as language?

Association areas are made up of neurons in the cortex that are devoted to making connections between the sensory information coming into the brain and stored memories, images, and knowledge. In other words, association areas help people make sense of the incoming sensory input. Although the association areas in the occipital and temporal lobes have already been mentioned, much of the brain's association cortex is in the frontal lobes. Some special association areas are worth talking about in more detail.

You've mentioned association cortex a few times. Do the other lobes of the brain contain association cortex as well?

motor cortex   section of the frontal lobe located at the back, responsible for sending motor commands to the muscles of the somatic nervous system.

association areas   areas within each lobe of the cortex responsible for the coordination and interpretation of information, as well as higher mental processing.

Broca's Area In the left frontal lobe of most people is an area of the brain devoted to the production of speech. (In a small portion of the population, this area is in the right frontal lobe.) More specifically, this area allows a person to speak smoothly and fluently. It is called *Broca's area* after nineteenth-century neurologist Paul Broca, who first studied people with damage to this area (Leonard, 1997). Damage to Broca's area causes a person to be unable to get words out in a smooth, connected fashion. People with this condition may know exactly what they want to say and understand what they hear others say, but they cannot control the actual production of their own words. Speech is halting and words are often mispronounced, such as saying "cot" instead of "clock" or "non" instead of "nine." Some words may be left out entirely, such as "the" or "for." This is called **Broca's aphasia**. *Aphasia* refers to an inability to use or understand either written or spoken language (Goodglass et al., 2001). (Stuttering is a somewhat different problem in getting words *started*, rather than mispronouncing them or leaving them out, but may also be related to Broca's area.)

Wernicke's Area In the left temporal lobe (again, in most people) is an area called *Wernicke's area*, named after the physiologist and Broca's contemporary, Carl Wernicke, who first studied problems arising from damage in this location. This area of the brain appears to be involved in understanding the meaning of words (Goodglass et al., 2001). A person with **Wernicke's aphasia** would be able to speak fluently and pronounce words correctly, but the words would be the wrong ones entirely. For example, Elsie suffered a stroke to the temporal lobe, damaging this area of the brain. In the emergency room the nurse tried to take her blood pressure, and when the cuff inflated, Elsie said, "Oh, that's so Saturday hard." Now, what does "Saturday hard" mean? Neither the nurse nor Elsie's daughter could figure that one out, but Elsie *thought* she was making sense. She also had trouble understanding what the people around her were saying to her. In another instance, Ernest suffered a stroke at the age of 80 and developed complete aphasia. As he recovered, he showed some telltale signs of Wernicke's aphasia. In one instance, he asked his wife to get him some milk out of the air conditioner. When she told him that he surely meant to say "refrigerator" he got angry and told her he knew what he was saying, "Now get me some milk out of the air conditioner, woman!"

Classic Studies in Psychology

Through the Looking Glass: Spatial Neglect

D r. V. S. Ramachandran reported in his fascinating book, *Phantoms in the Brain* (Ramachandran & Blakeslee, 1998), the case of a woman with an odd set of symptoms. When Ellen's son came to visit her, he was shocked and puzzled by his formerly neat and fastidious* mother's appearance. The woman who had always taken pride in her looks, who always had her hair perfectly done and her nails perfectly manicured, looked messy and totally odd. Her hair was uncombed on the left side. Her green shawl was hanging neatly over her right shoulder but hanging onto the floor on the left. Her lipstick was neatly applied to the right side of her lips, and *only to the right side—the left side of her face was completely bare of makeup!* Yet her eyeliner, mascara, and rouge were all neatly applied to the right side of her face.

What was wrong? The son called the doctor and was told that his mother's stroke had left her with a condition called **spatial neglect**, in which a person with damage to the right

Broca's aphasia condition resulting from damage to Broca's area, causing the affected person to be unable to speak fluently, to mispronounce words, and to speak haltingly.

Wernicke's aphasia condition resulting from damage to Wernicke's area, causing the affected person to be unable to understand or produce meaningful language.

spatial neglect condition produced by damage to the association areas of the right hemisphere resulting in an inability to recognize objects or body parts in the left visual field.

---

*Fastidious: having demanding standards, difficult to please.

parietal and occipital lobes of the cortex will ignore everything in the left visual field. Damage to areas of the frontal and temporal lobes may also play a part along with the parietal damage. Spatial neglect can affect the left hemisphere, but this condition occurs less frequently and in a much milder form than right-hemisphere neglect (Heilman et al., 1993; Corbetta et al., 2005; Springer & Deutsch, 1998).

This woman was not blind on the left side—she just would not notice anything there unless her attention was specifically called to it. Her son found that when he pointed out the condition of her makeup to her, she was able to recognize it. He found that she also ignored all of the food on the left side of her plate unless her attention was specifically called to it.

When the doctor examined this woman, he tried to get her to notice her left side by holding up a mirror. She responded correctly when asked what the mirror was and she was able to describe her appearance correctly, but when an assistant held a pen just within the woman's reach, reflected in the mirror on her left side, she tried to reach *through the mirror* to get the pen with her good right hand. When the doctor told her that he wanted her to grab the real object and not the image of it in the mirror, she told him that the pen was *behind* the mirror and even tried to reach around to get it.

Clearly, persons suffering from spatial neglect are not blind at all. They simply can no longer perceive the world in the same way as other people do. For these people, the left sides of objects, bodies, and spaces are somewhere "through the looking glass."

Questions for Further Discussion

1. If a person with spatial neglect only eats the food on the right side of the plate, what could caregivers do to help that person get enough to eat?

2. What other odd things might a person with spatial neglect do that a person with normal functioning would not? What other things might a person with spatial neglect fail to do?

THE CEREBRAL HEMISPHERES: ARE YOU IN YOUR RIGHT MIND?

I've heard that some people are right-brained and some are left-brained. Are the two sides of the brain really that different?

Most people tend to think of the two cerebral hemispheres as identical twins. Both sides have the same four lobes and are arranged in much the same way. But language seems to be confined to only the left hemisphere in about 90 percent of the population (Toga & Thompson, 2003). What other special tasks do the two halves of the **cerebrum** (the upper part of the brain consisting of the two hemispheres and the structures connecting them) engage in, and how do researchers know about such functions?

13.10 How does the left side of the brain differ from the right side?

Split-Brain Research   Roger Sperry was a pioneer in the field of hemisphere specialization. He won a Nobel Prize for his work in demonstrating that the left and right hemispheres of the brain specialize in different activities and functions (Sperry, 1968). In looking for a way to cure epilepsy (severe muscle spasms or seizures resulting from brain damage), Sperry cut through the corpus callosum, the thick band of neural fibers that joins the two hemispheres. In early research with animals, this technique worked and seemed to have no side effects. The first people to have this procedure done also experienced relief from their severe epileptic symptoms, but testing found that (in a sense) they now had two brains in one body.

The special testing involves sending messages to only one side of the brain, which is now possible because the connecting tissue, the corpus callosum, has been cut. Figure 13.15 shows what happens with a typical split-brain patient.

◄ I've heard that some people are right-brained and some are left-brained. Are the two sides of the brain really that different?

cerebrum the upper part of the brain consisting of the two hemispheres and the structures that connect them.

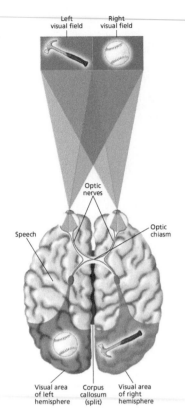

Figure 13.15 **The Split-Brain Experiment**

Roger Sperry created this experiment to demonstrate the specialization of the left and right hemispheres of the brain.

So there really are left-brained and right-brained people? ▶ And how could Michelle M. talk and read without a left hemisphere?

Table 13.2 Specialization of the Two Hemispheres

LEFT HEMISPHERE	RIGHT HEMISPHERE
Controls the right hand	Controls the left hand
Spoken language	Nonverbal
Written language	Visual-spatial perception
Mathematical calculations	Music and artistic processing
Logical thought processes	Emotional thought and recognition
Analysis of detail	Processes the whole
Reading	Pattern recognition
	Facial recognition

In a split brain patient, if a picture of a ball is flashed to the right side of the screen, the image of the ball will be sent to the left occipital lobe. The person will be able to say that he or she sees a ball. If a picture of a hammer is flashed to the left side of the screen, the person will not be able to verbally identify the object or be able to state with any certainty that something was seen. But if the left hand (controlled by the right hemisphere) is used, the person can point to the hammer he or she "didn't see." The right occipital lobe clearly saw the hammer, but the person could not verbalize that fact (Sperry, 1968). By doing studies such as these, researchers have found that the left hemisphere specializes in language, speech, handwriting, calculation (math), sense of time and rhythm (which is mathematical in nature), and basically any kind of thought requiring analysis. The right hemisphere appears to specialize in more global (widespread) processing involving perception, visualization, spatial perception, recognition of patterns, faces, emotions, melodies, and expression of emotions. It also comprehends simple language but does not produce speech.

Springer and Deutsch (1998) found that, in general, the left hemisphere processes information in a sequence and is good at breaking things down into smaller parts, or performing analysis. The right hemisphere, by contrast, processes information all at once and simultaneously, a more global or holistic* style of processing. Remember the discussion in Chapter Twelve of the early days of psychology, the structuralists, and the Gestalt psychologists? One could almost say that the left hemisphere of the brain is a structuralist who wants to break everything down into its smallest parts, and the right side of the brain is a Gestaltist, who wants to study only the whole. (See Table 13.2.)

So there really are left-brained and right-brained people? And how could Michelle M. talk and read without a left hemisphere?

Actually, unless one is a split-brain patient, the two sides of the brain are always working together as an integrated whole. For example, the right side might recognize someone's face, while the left side struggles to recall the person's name. People aren't really left- or right-brained, they are whole-brained. And in the case of Michelle M., neuroscientists think that her right hemisphere was able to "learn" what would normally be left hemisphere tasks through Michelle's own actions and her parents' constant encouragement—neuroplasticity in action!

*Holistic: relating to or concerned with complete systems or wholes.

The separate functions of the left and right sides of the brain are often confused with handedness, or the tendency to use one hand for most fine motor skills. While most right-handed people also have their left hemisphere in control of their other fine motor skills, such as speech, a few right-handers actually have their language functions in the right hemisphere, in spite of the dominance of the left hemisphere for controlling the right hand. Among left-handed people, there are also many who, although right-brain dominant, still have their language functions on the left side of the brain. Why? How much time do you have? There are far too many theories of why we use one hand over the other to cover in this text. ✲⦗Learn more on MPL

✲ **Learn more** curious facts about right and left handedness.
www.mypsychlab.com

The Chemical Connection: The Endocrine Glands

How do the glands fit into all of this? Aren't there more glands than just the adrenal glands? How do they affect our behavior?

Glands are organs in the body that secrete chemicals. Some glands, such as salivary glands and sweat glands, secrete their chemicals directly onto the body's tissues through tiny tubes, or ducts. This kind of gland affects the functioning of the body but doesn't really affect behavior. Other glands, called **endocrine glands**, have no ducts and secrete their chemicals directly into the bloodstream. (See Figure 13.16.) The chemicals secreted by this type of gland are called **hormones**. As mentioned earlier in the chapter when talking about the sympathetic division of the autonomic nervous system, these hormones flow into the bloodstream, which carries them to their target organs. The molecules of these hormones then fit into receptor sites on those organs to fulfill their function, affecting behavior as they do so.

◀ How do the glands fit into all of this? Aren't there more glands than just the adrenal glands? How do they affect our behavior?

13.11 How do the hormones released by glands interact with the nervous system and affect behavior?

The hormones affect behavior and emotions by controlling muscles and organs such as the heart, pancreas, and sex organs. Some theories of emotion state that the surge in certain hormones actually triggers the emotional reaction (Izard, 1988; Zajonc, 1980, 1984). Some of the hormones produced by endocrine glands also influence the activity of the brain, producing excitatory or inhibitory effects (Mai et al., 1987).

THE PITUITARY, MASTER OF THE HORMONAL UNIVERSE

The **pituitary gland** is located in the brain itself, just below the hypothalamus. The hypothalamus controls the glandular system by influencing the pituitary. That is because the pituitary gland is the *master gland*, the one that controls or influences all of the other endocrine glands. One part of the pituitary controls things associated with pregnancy, such as production of milk for nursing infants and the onset of labor, as well as the levels of salt and water in the body. Another part of the pituitary secretes several hormones that influence the activity of the other glands. Most notable of these hormones is a *growth hormone* that controls and regulates the increase in size as children grow from infancy to adulthood.

As the master gland, the pituitary forms a very important part of a feedback system, one that includes the hypothalamus and the organs targeted by the various hormones. The balance of hormones in the entire endocrine system is maintained by feedback from each of these "players" to the others.

endocrine glands glands that secrete chemicals called hormones directly into the bloodstream.

hormones chemicals released into the bloodstream by endocrine glands.

pituitary gland gland located in the brain that secretes human growth hormone and influences all other hormone-secreting glands (also known as the master gland).

Figure 13.16 The Endocrine Glands

The endocrine glands secrete hormones directly into the bloodstream, which carries them to organs in the body, such as the heart, pancreas, and sex organs.

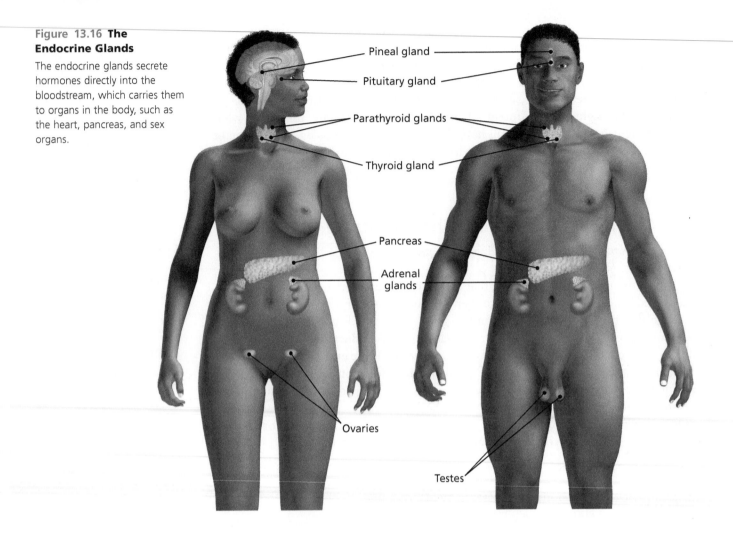

Pineal gland
Pituitary gland
Parathyroid glands
Thyroid gland
Pancreas
Adrenal glands
Ovaries
Testes

THE PINEAL GLAND

The **pineal gland** is also located in the brain, near the back. It secretes a hormone called *melatonin*, which regulates the sleep–wake cycle.

pineal gland endocrine gland located near the base of the cerebrum; secretes melatonin.

THE THYROID GLAND

The **thyroid gland** is located inside the neck and secretes a hormone called *thyroxin* that regulates metabolism (how fast the body burns its available energy).

thyroid gland endocrine gland found in the neck; regulates metabolism.

PANCREAS

The **pancreas** controls the level of blood sugar in the body by secreting *insulin* and *glucagons*. If the pancreas secretes too little insulin, it results in *diabetes*. If it secretes too much insulin, it results in *hypoglycemia*, or low blood sugar, which causes a person to feel hungry all the time and often become overweight as a result.

pancreas endocrine gland; controls the levels of sugar in the blood.

gonads sex glands; secrete hormones that regulate sexual development and behavior as well as reproduction.

THE GONADS

The **gonads** are the sex glands, including the **ovaries** in the female and the **testes** in the male. They secrete hormones that regulate sexual behavior and reproduction. They do not control all sexual behavior, though. In a very real sense, the brain itself is the master of the sexual system—human sexual behavior is not controlled totally

ovaries the female gonads.

testes the male gonads.

by instincts and the actions of the glands as in the animal world but also by psychological factors such as attractiveness.

THE ADRENAL GLANDS

Everyone has two **adrenal glands**, one on top of each kidney. The origin of the name is simple enough; *renal* comes from a Latin word meaning "kidney" and *ad* is Latin for "to," so *adrenal* means "to or on the kidney." Each adrenal gland is actually divided into two sections, the *adrenal medulla* and the *adrenal cortex*. It is the adrenal medulla that releases ephinephrine and norepinephrine when people are under stress and that aids in sympathetic arousal.

The adrenal cortex produces over 30 different hormones called *corticoids* (also called steroids) that regulate salt intake, help initiate* and control stress reactions, and also provides a source of sex hormones in addition to those provided by the gonads. One of the most important of these adrenal hormones is *cortisol*, released when the body experiences stress, both physical stress (such as illness, surgery, or extreme heat or cold) and psychological stress (such as an emotional upset). Cortisol is important in the release of glucose into the bloodstream during stress, providing energy for the brain itself, and the release of fatty acids from the fat cells that provide the muscles with energy.

adrenal glands endocrine glands located on top of each kidney that secrete over 30 different hormones to deal with stress, regulate salt intake, and provide a secondary source of sex hormones affecting the sexual changes that occur during adolescence.

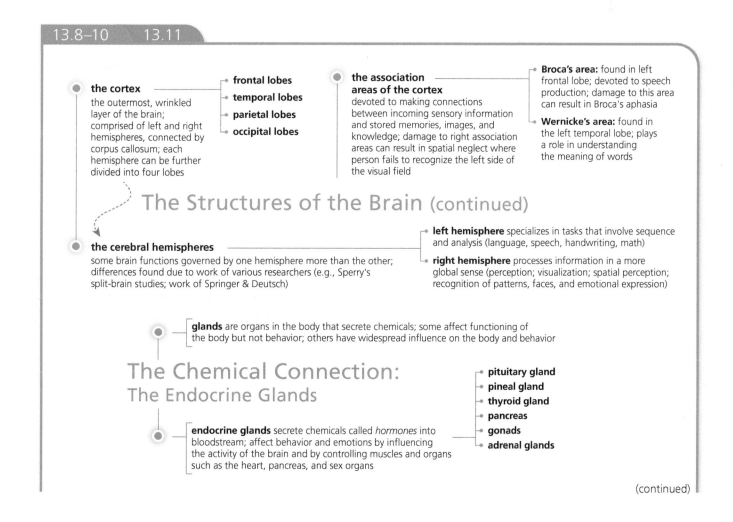

13.8–10   13.11

the cortex — frontal lobes / temporal lobes / parietal lobes / occipital lobes
the outermost, wrinkled layer of the brain; comprised of left and right hemispheres, connected by corpus callosum; each hemisphere can be further divided into four lobes

the association areas of the cortex
devoted to making connections between incoming sensory information and stored memories, images, and knowledge; damage to right association areas can result in spatial neglect where person fails to recognize the left side of the visual field

Broca's area: found in left frontal lobe; devoted to speech production; damage to this area can result in Broca's aphasia

Wernicke's area: found in the left temporal lobe; plays a role in understanding the meaning of words

The Structures of the Brain (continued)

the cerebral hemispheres
some brain functions governed by one hemisphere more than the other; differences found due to work of various researchers (e.g., Sperry's split-brain studies; work of Springer & Deutsch)

left hemisphere specializes in tasks that involve sequence and analysis (language, speech, handwriting, math)

right hemisphere processes information in a more global sense (perception; visualization; spatial perception; recognition of patterns, faces, and emotional expression)

glands are organs in the body that secrete chemicals; some affect functioning of the body but not behavior; others have widespread influence on the body and behavior

The Chemical Connection:
The Endocrine Glands

endocrine glands secrete chemicals called *hormones* into bloodstream; affect behavior and emotions by influencing the activity of the brain and by controlling muscles and organs such as the heart, pancreas, and sex organs

- pituitary gland
- pineal gland
- thyroid gland
- pancreas
- gonads
- adrenal glands

(continued)

---

*Initiate: begin or start.

Pick the best answer.

1. In which of the following lobes of the cortex would you find the primary auditory area?
   a. frontal
   b. temporal
   c. occipital
   d. parietal

2. The higher mental functions, such as thinking and problem solving, are found in the _____ lobe.
   a. frontal
   b. parietal
   c. temporal
   d. corpus

3. In an old *Twilight Zone* episode, a man wakes up one morning to find that people around him are using words that make no sense to him, and they also don't seem to understand him. His wife tells him that their son forgot his dinosaur today, and when he looks puzzled, she holds up the son's lunchbox and repeats, "You know, his dinosaur." This man's predicament is most like which of the following disorders?
   a. Wernicke's aphasia
   b. Broca's aphasia
   c. apraxia
   d. spatial neglect

4. When Dr. Ramachandran's spatial neglect patient was asked to reach for the pen, she _____.
   a. reached to the wrong side of the mirror.
   b. said she couldn't see the pen.
   c. tried to reach through the mirror.
   d. successfully grabbed the pen.

5. If you are a split-brain patient, which of the following would be TRUE?
   a. Objects in your left visual field would be easily named.
   b. Objects in your left visual field are invisible.
   c. Objects in your right visual field would be easily named.
   d. Objects in your right visual field are invisible.

6. Andrew never really grew to be very tall. The doctor told his parents that Andrew's _____ gland did not secrete enough growth hormone, causing his small stature.
   a. pituitary
   b. adrenal
   c. thyroid
   d. pancreas

7. If the pancreas secretes too little insulin, it causes _____.
   a. diabetes.
   b. hypoglycemia.
   c. hypothyroidism.
   d. virilism.

Applying Psychology to Everyday Life: Reflections on Mirror Neurons

You have probably heard the old phrase, "monkey see, monkey do." Neuroscientists have now discovered that the phrase "monkey see, monkey *cortex* do" is more appropriate. Psychologist Giacomo Rizzolatti and his colleagues at the University of Parma, Italy, while using implanted electrodes to examine neural activity in macaque monkeys, made an interesting discovery (Rizzolatti et al., 1996). The researchers wanted to determine which neurons were specifically involved in controlling the movement of the hands. They discovered that the same neurons that fired when the monkeys clutched a piece of food would also fire when the monkeys merely *watched the researchers* handle food. These neurons, which fire when an animal performs an action but also when an animal observes that same action being performed by another, are called **mirror neurons**. Brain-imaging techniques in human studies indicate that we, too, have mirror neurons (Buccino, et al., 2001; Buccino et al., 2004; Iacoboni et al., 1999).

Psychologists are very excited about what the existence of mirror neurons means for social interaction and its influence on the brain and perception. Have you ever winced and ducked when watching someone in a soccer game get hit? Blame those mirror neurons. Do you see someone looking happy and feel you just have to smile also? Mirror neurons again—monkey see, monkey *feel*. Researchers have known for decades that in the first few weeks of life human infants will imitate (although quite unconsciously) the facial expressions of adults (Meltzoff, 1990, 2007; Meltzoff & Moore, 1989). Now mirror neurons seem to provide the neurological explanation for why infants can do this. We are apparently social creatures from the very beginning, reacting to the mere sight of what we see others doing.

mirror neurons neurons that fire when an animal or person performs an action and also when an animal or person observes that same action being performed by another.

Does the knowledge researchers are gathering about mirror neurons have any practical applications? Some studies find that when a stroke patient needs to relearn a motor skill, watching another person perform that skill can be effective in regaining it (Binkofski & Buccino, 2006; Ertelt et al., 2007).

Experts in the field of *autism,* a disorder that is primarily social, are now becoming convinced that autism may be due at least in part to a faulty mirror system in the brain (Dapretto et al., 2006; Oberman et al., 2005; Oberman & Ramachandran, 2007). Autistic people may not like to touch or be touched, do not communicate well if at all, and tend not to make eye contact. In one study (Dapretto et al., 2006), autistic children and nonautistic children were asked to imitate the facial expressions they saw in a series of pictures, and researchers measured neural activity in the mirror neuron system. Although both groups of children were able to imitate the expressions in the pictures, the autistic children showed no neural activity in the mirror system while doing so. The control group of nonautistic children *did* show such mirror system activity. The researchers believe that this lack of a normally functioning mirror system in the autistic children may help explain why autistic people have difficulty with empathy (the ability to understand the emotions of others) as well as with language skills. Their mirror neuron systems respond only to what they themselves do and not to what they see other people doing—autistic people are "locked out" of that system of social reflection.

The implications for therapy with psychological disorders have not yet been fully explored. Could having depressed patients watch others enjoying themselves and laughing lift the depression? If a child with an intense fear of dogs watched someone calmly pet and play with a dog, would that help the child become less afraid? Is it possible that effective exercises could be developed to train or correct the defective mirror neuron systems of autistic children and adults, thereby enabling them to communicate and interact with others more socially? The future is ours to see— through the looking glass of social interactions.

As this boy imitates the motions his father goes through while shaving, certain areas of his brain are more active than others, areas that control the motions of shaving. But even if the boy were only **watching** his father, those same neural areas would be active—the neurons in the boy's brain would **mirror** the actions of the father he is observing.

Questions for Further Discussion

1. What are some other psychological disorders that might be treated by having the affected person observe someone else's behavior or facial expression?

2. In what ways might mirror neurons be involved in how children learn to speak and form words?

13 CHAPTER SUMMARY ((•─Hear more on **MPL** Listen to an audio file of your chapter. www.mypsychlab.com

An Overview of the Nervous System

13.1 What are the nervous system, neurons, and nerves, and how do they relate to one another?

- The nervous system is a complex network of cells that carries information to and from all parts of the body.

Neurons and Nerves: Building the Network

13.2 How do neurons use neurotransmitters to communicate with each other and with the body?

- The brain is made up of two types of cells, neurons and glial cells.

- Neurons have dendrites, which receive input, a soma or cell body, and axons that carry the neural message to other cells.

- Glial cells separate, support, and insulate the neurons from each other and make up 90 percent of the brain.

- Myelin insulates and protects the axons of neurons that travel in the body. These axons bundle together in "cables" called nerves. Myelin also speeds up the neural message.

- Neurons in the peripheral nervous system are also coated with neurilemma, which allows the nerves to repair themselves.

- A neuron contains charged particles called ions. When at rest, the neuron is negatively charged on the inside and positively charged on the outside. When stimulated, this reverses the charge by allowing positive sodium ions to enter the cell. This is the action potential.

- Neurons fire in an all-or-nothing manner. It is the speed and number of neurons firing that tell researchers the strength of the stimulus.

- Synaptic vesicles in the end of the axon terminal release neurotransmitter chemicals into the synapse, or gap, between one cell and the next. The neurotransmitter molecules fit into receptor sites on the next cell, stimulating or inhibiting that cell's firing. Neurotransmitters may be either excitatory or inhibitory.

- The first known neurotransmitter was acetylcholine. It stimulates muscles and helps in memory formation. Curare is a poison that blocks its effect.

- GABA is the major inhibitory neurotransmitter; high amounts of GABA are released when drinking alcohol.

- Serotonin is associated with sleep, mood, and appetite.

- Dopamine is associated with Parkinson's disease and schizophrenia.

- Endorphins are neural regulators that control our pain response.

- Most neurotransmitters are taken back into the synaptic vesicles in a process called reuptake.

- Acetylcholine is cleared out of the synapse by enzymes that break up the molecules.

The Central Nervous System— The "Central Processing Unit"

13.3 How do the brain and spinal cord interact?

- The central nervous system consists of the brain and the spinal cord.

- The spinal cord serves two functions. The outer part of the cord transmits messages to and from the brain, whereas the inner part controls lifesaving reflexes such as the pain response.

- Spinal cord reflexes involve afferent neurons, interneurons, and efferent neurons, forming a simple reflex arc.

- Great strides are being made in spinal cord repair and the growth of new neurons in the central nervous system.

Psychology in the News: Stem Cells: New Hope for Damaged Brains?

- Research suggests that stem cells can be obtained from adult bone marrow, making the repair and replacement of damaged neurons more feasible.

The Peripheral Nervous System— Nerves on the Edge

- The peripheral nervous system is all the neurons and nerves that are not part of the brain and spinal cord and that extend throughout the body.

- There are two systems within the peripheral nervous system, the somatic nervous system and the autonomic nervous system.

13.4 How do the somatic and autonomic nervous systems allow people and animals to interact with their surroundings and control the body's automatic functions?

- The somatic nervous system contains the sensory pathway, or neurons carrying messages to the central nervous system, and the motor pathway, or neurons carrying messages from the central nervous system to the voluntary muscles.

- The autonomic nervous system consists of the parasympathetic division and the sympathetic division. The sympathetic division is our fight-or-flight system, reacting to stress, whereas the parasympathetic division restores and maintains normal day-to-day functioning of the organs.

Peeking Inside the Brain

13.5 How do psychologists study the brain and how it works?

- We can study the brain by using deep lesioning to destroy certain areas of the brain in laboratory animals or by electrically stimulating those areas (ESB).

- We can use case studies of human brain damage to learn about the brain's functions but cannot easily generalize from one case to another.

- The EEG machine allows researchers to look at the activity of the surface of the brain through the use of electrodes placed on the scalp and connected to graph paper.

- CT scans are computer-aided X-rays of the brain and show a great deal of brain structure.

- MRI scans use a magnetic field and a computer to give researchers an even more detailed look at the structure of the brain. A related technique, fMRI, allows researchers to look at the activity of the brain over a time period.

- PET scans use a radioactive sugar injected into the bloodstream to track the activity of brain cells, which is enhanced and color-coded by a computer.

From the Bottom Up: The Structures of the Brain

13.6 What are the different structures of the bottom part of the brain and what do they do?

- The medulla is at the very bottom of the brain and top of the spinal column. It controls life-sustaining functions such as breathing and swallowing. The nerves from each side of the body also cross over in this structure to opposite sides.

- The pons is above the medulla and acts as a bridge between the lower part of the brain and the upper part. It influences sleep, dreaming, arousal, and coordination of movement on the left and right sides of the body.

- The reticular formation runs through the medulla and the pons and controls our selective attention and arousal.

- The cerebellum is found at the base and back of the brain and coordinates fine, rapid motor movement, learned reflexes, posture, and muscle tone.

13.7 What are the structures of the brain that control emotion, learning, memory, and motivation?

- The thalamus is the switching station that sends sensory information to the proper areas of the cortex.

- The hypothalamus controls hunger, thirst, sleep, sexual behavior, sleeping and waking, and emotions. It also controls the pituitary gland.

- The limbic system consists of the thalamus, hypothalamus, hippocampus, amygdala, and the fornix.

- The hippocampus is the part of the brain responsible for storing memories and remembering locations of objects.

- The amygdala controls our fear responses and memory of fearful stimuli.

13.8 What parts of the cortex control the different senses and the movement of the body?

- The cortex is the outer covering of the cerebrum and consists of a tightly packed layer of neurons about one-tenth of an inch in thickness. Its wrinkles, or corticalization, allow for greater cortical area and are associated with greater intelligence.

- The cortex is divided into two cerebral hemispheres connected by a thick band of neural fibers called the corpus callosum.

- The occipital lobes at the back and base of each hemisphere process vision and contain the primary visual cortex.

- The parietal lobes at the top and back of the cortex contain the somatosensory area, which processes our sense of touch, temperature, and body position. Taste is also processed in this lobe.

- The temporal lobes contain the primary auditory area and are also involved in understanding language.

- The frontal lobes contain the motor cortex, which controls the voluntary muscles, and are also where all the higher mental functions occur, such as planning, language, and complex decision making.

13.9 What parts of the cortex are responsible for higher forms of thought, such as language?

- Association areas of the cortex are found in all the lobes but particularly in the frontal lobes. These areas help people make sense of the information they receive from the lower areas of the brain.

- An area called Broca's area in the left frontal lobe is responsible for producing fluent, understandable speech. If damaged, the person has Broca's aphasia in which words will be halting and pronounced incorrectly.

- An area called Wernicke's area in the left temporal lobe is responsible for the understanding of language. If damaged, the person has Wernicke's aphasia in which speech is fluent but nonsensical. The wrong words are used.

Classic Studies in Psychology: Through the Looking Glass: Spatial Neglect

- Spatial neglect comes from damage to the association areas on one side of the cortex, usually the right side. A person with this condition will ignore information from the opposite side of the body or the opposite visual field.

13.10 How does the left side of the brain differ from the right side?

- Studies with split-brain patients, in which the corpus callosum has been severed to correct epilepsy, reveal that the left side of the brain seems to control language, writing, logical thought, analysis, and mathematical abilities. The left side also processes information sequentially.

- The right side of the brain processes information globally and controls emotional expression, spatial perception, recognition of faces, patterns, melodies, and emotions. The left hemisphere can speak but the right cannot.

The Chemical Connection: The Endocrine Glands

13.11 How do the hormones released by glands interact with the nervous system and affect behavior?

- Endocrine glands secrete chemicals called hormones directly into the bloodstream, influencing the activity of the muscles and organs.

- The pituitary gland is found in the brain just below the hypothalamus. It has two parts, the anterior and the posterior. It controls the levels of salt and water in the system and, in women, the onset of labor and lactation, as well as secreting growth hormone and influencing the activity of the other glands.

- The pineal gland is also located in the brain. It secretes melatonin, a hormone that regulates the sleep–wake cycle in response to changes in light.

- The thyroid gland is located inside the neck. It controls metabolism (the burning of energy) by secreting thyroxin.

- The pancreas controls the level of sugar in the blood by secreting insulin and glucagons. Too much insulin produces hypoglycemia, whereas too little causes diabetes.

- The gonads are the ovaries in women and testes in men. They secrete hormones to regulate sexual growth, activity, and reproduction.

- The adrenal glands, one on top of each kidney, control the stress reaction through the adrenal medulla's secretion of epinephrine and norepinephrine. The adrenal cortex secretes over 30 different corticoids (hormones) controlling salt intake, stress, and sexual development.

Applying Psychology to Everyday Life: Reflections on Mirror Neurons

- Italian scientist Rizzolatti and colleagues discovered the existence of mirror neurons, neurons that not only fire when performing an action but also fire when the organism merely watches an action being performed by another.

- Mirror neurons may explain much of human social interaction, and may be useful in understanding disorders such as autism. There may also be practical applications in the treatment of stroke patients who need to regain lost skills and in therapy for psychological disorders such as depression.

TEST YOURSELF

✓ Practice more on MPL Ready for your test? More quizzes and a customized study plan. www.mypsychlab.com

Pick the best answer.

1. In the structure of the neuron, the _____ sends information to other cells.
   - **a.** axon
   - **b.** dendrite
   - **c.** soma
   - **d.** myelin

2. Which type of cell makes up 10 percent of the brain?
   - **a.** glial cells
   - **b.** neurons
   - **c.** stem cells
   - **d.** afferent cells

3. Damaged nerve fibers in the body can repair themselves because they are coated with _____, which forms a protective tunnel around the nerve fibers.
   - **a.** glial
   - **b.** soma
   - **c.** myelin
   - **d.** neurilemma

4. When a neuron is in the resting potential state, where are the sodium ions?
   - **a.** inside the cell
   - **b.** outside the cell
   - **c.** inside the soma
   - **d.** in the synapse

5. How does one neuron communicate with another neuron?
   - **a.** An electrical spark jumps over the gap between cells.
   - **b.** Charged particles leap from one cell to the next.
   - **c.** Chemicals in the end of one neuron float across the gap to fit into holes on the next neuron.
   - **d.** The end of one neuron extends to touch the other neuron.

6. Which neurotransmitter is associated with the control of the pain response?
   - **a.** acetylcholine
   - **b.** GABA
   - **c.** serotonin
   - **d.** endorphin

7. Which of the following is the correct path of a reflex arc?
   - **a.** efferent neuron to interneuron to afferent neuron
   - **b.** efferent neuron to afferent neuron to interneuron
   - **c.** afferent neuron to interneuron to efferent neuron
   - **d.** afferent neuron to efferent neuron to the brain

8. Voluntary muscles are controlled by the _____ nervous system.
   - **a.** somatic
   - **b.** autonomic
   - **c.** sympathetic
   - **d.** parasympathetic

9. Your heart races. You begin to breathe faster. Your pupils enlarge and your appetite is gone. Your _____ division has just been activated.
   - **a.** sympathetic
   - **b.** parasympathetic
   - **c.** autonomic
   - **d.** somatic

10. The _____ division controls ordinary, day-to-day bodily functions.
    - **a.** sympathetic
    - **b.** parasympathetic
    - **c.** central
    - **d.** somatic

11. Which of the following techniques for imaging the brain would *not* be advisable for a person with a metal plate in his or her head?
    - **a.** EEG
    - **b.** CT
    - **c.** MRI
    - **d.** PET

12. Which technique of studying the brain actually damages neurons?
    - **a.** EEG
    - **b.** deep lesioning
    - **c.** ESB
    - **d.** MRI

13. Maria suffered a stroke that damaged a part of her brain. She fell into a sleeplike coma and could not be awakened. If we know that the area of damage is somewhere in the brain stem, which structure is most likely damaged?
    - **a.** medulla
    - **b.** pons
    - **c.** reticular formation
    - **d.** cerebellum

14. Alex, who is 2 months old, is having his picture taken. The photographer tries to sit him up, but Alex keeps sinking down. Alex cannot sit upright yet because the _____ in his brain stem is not yet fully developed.
    - **a.** medulla
    - **b.** pons
    - **c.** reticular formation
    - **d.** cerebellum

15. Which sense is NOT sent to the cortex by the thalamus?
    - **a.** hearing
    - **b.** smell
    - **c.** taste
    - **d.** vision

16. Which part of the brain is the link between the brain and the glandular system?
    - **a.** hippocampus
    - **b.** thalamus
    - **c.** hypothalamus
    - **d.** amygdala

17. Jeff is undergoing brain surgery to remove a tumor. The surgeon applies electrical simulation to various areas around the tumor, causing Jeff to report tingling sensations in various areas of his skin. The tumor is most likely in which lobe of Jeff's brain?
    - **a.** frontal
    - **b.** temporal
    - **c.** occipital
    - **d.** parietal

18. George has a small stroke that results in a partial paralysis of his left side. The damaged area is most likely in his _____ lobe.
    - **a.** right frontal
    - **b.** left frontal
    - **c.** right parietal
    - **d.** left temporal

19. Linda is recovering from damage to her brain. Her main symptom is a speech problem; instead of saying, "I am going to P. T. (physical therapy) at nine o'clock" she says, "I go . . . P. T. . . . non o'cot." Linda's problem is _____.
    - **a.** spatial neglect.
    - **b.** visual agnosia.
    - **c.** Broca's aphasia.
    - **d.** Wernicke's aphasia.

20. Recognizing the face of someone you run into at the mall is a function of the _____ hemisphere; being able to retrieve that person's name from memory is a function of the _____ hemisphere.
    a. left; right
    b. right; left
    c. right; right
    d. left; left

21. Heather is beautifully proportioned, but at 18 years of age she is still no taller than the average 10-year-old. Heather most likely had a problem in her _____ gland(s) while she was growing up.
    a. pituitary
    b. adrenal
    c. thyroid
    d. pineal

22. The action of hormones in the bloodstream is most similar to which of the following?
    a. the action of sodium ions in the action potential
    b. the action of myelin surrounding the axons
    c. the action of glial cells in the brain
    d. the action of neurotransmitters in the synapse

23. Melatonin is secreted by the _____ gland(s).
    a. pituitary
    b. adrenal
    c. thyroid
    d. pineal

13.1–2   p. 256

Neurons and Nerves
(the brain is comprised of glial cells and neurons)

glial cells
provide physical and metabolic
support to neurons

neurons
specialized cells
in nervous system

• have specialized
components

• have an electrical
charge at rest—
the resting potential
(see Fig. 13.3, p. 250)

• are affected by
neurotransmitters
(see Table 13.1, p. 254)

• are separated
by a gap called
the synapse

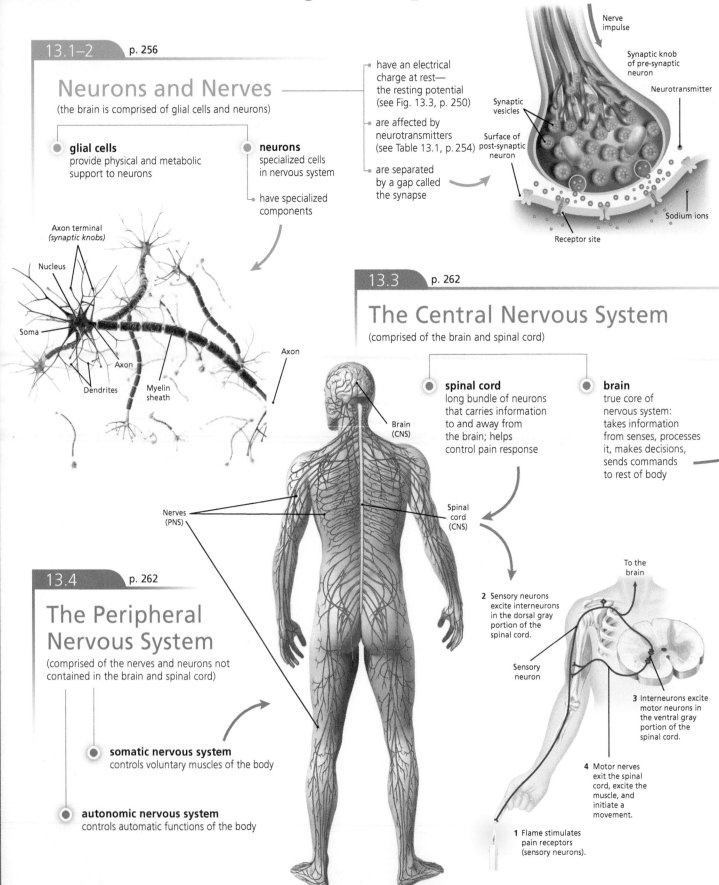

Nerve
impulse

Synaptic knob
of pre-synaptic
neuron

Neurotransmitter

Synaptic
vesicles

Surface of
post-synaptic
neuron

Sodium ions

Receptor site

Axon terminal
(synaptic knobs)

Nucleus

Soma

Axon

Dendrites

Myelin
sheath

Axon

13.3   p. 262

The Central Nervous System
(comprised of the brain and spinal cord)

spinal cord
long bundle of neurons
that carries information
to and away from
the brain; helps
control pain response

brain
true core of
nervous system:
takes information
from senses, processes
it, makes decisions,
sends commands
to rest of body

Brain
(CNS)

Spinal
cord
(CNS)

Nerves
(PNS)

13.4   p. 262

The Peripheral
Nervous System
(comprised of the nerves and neurons not
contained in the brain and spinal cord)

somatic nervous system
controls voluntary muscles of the body

autonomic nervous system
controls automatic functions of the body

To the
brain

2 Sensory neurons
excite interneurons
in the dorsal gray
portion of the
spinal cord.

Sensory
neuron

3 Interneurons excite
motor neurons in
the ventral gray
portion of the
spinal cord.

4 Motor nerves
exit the spinal
cord, excite the
muscle, and
initiate a
movement.

1 Flame stimulates
pain receptors
(sensory neurons).

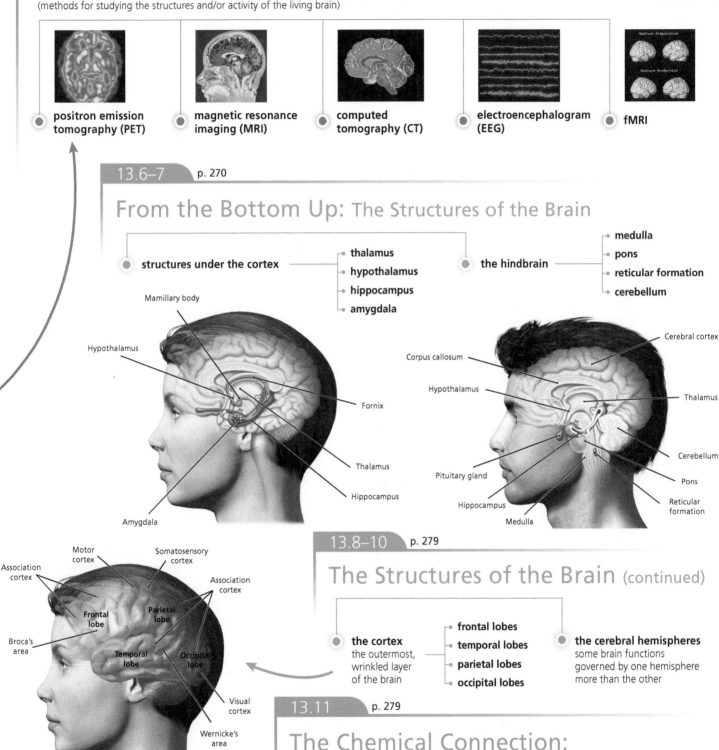

13.5   p. 270

Peeking Inside the Brain
(methods for studying the structures and/or activity of the living brain)

- **positron emission tomography (PET)**
- **magnetic resonance imaging (MRI)**
- **computed tomography (CT)**
- **electroencephalogram (EEG)**
- **fMRI**

13.6–7   p. 270

From the Bottom Up: The Structures of the Brain

- **structures under the cortex**
  - thalamus
  - hypothalamus
  - hippocampus
  - amygdala
- **the hindbrain**
  - medulla
  - pons
  - reticular formation
  - cerebellum

Mamillary body
Hypothalamus
Fornix
Thalamus
Hippocampus
Amygdala

Corpus callosum
Hypothalamus
Pituitary gland
Hippocampus
Medulla
Cerebral cortex
Thalamus
Cerebellum
Pons
Reticular formation

Association cortex
Motor cortex
Somatosensory cortex
Association cortex
Frontal lobe
Parietal lobe
Broca's area
Temporal lobe
Occipital lobe
Visual cortex
Wernicke's area

13.8–10   p. 279

The Structures of the Brain (continued)

- **the cortex**
  the outermost, wrinkled layer of the brain
  - frontal lobes
  - temporal lobes
  - parietal lobes
  - occipital lobes
- **the cerebral hemispheres**
  some brain functions governed by one hemisphere more than the other

13.11   p. 279

The Chemical Connection: The Endocrine Glands

- **glands**
  organs in the body that secrete chemicals
- **endocrine glands**
  secrete chemicals called *hormones* into bloodstream
  - pituitary gland
  - pineal gland
  - thyroid gland
  - pancreas
  - gonads
  - adrenal glands

Taken from *Essential Environment: The Science Behind the Stories*, Second Edition by Jay Withgott and Scott Brennan

14 Nonrenewable Energy Sources, Their Impacts, and Energy Conservation

Caribou crossing haul road at Prudhoe Bay

Upon successfully completing this chapter, you will be able to:

▶ Survey the energy sources that we use

▶ Describe the nature and origin of coal, natural gas, and petroleum, and evaluate their extraction and use

▶ Outline the future depletion of global oil supplies and assess the concerns over "peak oil"

▶ Review and assess environmental, political, social, and economic impacts of fossil fuel use

▶ Specify strategies for conserving energy

▶ Describe nuclear energy and how it is harnessed

▶ Assess the benefits and drawbacks of nuclear power and outline the societal debate over this energy source

Central Case: Oil or Wilderness on Alaska's North Slope?

East of the National Petroleum Reserve are state lands that experienced widespread development and extraction after oil was discovered at Prudhoe Bay in 1968. Since drilling began in 1977, over 14 billion barrels (1 barrel = 159 L or 42 gal) of crude oil have been extracted from 19 oil fields spread over 160,000 ha (395,000 acres) of this region. The oil is transported across the state of Alaska by the 1,300-km (800-mi) trans-Alaska pipeline south to the port of Valdez, where it is loaded onto tankers.

East of the Prudhoe Bay region lies the Arctic National Wildlife Refuge (ANWR), an area the size of South Carolina consisting of federal lands set aside in 1960 and 1980 mainly to protect wildlife and preserve pristine ecosystems of tundra, mountains, and seacoast. This scenic region is home to 160 nesting bird species, numerous fish and marine mammals, grizzly bears, polar bears, Arctic foxes, timber wolves, and musk oxen. In most years, thousands of caribou arrive from the south to spend the summer, giving birth to and raising their calves. Because of the vast caribou herd and the other large mammals, ANWR has been called "the Serengeti of North America."

ANWR has been the focus of debate for decades. Advocates of oil drilling have tried to open its lands for development, and proponents of wilderness preservation have fought for its preservation. Scientists, oil industry experts, politicians, environmental groups, citizens, and Alaska residents have all been part of the debate. So have the two Native groups in the area, the Gwich'in and the Inupiat, who disagree over whether the refuge should be opened to oil development. The Gwich'in depend on hunting caribou and fear that oil industry activity will reduce caribou herds, whereas the Inupiat, who rely less on caribou, see oil extraction as one of the few opportunities for economic development in the area.

In a compromise in 1980, the U.S. Congress put most of the refuge off limits to oil but reserved for future decision making a 600,000-ha (1.5-million-acre) area of coastal plain. This region, called the 1002 Area (after Section 1002 of the bill that established it),

A bove the Arctic Circle, at the top of the North American continent, the land drops steeply down from the jagged mountains of Alaska's spectacular Brooks Range and stretches north in a vast, flat expanse of tundra until it meets the icy waters of the Arctic Ocean. Few Americans have been to this remote region, yet it has come to symbolize a struggle between two values in our modern life.

For some U.S. citizens, Alaska's North Slope is one of the last great expanses of wilderness in their sprawling industrialized country—one of the last places humans have left untouched. For these millions of Americans, simply knowing that this wilderness still exists is of tremendous value. For millions of others, this land represents something else entirely—a source of petroleum, the natural resource that, more than any other, fuels our society and shapes our way of life. To these people, it seems wrong to leave such an important resource sitting unused in the ground. Those who advocate drilling for oil here accuse wilderness preservationists of neglecting the country's economic interests, whereas advocates for wilderness argue that drilling will sacrifice the nation's natural heritage for little gain.

Ever since oil was found seeping from the ground in this area a century ago, these two visions for Alaska's North Slope have competed. Now they exist side by side across three regions of this vast swath of land (Figure 14.1). The westernmost portion of the North Slope was set aside in 1923 by the U.S. government as an emergency reserve for petroleum. This parcel of land, the size of Indiana, is today called the National Petroleum Reserve–Alaska and was intended to remain untapped for oil unless the nation faced an emergency. So far, most of this region's 9.5 million ha (23.5 million acres) remains undeveloped.

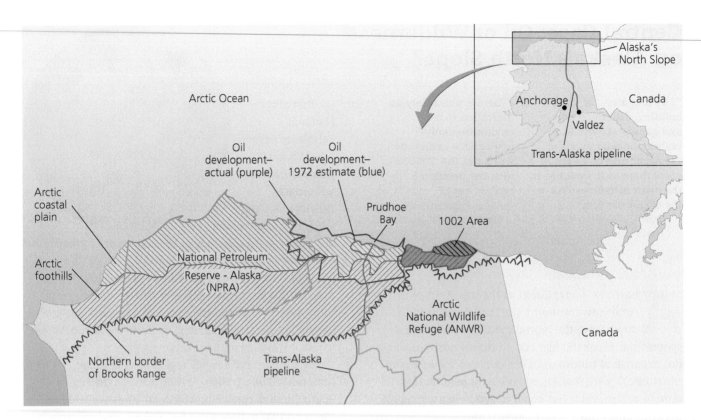

FIGURE 14.1 Alaska's North Slope is the site of both arctic wilderness and oil exploration. In the western portion of this region, the U.S. government established the National Petroleum Reserve–Alaska as an area in which to drill for oil if it is needed in an emergency. It is well explored but not widely developed. To the east of this area, the Prudhoe Bay region is the site of widespread oil extraction, and since 1977 it has produced over 14 billion barrels of oil. Oil development has expanded much farther than experts estimated it would in 1972. Farther east lies the Arctic National Wildlife Refuge, home to untrammeled Arctic wilderness and the focus of debate for years. Proponents of oil extraction and proponents of wilderness preservation have been battling over whether the 1002 Area of the coastal plain north of the Brooks Range should be opened to oil development.

remains undeveloped for oil but can be opened for development by a vote of both houses of Congress. Its unsettled status has made it the center of the oil-versus-wilderness debate, and Congress has been caught between passionate feelings on both sides for a quarter of a century.

In 2005 and 2006, the Republican-controlled Congress made several efforts to open the refuge to drilling—more than once with provisions slipped into unrelated budget legislation. As of this writing, each attempt had been narrowly blocked.

Behind the noisy policy debate over ANWR, scientists have attempted to inform the dialogue through research. Geologists have tried to ascertain how much oil lies underneath the refuge. Biologists have tried to predict the impacts of oil drilling on Arctic ecosystems. Many environmental scientists have concluded that a small amount of conservation would free up more oil than drilling in ANWR would produce. Moreover, scientists and nonscientists alike are debating the relevance of the oil beneath the refuge for the security and prosperity of the nation. We will examine these questions by revisiting Alaska's North Slope as we survey the fossil fuel energy we use to heat and light our homes, power our machinery, and provide the comforts, conveniences, and mobility to which technology has accustomed us.

Sources of Energy

The debate over drilling for oil in the Arctic National Wildlife Refuge is a thoroughly modern debate, pitting the culturally new concept of wilderness preservation against the desire to exploit a resource that has come to guide the world's economy only in the past 150 years. However, people have used—and fought over—energy in one way or another for all of our history.

We use a variety of energy sources

Our planet receives energy from several sources, and people have developed many ways to harness renewable and nonrenewable forms of energy (Table 14.1). Most of Earth's energy comes from the sun. We can harness energy from the sun's radiation directly, but solar radiation also makes possible several other energy sources. Sunlight drives the growth of plants, from which we take wood as a fuel source. After their death, plants may impart their stored chemical energy to **fossil fuels** (such as oil, coal, and natural gas), which are highly combustible substances formed from the remains of organisms from past geological ages. Solar radiation also helps drive wind patterns and the hydrologic cycle, making possible other forms of energy, such as wind power and hydroelectric power.

A great deal of energy also emanates from Earth's core, enabling us to harness geothermal power. A much smaller amount of energy results from the gravitational pull of the moon and sun, and we are just beginning to harness power from the ocean tides that these forces generate. An immense amount of energy resides within the bonds among protons and neutrons in atoms, and this energy provides us with nuclear power.

Energy sources such as sunlight, geothermal energy, and tidal energy are considered *renewable* because they will not be depleted by our use of them. In contrast, energy sources such as oil, coal, and natural gas are considered *nonrenewable*, because at our current rates of consumption we will use up Earth's accessible store of them in a matter of decades to centuries. Nuclear power as currently harnessed through fission of uranium (▸ pp. 309–310) is considered nonrenewable to the extent that uranium ore is in limited supply. Although these nonrenewable fuels result from ongoing natural processes, the timescales on which they are created are so long that, once the fuels are depleted, they cannot be replaced in any time span useful to our civilization. It takes a thousand years for the biosphere to generate the amount of organic matter that must be buried to produce a single day's worth of fossil fuels for our society. For this reason, and because fossil fuels exert severe environmental impacts, renewable energy sources increasingly are being developed as alternatives to fossil fuels.

Citizens of developed nations generally consume far more energy than do those of developing nations. (Figure 14.2). Developing nations devote a greater proportion of energy to subsistence activities, such as growing and preparing food and heating homes, whereas industrialized countries use a greater proportion for transportation and industry. Because industrialized nations rely more on mechanized equipment and technology, they use more fossil fuels. In the United States, fossil fuels supply 89% of energy needs.

Fossil fuels provide most of the energy we consume because their high energy content makes them efficient to burn, ship, and store. Besides providing for transportation, heating, and cooking, we use these fuels to generate **electricity**, a secondary form of energy that is easier to transfer over long distances and apply to

Table 14.1 Energy Sources We Use Today		
Energy source	**Description**	**Type of energy**
Crude oil	Fossil fuel extracted from ground	Nonrenewable
Natural gas	Fossil fuel extracted from ground	Nonrenewable
Coal	Fossil fuel extracted from ground	Nonrenewable
Nuclear energy	Energy from atomic nuclei of uranium mined from ground and processed	Nonrenewable
Biomass energy	Chemical energy from photosynthesis stored in plant matter	Renewable
Hydropower	Energy from running water	Renewable
Solar energy	Energy from sunlight directly	Renewable
Wind energy	Energy from wind	Renewable
Geothermal energy	Earth's internal heat rising from core	Renewable
Tidal and wave energy	Energy from tidal forces and ocean waves	Renewable

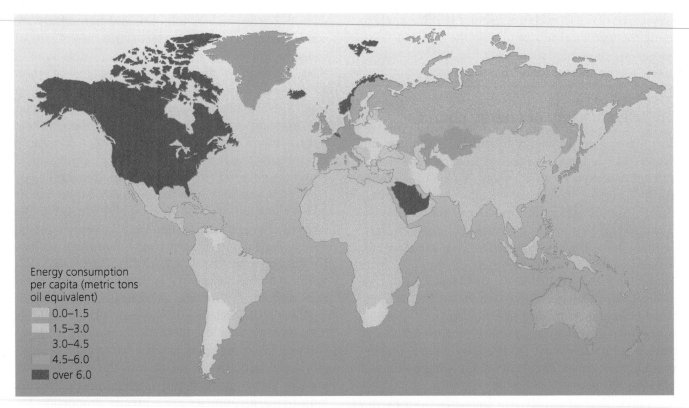

FIGURE 14.2 Regions vary greatly in their per capita consumption of energy. Per person, the most-industrialized nations use up to 100 times more energy than do the least-industrialized nations. This map combines all types of energy, standardized to metric tons of "oil equivalent," that is, the amount of fuel needed to produce the energy gained from combusting one metric ton of crude oil. Data from British Petroleum. 2005. *Statistical review of world energy 2005.*

a variety of uses. Global consumption of the three main fossil fuels has risen steadily for years and is now at its highest level ever (Figure 14.3).

Fossil fuels are indeed fuels created from "fossils"

The fossil fuels we burn today in our vehicles, homes, industries, and electrical power plants were formed from the tissues of organisms that lived 100–500 million years ago. The energy these fuels contain came originally from the sun and was converted to chemical-bond energy as a result of photosynthesis. The chemical energy in these organisms' tissues was then concentrated as these tissues decomposed and their hydrocarbon compounds were altered and compressed (Figure 14.4).

Most organisms, after death, do not end up as part of a coal, gas, or oil deposit. A tree that falls and decays as a rotting log undergoes mostly **aerobic** decomposition; in the presence of air, bacteria and other organisms that use oxygen break down plant and animal remains into simpler molecules that are recycled through the ecosystem.

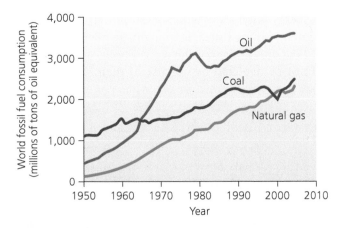

FIGURE 14.3 Global consumption of fossil fuels has risen greatly over the past half century. Oil use rose steeply during the 1960s to overtake coal, and today it remains our leading energy source. Data from Worldwatch Institute. 2005. *Vital signs 2005.*

Fossil fuels are produced only when organic material is broken down in an **anaerobic** environment, one with little or no oxygen. Such environments include the bottoms of lakes, swamps, and shallow seas.

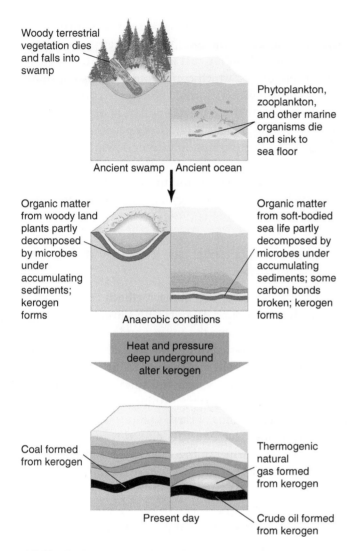

FIGURE 14.4 The fossil fuels we use for energy today consist of the remains of organic material from plants (and to a lesser extent, animals) that died millions of years ago. Their formation begins when organisms die and end up in oxygen-poor conditions, such as when trees fall into lakes and are buried by sediment, or when phytoplankton and zooplankton drift to the seafloor and are buried. Organic matter that undergoes slow anaerobic decomposition deep under sediments forms kerogen. Geothermal heating acts on kerogen to create crude oil and natural gas. Natural gas can also be produced nearer the surface by anaerobic bacterial decomposition of organic matter. Oil and gas come to reside in porous rock layers beneath dense, impervious layers. Coal is formed when plant matter is compacted so tightly that there is little decomposition.

Fossil fuel reserves are unevenly distributed

Fossil fuel deposits are localized and unevenly distributed over Earth's surface, so some regions have substantial reserves of fossil fuels whereas others have very few. How long each nation's fossil fuel reserves will last

Table 14.2	Nations with Largest Proven Reserves of Fossil Fuels	
Oil (% world reserves)	**Natural gas** (% world reserves)	**Coal** (% world reserves)
Saudi Arabia, 22.0	Russia, 26.6	United States, 27.1
Iran, 11.5	Iran, 14.9	Russia, 17.3
Iraq, 9.6	Qatar, 14.3	China, 12.6
Kuwait, 8.5	Saudi Arabia, 3.8	India, 10.2
United Arab Emirates, 8.1	United Arab Emirates, 3.4	Australia, 8.6
Venezuela, 6.6	United States, 3.0	South Africa, 5.4
Russia, 6.2	Nigeria, 2.9	Ukraine, 3.8
Kazakhstan, 3.3	Algeria, 2.5	Kazakhstan, 3.4
Libya, 3.3	Venezuela, 2.4	Poland, 1.5
Nigeria, 3.0	Iraq, 1.8	Brazil, 1.1

Data from British Petroleum. 2006. *Statistical review of world energy 2006.*

depends on how much the nation extracts, how much it consumes, and how much it imports from and exports to other nations. Nearly two-thirds of the world's proven reserves of crude oil lie in the Middle East. The Middle East is also rich in natural gas, but Russia contains more than twice as much natural gas as any other country. Russia is also rich in coal, as is China, but the United States possesses more coal than any other nation (Table 14.2).

Coal

Coal is organic matter (generally woody plant material) that was compressed under very high pressure to form dense, solid carbon structures. Coal typically results when little decomposition takes place because the material cannot be digested or appropriate decomposers are not present. The proliferation 300–400 million years ago of swampy environments where organic material was buried has resulted in substantial coal deposits throughout the world. In fact, coal is the world's most abundant fossil fuel.

Coal varies in its qualities

Coal varies from deposit to deposit in its water content and in the amount of potential energy it contains. Organic material that is broken down anaerobically but remains wet, near the surface, and poorly compressed is

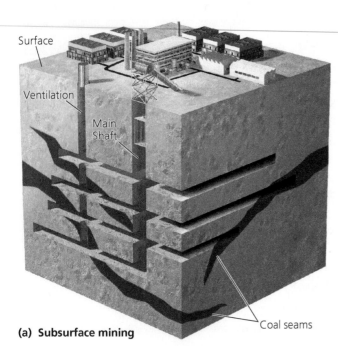

(a) Subsurface mining

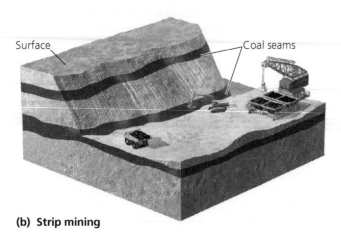

(b) Strip mining

FIGURE 14.5 Coal is mined in two major ways. In subsurface mining (**a**), miners work below ground in shafts and tunnels blasted through the rock; these passageways provide access to underground seams of coal. This type of mining poses dangers and long-term health risks to miners. In strip mining (**b**), soil is removed from the surface, exposing coal seams from which coal is mined. This type of mining can cause substantial environmental impact.

called *peat*. As peat decomposes further, as it is buried more deeply under sediments, as pressure and heat increase, and as time passes, water is squeezed from the material, and carbon compounds are packed more tightly together, forming coal. The greater the compression, the greater is the energy content per unit volume.

Coal deposits also vary in the amount of impurities they contain, including sulfur, mercury, arsenic, and other trace metals. Coal in the eastern United States tends to be high in sulfur because it was formed in marine sediments, where sulfur from seawater was present. When high-sulfur coal is burned, it produces sulfate air pollutants, which contribute to industrial smog and acidic deposition. Combustion of mercury-rich coal emits mercury that can bioaccumulate in organisms' tissues, poisoning animals as it moves up food chains. Such pollution problems commonly occur downwind of coal-fired power plants. Scientists and engineers are seeking ways to cleanse coal of its impurities so that it can continue to be used as an energy source while minimizing impact on the environment (▸ p. 303).

Coal is mined from the surface and from below ground

We extract coal using two major methods (Figure 14.5). We reach underground deposits with **subsurface mining**. Shafts are dug deep into the ground, and networks of tunnels are dug or blasted out to follow coal seams. Coal is removed systematically and shipped to the surface. When coal deposits are at or near the surface, strip-mining methods are used. In **strip mining**, heavy machinery removes huge amounts of earth to expose and extract the coal. The pits are subsequently refilled with the soil that was removed. Strip-mining operations can occur on immense scales; in some cases entire mountaintops are lopped off (▸ p. 303).

We generate electricity with coal

In the early days of the industrial revolution, we used coal for direct heating and for running steam engines. Today we burn coal largely to generate electricity. In coal-fired power plants, coal combustion converts water to steam, which turns a turbine to create electricity (Figure 14.6). Today coal provides over half the electrical generating capacity of the United States. China and the United States are the primary producers and consumers of coal (Table 14.3).

Table 14.3 Top Producers and Consumers of Coal	
Production (% world production)	**Consumption** (% world consumption)
China, 38.4	China, 36.9
United States, 20.0	United States, 19.6
Australia, 7.0	India, 7.3
India, 6.9	Japan, 4.1
South Africa, 4.8	Russia, 3.8

Data from British Petroleum. 2006. *Statistical review of world energy 2006.*

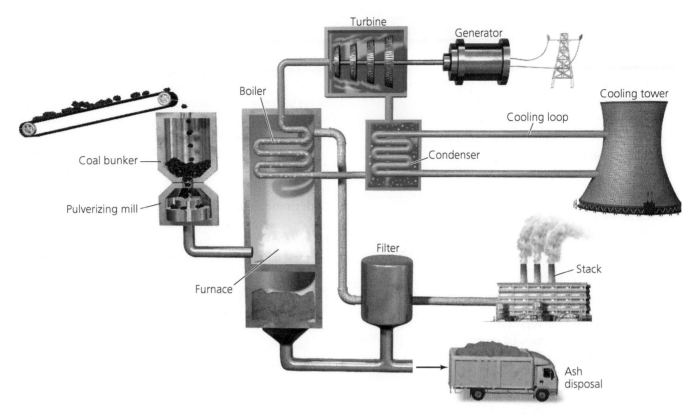

FIGURE 14.6 Coal is the primary fuel source used to generate electricity in the United States. Pieces of coal are pulverized and blown into a high-temperature furnace. Heat from the combustion boils water, and the resulting steam turns a turbine, generating electricity by passing magnets past copper coils. The steam is then cooled and condensed in a cooling loop and returned to the furnace. "Clean coal" technologies (▶ p. 303) help filter out pollutants from the combustion process, and toxic ash residue is disposed of in hazardous waste disposal sites.

Natural Gas

Natural gas is the fastest-growing fossil fuel in use today and provides for one-quarter of global commercial energy consumption. World supplies of natural gas are projected to last perhaps 60 more years.

Natural gas is formed in two ways

Natural gas can arise from either of two processes. *Biogenic* gas is created at shallow depths by the anaerobic decomposition of organic matter by bacteria. An example is the "swamp gas" you can sometimes smell when stepping into the muck of a swamp. In contrast, *thermogenic* gas results from compression and heat deep underground. Thermogenic gas may be formed directly, along with crude oil, or it may be formed from crude oil that is altered by heating. Biogenic gas is nearly pure methane, (CH_4), but thermogenic gas contains small amounts of other hydrocarbon gases as well. Most gas extracted commercially is thermogenic and found above deposits of crude oil or seams of coal, so its extraction often accompanies the extraction of those fossil fuels. Natural gas deposits are greatest in Russia and the United States, and these two nations lead the world in both gas production and gas consumption (Table 14.4).

Natural gas extraction becomes more challenging with time

To access some natural gas deposits, prospectors need only drill an opening, because pressure and low molecular weight drive the gas upward naturally. The first gas fields to be tapped were of this type. Most fields remaining today, however, require that gas be pumped to Earth's surface. As with oil and coal, many of the most accessible natural gas reserves have already been exhausted. Thus, much extraction today makes use of sophisticated techniques to break into rock formations and pump gas to the surface. One such "fracturing technique" is to pump salt water under high pressure into rocks to crack them. Sand or small glass beads are inserted to hold the cracks open once the water is withdrawn.

Table 14.4 Top Producers and Consumers of Natural Gas	
Production (% world production)	**Consumption** (% world consumption)
Russia, 21.6	United States, 23.0
United States, 19.0	Russia, 14.7
Canada, 6.7	United Kingdom, 3.4
United Kingdom, 3.2	Canada, 3.3
Algeria, 3.2	Iran, 3.2

Data from British Petroleum. 2006. *Statistical review of world energy 2006.*

Oil

The world's most-used fuel is oil, which today accounts for 37% of global commercial energy consumption. Its use worldwide over the past decade has risen roughly 16%, and today our global society produces and consumes nearly 750 L (200 gal) of oil each year for every man, woman, and child. Table 14.5 shows the top oil-producing and oil-consuming nations.

Heat and pressure underground form petroleum

The sludgelike liquid we know as **crude oil**, or **petroleum**, tends to form under temperature and pressure conditions often found 1.5–3 km (1–2 mi) below the surface. The crude oil of Alaska's North Slope was formed when dead plant material (and small amounts of animal material) drifted down through coastal marine waters millions of years ago and was buried in ocean sediments. These organic remains were then transformed by time, heat, and pressure into the petroleum of today.

Table 14.5 Top Producers and Consumers of Oil	
Production (% world production)	**Consumption** (% world consumption)
Saudi Arabia, 13.5	United States, 24.6
Russia, 12.1	China, 8.5
United States, 8.0	Japan, 6.4
Iran, 5.1	Russia, 3.4
Mexico, 4.8	Germany, 3.2

Data from British Petroleum. 2006. *Statistical review of world energy 2006.*

Petroleum geologists infer the location and size of deposits

Because petroleum forms only under certain conditions, it occurs in isolated deposits, tending to collect in porous layers beneath dense, impermeable layers. Oil deposits are not large black underground pools, but instead consist of small droplets within holes in porous rock, like a hard sponge full of oil. Geologists searching for oil (or other fossil fuels) drill rock cores and conduct ground, air, and seismic surveys to map underground rock formations, understand geological history, and predict where fossil fuel deposits might lie. Using such techniques, geologists from the U.S. Geological Survey (USGS) in 1998 estimated, with 95% certainty, the total amount of oil underneath ANWR's 1002 Area to be between 11.6 and 31.5 billion barrels. The geologists' average estimate of 20.7 billion represents their best guess as to the number of barrels of oil the 1002 Area holds.

Some portion of oil will be impossible to extract using current technology. Thus, estimates are generally made of *technically recoverable* amounts of fuels. In its 1998 estimates, the USGS calculated technically recoverable amounts of oil under the 1002 Area to be between 4.3 and 11.8 billion barrels, with an average estimate of 7.7 billion barrels (an amount equal to roughly one year's supply for the United States at current consumption rates). However, oil companies will not be willing to extract these entire amounts. Some oil will be so difficult to extract that the expense of doing so would exceed the income the company would receive from the oil's sale. USGS scientists calculated that at a price of $30 per barrel, 3.0–10.4 billion barrels would be economically worthwhile to recover from the 1002 Area. The USGS did not present estimates for today's much higher prices, but as prices climb, *economically recoverable* amounts approach technically recoverable amounts.

Thus, technology sets a limit on the amount that *can* be extracted, whereas economics determines how much *will* be extracted. The amount of oil, or any other fossil fuel, in a deposit that is technologically and economically feasible to remove under current conditions is termed the **proven recoverable reserve** of that fuel.

We drill to extract oil

Once geologists have identified an oil deposit, an oil company will typically conduct *exploratory drilling*, drilling small holes that descend to great depths. If enough oil is encountered, extraction begins. Just as you would squeeze a sponge to remove its liquid, pressure is required to extract oil from porous rock. Oil is typically already under pressure—from above by rock or trapped gas, from below by groundwater, or internally from natural gas dissolved in the oil. All these forces are held in place by surrounding rock until drilling reaches the deposit, whereupon oil will often rise to the surface of its own accord. Once pressure is relieved, however, oil becomes more difficult to extract, and may need to be pumped out.

We drill for oil and natural gas not just on land but also in the seafloor on the continental shelves. Offshore drilling has required us to develop technology that can withstand wind, waves, and ocean currents. Some drilling platforms are fixed standing platforms built with unusual strength. Others are resilient floating platforms anchored in place above the drilling site. Over 25% of the oil and gas extracted in the United States comes from offshore sites, primarily in the Gulf of Mexico and off the southern

California coast. This is why Hurricanes Katrina and Rita in 2005 disrupted U.S. oil supplies. By battering offshore oil platforms in the Gulf, and by damaging refineries onshore, the storms interrupted a substantial portion of the nation's oil supply, and prices rose accordingly.

Petroleum products have many uses

Once we extract crude oil, we refine it. Crude oil is a mixture of hundreds of different types of hydrocarbon molecules characterized by carbon chains of different lengths. A chain's length affects its chemical properties, which has consequences for human use, such as whether a given fuel burns cleanly in a car engine. Oil refineries sort the various hydrocarbons of crude oil, separating those intended for use in gasoline engines from those, such as tar and asphalt, used for other purposes (Figure 14.7).

(a) Distillation columns

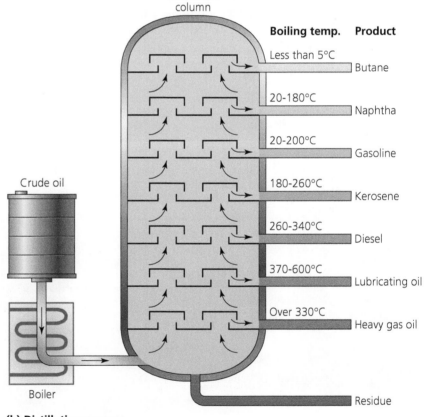

(b) Distillation process

FIGURE 14.7 Crude oil is shipped to petroleum refineries, where distillation columns (a) are used to refine it into a number of different types of fuel. In the distillation process (b), crude oil is boiled, causing its many hydrocarbon constituents to volatilize and proceed upward through a distillation column. Constituents that boil only at the highest temperatures and condense readily once the temperature drops will condense at low levels in the column. Constituents that volatilize readily at lower temperatures will continue rising through the column and condense at higher levels, where temperatures are lower. In this way, heavy oils (generally consisting of long hydrocarbon molecules) are separated from lighter oils (generally those with short hydrocarbon molecules).

Separating crude oil's components helps us create many types of petroleum products. Since the 1920s, refining techniques and chemical manufacturing have greatly expanded our uses of petroleum to include a wide array of products and applications, from lubricants to plastics to fabrics to pharmaceuticals. Today, petroleum-based products are all around us in our everyday lives (Figure 14.8).

Because petroleum products have become so central to our lives, it should concern us that oil production will soon decline as we continue to deplete the world's oil reserves.

We may already have depleted half our oil reserves

Many scientists and oil industry analysts calculate that we have already extracted about half of the world's oil reserves. So far we have used up about 1 trillion barrels of oil, and most estimates hold that an additional 1 trillion barrels, or somewhat more, remain. To estimate how long this remaining oil will last, analysts calculate the reserves-to-production ratio, or **R/P ratio**, by dividing the amount of total remaining reserves by the annual rate of production (i.e., extraction and processing). At current levels of production (30 billion barrels globally per year), most analysts estimate that world oil supplies will last about 40 more years.

Unfortunately, this does not mean that we have 40 years to figure out what to do once the oil runs out. A growing number of scientists and analysts insist that we will face a crisis not when the last drop of oil is pumped, but when the rate of production first begins to decline. They point out that when production declines as demand continues to increase (because of rising global population and consumption), we will experience an oil shortage immediately. Because production tends to decline once reserves are depleted halfway, most of these experts calculate that this crisis will likely begin within the next several years.

To understand the basis of these concerns, we need to turn back the clock to 1956. In that year, Shell Oil geologist M. King Hubbert calculated that U.S. oil production would peak around 1970. His prediction was ridiculed at

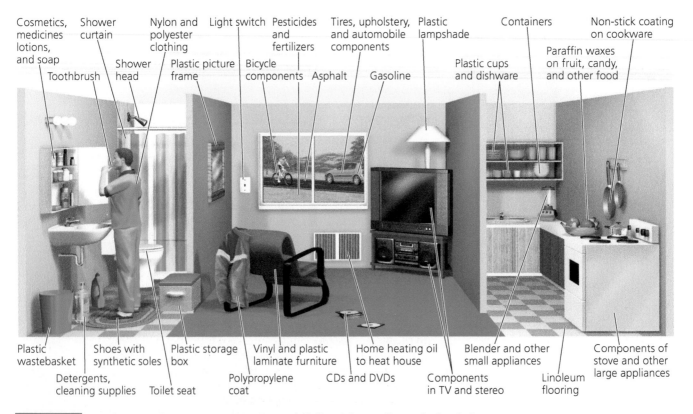

FIGURE 14.8 Petroleum products are everywhere in our daily lives. The gasoline and other fuels we use for transportation and heating are just a few of the many products we derive from petroleum. These products include many of the fabrics that we wear and most of the plastics that help make up countless items we use every day.

the time, but it proved to be accurate; U.S. production peaked in that very year and has continued to fall since then (Figure 14.9a). The peak in production came to be known as **Hubbert's peak**. In 1974, Hubbert analyzed data on technology, economics, and geology to predict that global oil production would peak in 1995. It grew past 1995, but many scientists using better data today predict that at some point in the coming decade, production will begin to decline (Figure 14.9b). Discoveries of new oilfields peaked 30 years ago, and since then we have been extracting and consuming more oil than we have been discovering.

Predicting an exact date for the coming decline in production is difficult, and we will not know for certain when we have reached the peak until a few years after we have passed it. But the divergence of supply

and demand will likely have momentous economic, social, and political consequences that will profoundly affect the lives of each and every one of us. One prophet of "peak oil," writer James Howard Kunstler, has sketched a frightening scenario of our post-peak world during what he calls "the long emergency": Lacking cheap oil with which to transport goods long distances, today's globalized economy would collapse and our economies would become intensely localized. Large cities could no longer be supported without urban agriculture, and even by expanding agricultural land we could only feed a fraction of the world's 6.5 billion people without petroleum-based fertilizers and pesticides. The American suburbs would be hit particularly hard because of their utter dependence on the automobile; Kunstler argues that they will become

FIGURE 14.9 Because fossil fuels are nonrenewable resources, supplies at some point pass the midway point of their depletion, and annual production begins to decline. U.S. oil production peaked in 1970, just as geologist M. King Hubbert had predicted decades previously; this high point is referred to as "Hubbert's peak" **(a)**. Today many analysts believe global oil production is about to peak. Shown **(b)** is the latest projection, from a 2004 analysis by scientists at the Association for the Study of Peak Oil. Go to **GRAPHit!** at www.aw-bc.com/withgott. Data from (a) Deffeyes, K. S. 2001. *Hubbert's peak: The impending world oil shortage.* (b) Colin J. Campbell and Association for the Study of Peak Oil, 2004.

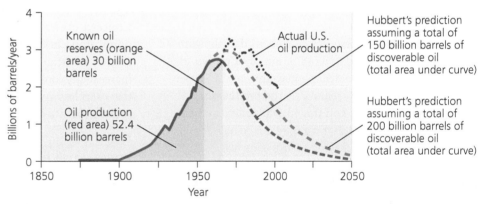

(a) Hubbert's prediction of peak in U.S. oil production, with actual data

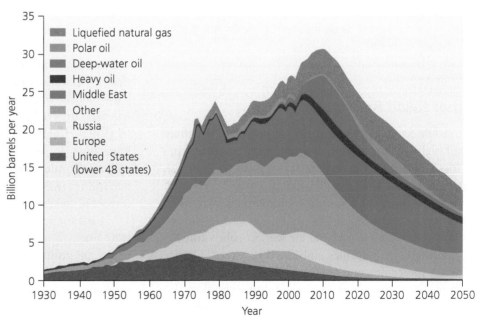

(b) Modern prediction of peak in global oil production

the slums of the future, a bleak landscape littered with the hulls of rusted-out SUVs.

More optimistic observers argue that as oil supplies dwindle, rising prices will create powerful incentives for businesses, governments, and individuals to conserve energy and develop renewable energy sources—and that these developments will save us from major disruptions caused by the coming oil peak. Indeed, to achieve a sustainable society, we will need to switch to renewable energy sources, and energy conservation (▸ pp. 307–309) can extend the time we have in which to make this transition. However, the research needed to develop new technologies and the work needed to construct their infrastructure both depend on cheap oil, and the time we will have to make this enormous transition will be quite limited.

Weighing the **Issues:**
The End of Oil

Physicist David Goodstein has calculated that the gap between rising demand and falling supply after world oil production begins to decline may amount to 5% per year. As a result, just 10 years after the production peak we will have only half the oil availability we had at the peak. He worries that we may not be able to modify our infrastructure and institutions fast enough to accommodate other energy sources before the economic impacts of an oil shortage undermine our ability to do so.

Do you think our society could adapt to a 50% decrease in oil availability over 10 years? How do you think we would most likely respond? How do you think we should respond?

Other fossil fuels exist

Although crude oil, natural gas, and coal are the three fossil fuels that power our civilization today, other types of fossil fuels exist. *Oil sands* or *tar sands* are dense, hard, oily substances that can be mined from the ground. *Shale oil* is essentially kerogen, sedimentary rock filled with organic matter that was not buried deeply enough to form oil. *Methane hydrates* are ice-like solids consisting of methane molecules embedded in a crystal lattice of water molecules, and are found in many seafloor sediments. These sources are abundant, but technology for extracting usable fuel from them is largely undeveloped and requires substantial inputs of energy, so that their extraction will likely remain inefficient and expensive.

Many advocates of sustainability believe it would be a mistake to try to switch to these sources once our conventional fossil fuels become scarce. Such sources will require extensive mining and will emit at least as much carbon dioxide, methane, and other air pollutants as do coal, oil, and gas. As such, they will exacerbate the severe environmental impacts that fossil fuels are already causing.

Impacts of Fossil Fuel Use

Our society's love affair with fossil fuels and the many petrochemical products we have developed from them has boosted our material standard of living beyond what our ancestors could have dreamed, has eased constraints on travel, and has helped lengthen our life spans. However, it has also harmed the environment and human health, and it serves as a source of political and economic instability. Concern over environmental, social, political, and economic impacts is a prime reason many scientists, environmental advocates, businesspeople, and policymakers are increasingly looking toward renewable sources of energy that exert less impact on natural systems and may be more socially sustainable.

Fossil fuel emissions cause pollution and drive climate change

When we burn fossil fuels, we alter certain flux rates in Earth's carbon cycle. We essentially take carbon that has been effectively retired into a long-term reservoir underground and release it into the air. This occurs as carbon from within the hydrocarbon molecules of fossil fuels unites with oxygen from the atmosphere during combustion, producing carbon dioxide (CO_2). Carbon dioxide is a greenhouse gas, and CO_2 from fossil fuel combustion has been inferred to warm our planet and drive changes in global climate. Because global climate change may have diverse, severe, and widespread ecological and socioeconomic impacts, carbon dioxide pollution is becoming recognized as the greatest environmental impact of fossil fuel use.

Fossil fuels release more than carbon dioxide when they burn. Methane is a potent greenhouse gas, and other air pollutants from fossil fuel combustion can affect human health and the environment. Deposition of mercury and other pollutants from coal-fired power plants is increasingly recognized as a substantial health risk. Power plants and vehicles release sulfur dioxide (SO_2) and nitrogen oxides (NO_X), which contribute to industrial and photochemical smog and acidic deposition. Gasoline combustion in automobiles releases pollutants that irritate the nose, throat, and lungs, as well as hydrocarbons (such as benzene and toluene) and impurities (such as lead and arsenic) known to cause cancer or other serious health risks.

To try to make emissions from coal combustion less toxic, U.S. policymakers have appropriated billions of dollars in recent years toward developing "clean coal" technologies. Such technologies include *scrubbers*, which are materials based on minerals such as calcium or sodium that absorb and remove sulfur dioxide from smokestack emissions. They also include chemical reactions that strip away nitrogen oxides, breaking them down into elemental nitrogen and water. In addition, multilayered filtering devices are used to capture tiny ash particles. The most successful of these efforts have reduced emissions by up to 95% at some power plants. However, some energy analysts and environmental advocates question a policy emphasis on clean coal. Coal, they maintain, is an inherently dirty means of generating power and should be replaced outright with cleaner energy sources.

Coal mining affects health and the environment

Surface strip mining for coal can destroy large swaths of habitat, cause extensive soil erosion, and lead to water pollution. Regulations in the United States require mining companies to restore strip-mined land following mining, but impacts are severe and long-lasting just the same. Most other nations exercise less oversight.

Mountaintop removal (Figure 14.10) has even greater impacts than conventional strip mining. When tons of rock and soil are removed from atop a mountain, it is difficult to keep material from sliding downhill, where immense areas of habitat can be degraded or destroyed and creek beds can be polluted and clogged. Loosening of U.S. government restrictions in 2002 enabled mining companies to legally dump mountaintop rock and soil into valleys and rivers below, regardless of the consequences for ecosystems, wildlife, and local residents.

Subsurface mining raises the greatest health concerns for miners and is one of our society's most dangerous occupations. Besides risking injury or death from dynamite blasts and collapsing tunnels, miners constantly inhale coal dust, which can lead to respiratory diseases, including fatal black lung disease.

Fossil fuels pollute water

Our extraction and use of coal and oil can also pollute rivers, oceans, and groundwater. Water pollution from oil results from large tanker spills but mostly from a variety of non-point sources. Strip mining for coal often causes chemical runoff into waterways through the process of **acid drainage**, which occurs when sulfide minerals in newly exposed rock surfaces react

FIGURE 14.10 Strip mining in some areas is taking place on massive scales, such that entire mountain peaks are leveled, as at this site in West Virginia. Such "mountaintop removal" can cause enormous amounts of erosion into streams that flow from near the mine into surrounding valleys, affecting ecosystems over large areas, as well as the people who live there.

with oxygen and rainwater to produce sulfuric acid. As the sulfuric acid runs off, it leaches metals from the rocks, many of which can be toxic to organisms.

With both air and water pollution, the costs of alleviating all these health and environmental impacts are high, and the public eventually pays them in an inefficient manner. The reason is that the costs are generally not internalized in the relatively cheap, subsidized prices of fossil fuels.

Oil and gas extraction can alter the environment

Drilling for oil or gas in itself has fairly minimal environmental impact, but much more than drilling is involved in the development of an oil or gas field. Road networks must be constructed, and many sites may be explored in the course of prospecting. These activities can fragment habitats and can be noisy and disruptive enough to affect wildlife. The extensive infrastructure that must be erected to support a full-scale drilling operation typically includes housing for workers, access roads, transport pipelines, and waste piles for removed soil. Ponds may be constructed for collecting sludge, the toxic leftovers that remain after the useful components of oil have been removed.

To predict the possible ecological effects of drilling in ANWR's 1002 Area, scientists have examined the effects of development on arctic vegetation, air quality, water quality, and wildlife (including caribou, grizzly bears, and a variety of bird species) in Prudhoe Bay and other Alaska locales with environments similar to that of ANWR's coastal plain (Figure 14.11). Scientists have compared different areas and have contrasted single areas or populations before and after drilling. In addition, scientists have run small-scale manipulative experiments when possible, for example, to study the effects of ice roads and secondary extraction methods such as seawater flushing. In one way or another they have examined the effects of road building, oil pad construction, worker presence, oil spills, accidental fires, trash buildup, permafrost melting, off-road vehicle trails, and dust from roads.

Based on these studies, many scientists anticipate damage to vegetation and wildlife if drilling takes place in ANWR. Vegetation can be killed when saltwater pumped in for flushing deposits is spilled or when plants are buried under gravel pits or roads. Plants grow slowly in the Arctic, so even minor changes can have long-lasting repercussions. For example, tundra vegetation at Prudhoe Bay still has not fully recovered from temporary

FIGURE 14.11 Alaska's North Slope is home to a variety of large mammals, including grizzly bears, polar bears, wolves, arctic foxes, and large herds of caribou. Whether and how oil development may negatively affect these animals are highly controversial issues, and scientific studies are ongoing. The caribou herd near Prudhoe Bay has increased since oil extraction began there, but not by as much as have herds in other parts of Alaska. Grizzly bears such as the ones shown here can sometimes be found near, or even walking atop, the trans-Alaska pipeline.

roads last used 30 years ago during the exploratory phase of development. In addition, air and water quality can be degraded by fumes from equipment and drilling operations, burning of natural gas associated with oil extraction, sludge ponds, waste pits, and oil spills.

Other scientists contend that drilling operations in ANWR would have little environmental impact. Roads would be built of ice that will melt in the summer, they point out, and most drilling activity would be confined to the winter, when caribou are elsewhere. Moreover, drilling proponents maintain, much of the technology used at Prudhoe Bay is now outdated, and ANWR would be developed with more environmentally sensitive technology and approaches.

Oil supply and prices affect the economies of nations

Hurricanes Katrina and Rita and the increased gasoline prices they caused in 2005 served to remind us how much we rely on a cheap and ever-increasing supply of petroleum. The hurricanes' economic impact should have come as no surprise, for we have experienced "oil shocks" before. In 1973, with domestic sources in decline, the United States was importing more and more

Drilling in the Arctic National Wildlife Refuge

Should we drill for oil in the Arctic National Wildlife Refuge?

ANWR Oil Means Better Living, Not Eco-Apocalypse

Oil development has taken place in the Arctic for over 30 years. Originally there were fears for the environment, just as we are hearing today. The Inupiat feared harm to the caribou and to their lifestyles while environmentalists claimed that oil development meant environmental apocalypse and that, moreover, it would yield only 2 years' supply of oil.

Well, "2 years" of oil turned into over 28; 3,000 caribou turned into over 32,000; and the Inupiat have turned into the number-one supporters of development. Technology has allowed a 140-acre drill pad to be reduced to 5 acres in size. Improvements in directional drilling now allow us to extract oil 8 miles from drill-point. The EPA, the North Slope Borough, and Alaska Department of Fish and Game monitor activities daily, so one can hardly claim an eco-apocalypse. Misinformation is rife in the ANWR debate.

Furthermore, the NIMBY argument doesn't work with ANWR; the people who live off the 1002 Area want this badly. To them, drilling in the 1002 Area will provide jobs, schools, clinics—a future. They have seen firsthand how their fears of 30 years ago were unfounded. They have seen their communities prosper.

The energy future of the United States should be multi-sourced. Wind turbines, solar panels, and hydrogen cells *all* need oil to build their working parts. None of these sources can produce plastic, bitumen, tires, paints, medicines, or a thousand other oil-based products we use daily. One can scream against oil, yet every one of us uses it every day in every aspect of our lives. We don't know any alternative. We should invest heavily in finding alternatives, but we should not think for a second that we can cut off our oil supply, domestic or foreign, and live as happily as we do now.

Adrian Herrera is a consultant for the lobby group Arctic Power, lobbying Congress to open the 1002 Area of ANWR to responsible oil development. Formerly, Herrera worked as an engineering assistant at Prudhoe Bay and for an independent ecological research company tasked with monitoring the wildlife and environment in and around the oil fields. He is an Alaskan resident of over 30 years and has worked and lived in the Arctic extensively.

Drilling the Arctic Refuge Is Not a Solution to Our Energy Problems—It's a Distraction

The Arctic National Wildlife Refuge is one of the last unspoiled wild areas in the United States. Its 1.5-million-acre coastal plain is rich in biodiversity, home to nearly 200 species, including polar bears, musk oxen, caribou, and millions of migratory birds.

There is no way to drill in the refuge without permanently harming this unique ecosystem or destroying the culture of the native Gwich'in people, who have depended on caribou for thousands of years. The little oil beneath the refuge is scattered in more than 30 small deposits. To extract it, roads, pipelines, airstrips, and other industrial infrastructure would be built across the entire area.

Drilling the Arctic Refuge would do nothing to lower gas prices or lessen our nation's dependence on imported oil. According to the U.S. Geological Survey, the refuge holds less economically recoverable oil than what Americans consume in a year, and it would take 8–10 years for that oil to reach the market. A recent U.S. Energy Department report found that oil from the Arctic Refuge would have little impact on the price of gasoline, lowering gas prices by less than a penny and a half per gallon—in 2025.

If we boosted the fuel economy performance of our cars and trucks by just 1 mile per gallon annually over the next 15 years, we would save more than 10 times the oil that could be recovered from the refuge. We have the technology today to accomplish that goal.

The United States has 3% of the world's oil reserves but consumes 25% of all oil produced each year. We cannot drill our way to lower gas prices. By focusing on efficiency and alternative fuels, we can improve our energy security and preserve the Arctic Refuge for future generations.

Karen Wayland is the Natural Resources Defense Council's legislative director and an adjunct professor at Georgetown University. Dr. Wayland, who holds a dual Ph.D. in geology and resource development, was a legislative fellow for Sen. Harry Reid (D-Nev.) on nuclear waste, water, energy, and Native American issues before joining NRDC's staff.

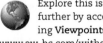

Explore this issue further by accessing **Viewpoints** at www.aw-bc.com/withgott.

oil, depending on a constant flow from abroad to keep cars on the road and industries running. Then the predominantly Arab nations of the *Organization of Petroleum Exporting Countries (OPEC)* resolved to stop selling oil to the United States. OPEC wished to raise prices by restricting supply, and opposed U.S. support of Israel in the Arab-Israeli Yom Kippur War. The embargo created panic in the West and caused oil prices to sky-rocket, spurring inflation. Short-term oil shortages drove American consumers to wait in long lines at gas pumps.

To counter dependence on a few major supplier nations, the United States has diversified its sources of petroleum and now receives most of it from non–Middle Eastern nations, including Venezuela, Canada, Mexico, and Nigeria. Major trade relations among nations and regions of the world are depicted in Figure 14.12.

The fact that so many nations' economies are utterly tied to fossil fuels means that those economies are tremendously vulnerable to supplies' becoming suddenly unavailable or extremely costly. In the United States, concern over reliance on foreign oil sources has repeatedly driven the proposal to open ANWR to drilling, despite critics' charges that such drilling would do little to decrease the nation's dependence. The United States currently imports 65% of its crude oil. With the majority of world oil reserves located in the politically unstable Middle East, crises such as the 1973 embargo are a constant concern for U.S. policy-makers. The United States has cultivated a close relationship with Saudi Arabia, the owner of 22% of world oil reserves, even though that country's political system allows for little of the democracy that U.S. leaders claim to cherish and promote. The world's third-largest holder of oil reserves, at almost 10%, is Iraq, which is why many people around the world believe the U.S.-led invasion of Iraq in 2003 was motivated primarily to secure access to oil.

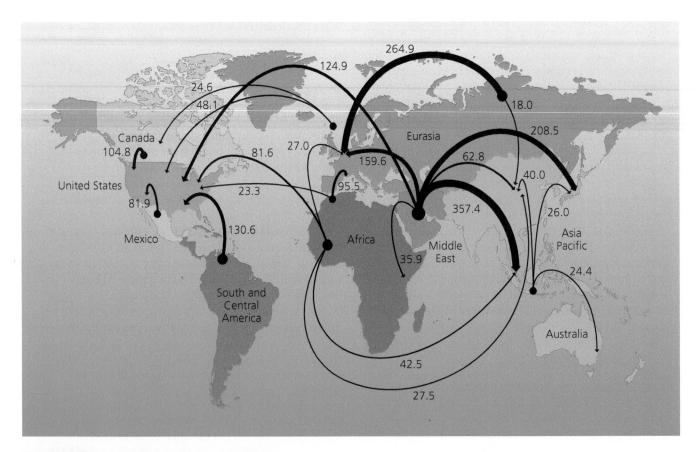

FIGURE 14.12 The global trade in oil is lopsided; relatively few nations account for most exports, and some nations are highly dependent on others for energy. The United States obtains most of its imported oil from Venezuela and Saudi Arabia, followed by Canada, Mexico, Nigeria, and the North Sea. Canada imports some North Sea oil while exporting more to the United States. Thickness of arrows in the figure is in proportion to the amount of oil traded, and numbers indicate millions of metric tons. Data from British Petroleum. 2005. *Statistical review of world energy 2005.*

Residents may or may not benefit from their fossil fuel reserves

People who live in areas where fossil fuels are extracted may experience benefits or drawbacks. In Alaska, citizens have seen economic gain from Prudhoe Bay's development. Alaska's constitution requires that one-quarter of state oil revenues be placed in the Permanent Fund, which pays yearly dividends to all Alaska residents. Since 1982, each Alaska resident has received annual payouts ranging from $331 to $1,964. Because development of ANWR would add to this fund and create jobs, most Alaska residents support oil drilling in ANWR. The Native people who live on the North Slope are split over the proposed drilling. The Inupiat want income for health care, police and fire protection, and other services that are scarce in this remote region. The Gwich'in oppose drilling because they fear it will threaten the caribou herds and Arctic ecosystems they depend on.

Alaska's distribution of revenue among its citizenry is unusual. In most parts of the world where fossil fuels are extracted, local residents have not seen benefits. In Nigeria, oil was discovered in 1958 in the territory of the native Ogoni people, and the Shell Oil Company moved in to develop oil fields. Although Shell extracted $30 billion of oil from Ogoni land over the years, the Ogoni still live in poverty, with no running water or electricity. The profits from oil extraction on Ogoni land have gone to Shell and to the military dictatorships of Nigeria. The development resulted in oil spills, noise, and constantly burning gas flares, all of which caused illness among people living nearby. From 1962 until his death in 1995, Ogoni activist and leader Ken Saro-Wiwa worked for fair compensation to the Ogoni for oil extraction and environmental degradation on their land. After years of persecution by the Nigerian government, Saro-Wiwa was arrested in 1994, given a trial widely regarded in the international human rights community as a sham, and put to death by military tribunal.

Energy Conservation

Given that fossil fuel supplies are limited and that their use has health, environmental, political, and socioeconomic consequences, a sustainable future requires that we move toward replacing them with clean and renewable energy sources. As we make this historic transition, it will benefit us to minimize our energy use so as to prolong the availability of fossil fuels. **Energy conservation** is the practice of reducing energy use to extend the lifetimes of

our nonrenewable energy supplies, be less wasteful, and reduce our environmental impact.

Energy conservation has often been a function of economic need

In the United States, many people first saw the value of conserving energy following the OPEC embargo of 1973–1974. In response to that event, the U.S. government enacted policies such as a mandated increase in the miles-per-gallon (mpg) fuel efficiency of automobiles and a reduction in the national speed limit to 55 miles per hour.

Three decades later, many of these conservation initiatives have been abandoned. Government funding for research into alternative energy sources has decreased, speed limits have increased, and recent bills to raise the mandated average fuel efficiency of vehicles have failed in Congress. The average fuel efficiency of new vehicles has fallen from a high of 22.1 mpg in 1988 to 21.0 mpg in 2005 (Figure 14.13). This decrease is due to increased sales of light trucks (averaging 18.2 mpg), including sport-utility vehicles, relative to cars (averaging 24.7 mpg). Transportation accounts for two-thirds of U.S. oil use, and passenger vehicles consume over half this energy. Thus, the failure to improve vehicular fuel economy over the past 20 years, despite the existence of technology to do so, has added greatly to U.S. oil consumption.

Moreover, because the government heavily subsidizes fossil fuel production, market prices do not tell us the true costs of fossil fuels. This disparity decreases our economic incentives to conserve.

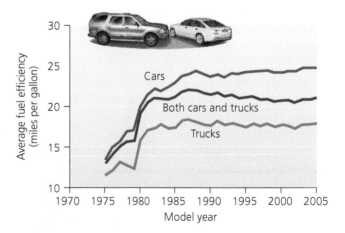

FIGURE 14.13 Fuel efficiency of automobiles in the United States rose dramatically in the late 1970s as a result of legislative mandates, but it has declined slightly since 1988. The decline is due to a lack of further legislation for improved fuel economy and to the increased popularity in recent years of sport-utility vehicles. Data from U.S. Environmental Protection Agency. 2005. *Light-duty automotive technology and fuel economy trends: 1975 through 2005.*

More Miles, Less Gas

If you drive an automobile, what gas mileage does it get? How does it compare to the vehicle averages in Figure 14.13? If your vehicle's fuel efficiency were 10 mpg greater, and you drove the same amount, how many gallons of gasoline would you no longer need to purchase each year? How much money would you save? If all U.S. vehicles were mandated to increase fuel efficiency by 10 mpg, how much gasoline do you think the over 200 million Americans who drive could conserve? What other strategies can you think of to conserve fossil fuels, and how might they compare in effectiveness to a rise in fuel efficiency standards?

Many critics of oil drilling in the Arctic National Wildlife Refuge point out the vast amounts of oil wasted by our fuel-inefficient automobiles. They argue that a small amount of conservation would save the nation far more oil than it would ever obtain from ANWR. As we noted, the USGS's average estimate for recoverable oil in the 1002 Area, 7.7 billion barrels, represents just one year's supply for the United States at current consumption rates. Spread over a period of extraction of many years, the proportion of U.S. oil needs that ANWR would fulfill appears strikingly small (Figure 14.14).

Personal choice and increased efficiency are two routes to conservation

We can conserve energy in two primary ways. As individuals, we can make conscious choices to reduce our own energy consumption by driving less, turning off lights when rooms are not being used, turning down thermostats, and cutting back on the use of machines and appliances. Such steps save us money while also helping conserve resources.

We can also conserve energy as a society by making our energy-consuming devices and processes more efficient. With automobiles, we already possess the technology to increase fuel efficiency far above the current average of 21 mpg. We could accomplish such improvement with more efficient gasoline engines or with alternative technology vehicles such as electric/gasoline hybrids (Figure 14.15).

The efficiency of power plants can be improved through **cogeneration**, in which excess heat produced during electricity generation is captured and used to heat workplaces and homes and to produce other kinds

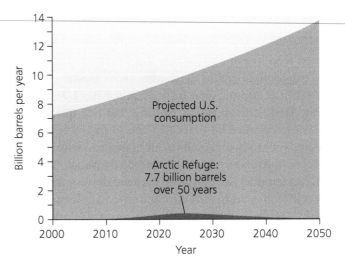

FIGURE 14.14 Opponents of oil drilling in the Arctic National Wildlife Refuge contend that the amount of oil estimated to be recoverable would make only a small contribution toward overall U.S. oil demand. In this graph, the best USGS estimate of oil from ANWR's 1002 Area is shown in red, in the context of total U.S. oil consumption, assuming that current consumption trends are extrapolated into the future and oil production takes place over many years. The actual ANWR contribution, if it comes to pass, would depend greatly on the amount of oil actually present under ANWR, the time it would take to extract it, and future trends in consumption. Adapted from Natural Resources Defense Council. 2002. *Oil and the Arctic National Wildlife Refuge*; and U.S. Geological Survey. 2001. *Arctic National Wildlife Refuge, 1002 Area, petroleum assessment, 1998, including economic analysis.*

of power. Cogeneration can nearly double the efficiency of a power plant.

In homes and public buildings, inadequate insulation causes a significant amount of heat loss in winter and heat retention in summer. Improvements in the design of homes and offices can reduce energy required to heat and cool them. Such design changes may involve the building's location, insulation, or even the color of its roof (light colors keep buildings cooler by reflecting the sun's rays).

Among consumer products, scores of appliances, from refrigerators to light bulbs, have been reengineered through the years to increase energy efficiency. Even so, there remains room for improvement. Energy-efficient lighting, for example, can reduce energy use by 80%, and federal standards for energy-efficient appliances have already reduced per-person home electricity use below what it was in the 1970s. While manufacturers can improve the energy efficiency of appliances, consumers need to "vote with their wallets" by purchasing these energy-efficient appliances, so that they are kept commercially available. The U.S. Environmental Protection Agency (EPA) estimates that if all U.S. households purchased energy-efficient appliances, the

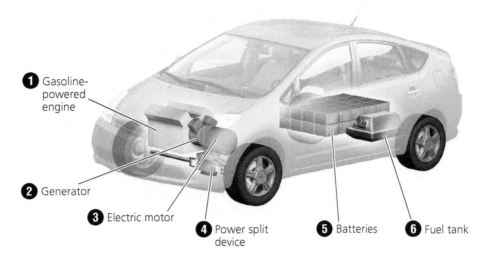

① Gasoline-
    powered
    engine

② Generator

③ Electric motor

④ Power split
    device

⑤ Batteries

⑥ Fuel tank

FIGURE 14.15 A hybrid car, such as the Toyota Prius diagrammed here, uses a small, clean, and efficient gasoline-powered engine (1) to produce power that the generator (2) can convert to electricity to drive the electric motor (3). The power split device (4) integrates the engine, generator, and motor, serving as a continuously variable transmission. The car automatically switches between all-electrical power, all-gas power, and a mix of the two, depending on the demands being placed on the engine. Typically, the motor provides power for low-speed city driving and adds extra power on hills. The motor and generator charge a pack of nickel-metal-hydride batteries (5), which can in turn supply power to the motor. Energy for the engine comes from gasoline carried in a typical fuel tank (6).

national annual energy expenditure would be reduced by $200 billion. For the individual consumer, most studies show that the savings on utility bills rapidly offset the higher costs of energy-efficient appliances.

In the energy bill endorsed by the Bush administration and passed by the U.S. Congress in 2005, some conservation measures were adopted, including tax credits for consumers who buy hybrid cars or improve energy efficiency in their homes. However, these measures were a relatively minor component of the legislation, and most of its funding went toward subsidies for production in various energy sectors. Among the beneficiaries was the nuclear power industry. Increasing numbers of people across the political spectrum recognize that we may see a resurgence of nuclear power as one alternative to fossil fuels.

Nuclear Power

Nuclear power occupies an odd and conflicted position in our modern debate over energy. Free of the air pollution produced by fossil fuel combustion, it has long been put forth as an environmentally friendly alternative to fossil fuels. At the same time, nuclear power's great promise has been clouded by nuclear weaponry, the dilemma of radioactive waste disposal, and the long shadow of Chernobyl and other power plant accidents.

First developed commercially in the 1950s, nuclear power has expanded 15-fold worldwide since 1970, experiencing most of its growth during the 1970s and 1980s. The United States generates the most electricity from nuclear energy—nearly a third of the world's production—yet only 20% of U.S. electricity comes from nuclear power. A number of other nations rely more heavily on nuclear power (Table 14.6).

Fission releases nuclear energy in reactors to generate electricity

Strictly defined, **nuclear energy** is the energy that holds together protons and neutrons within the nucleus of an atom. We harness this energy by converting it to thermal energy, which can then be used to generate electricity. The reaction that drives the release of nuclear energy in power plants is **nuclear fission**, the splitting apart of atomic nuclei (Figure 14.16). In fission, the nuclei of large, heavy atoms, such as uranium or plutonium, are bombarded with neutrons. Ordinarily neutrons move too quickly to split nuclei when they collide with them, but if neutrons are slowed down they can break apart nuclei. Each split nucleus emits multiple neutrons, together with substantial heat and radiation. These neutrons (two to three in the case of fissile uranium-235 isotopes) can in turn bombard other uranium-235 (^{235}U) atoms in the vicinity, resulting in a self-sustaining chain reaction.

Table 14.6 Top Consumers of Nuclear Power

Nation	Nuclear power consumed*	Number of plants†	Percentage of electricity generation from nuclear power plants‡
United States	185.9	104	19
France	102.4	59	78
Japan	66.3	53	23
Germany	36.9	18	28
Russia	33.9	30	16
South Korea	33.2	19	37
Canada	20.8	16	13
Ukraine	20.1	13	45
United Kingdom	18.5	27	22
Sweden	16.3	11	50

Data from International Atomic Energy Agency, British Petroleum, and International Energy Agency.

*In million metric tons of oil equivalent, 2005 data.

† 2003 data.

‡ 2003 data.

If not controlled, this chain reaction becomes a runaway process of positive feedback—the process that creates the explosive power of a nuclear bomb. Inside a nuclear power plant, however, fission is controlled so that only one of the two or three neutrons emitted with each fission event goes on to induce another fission event. In this way, the chain reaction maintains a constant output of energy at a controlled rate.

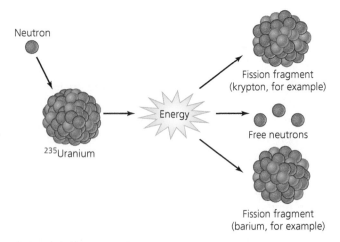

FIGURE 14.16 In nuclear fission, atoms of uranium-235 are bombarded with neutrons. Each collision splits uranium atoms into smaller atoms and releases two or three neutrons, along with energy and radiation. Because the neutrons can continue to split uranium atoms and set in motion a runaway chain reaction, engineers at nuclear plants must absorb excess neutrons with control rods to regulate the rate of the reaction.

For fission to begin in a nuclear reactor, the neutrons bombarding uranium are slowed down with a substance called a *moderator*, most often water or graphite. As fission proceeds, it becomes necessary to soak up the excess neutrons produced when uranium nuclei divide, so that on average only a single uranium atom from each nucleus goes on to split another nucleus. For this purpose, *control rods*, made of a metallic alloy that absorbs neutrons, are placed into the reactor among the water-bathed *fuel rods* of uranium. Engineers move these control rods into and out of the water to maintain the fission reaction at the desired rate. All this takes place within the reactor core and is the first step in the electricity-generating process of a nuclear power plant (Figure 14.17).

Nuclear energy comes from processed and enriched uranium

Uranium is used for nuclear power because it is radioactive, emitting subatomic particles and high-energy radiation as it decays into a series of daughter isotopes. Over 99% of the uranium in nature occurs as the isotope uranium-238. Uranium-235 (with three fewer neutrons) makes up less than 1% of the total. Because ^{238}U does not emit enough neutrons to maintain a chain reaction when fissioned, we use ^{235}U for commercial nuclear power. So, mined uranium ore must be processed to enrich the concentration of ^{235}U to at least 3%. The enriched uranium is formed into small pellets of uranium dioxide (UO_2), which are incorporated into the fuel rods used in reactors. After several years in a reactor, enough uranium has decayed so that the fuel loses its ability to generate adequate energy, and it must be replaced. Some spent fuel is reprocessed to recover what usable energy may be left, but most is disposed of as radioactive waste.

Uranium is an uncommon mineral, and uranium ore is in finite supply, so nuclear power is generally considered a nonrenewable energy source.

Nuclear power delivers energy more cleanly than fossil fuels

Using conventional fission, nuclear power plants generate electricity without creating the air pollution from stack emissions that fossil fuels do. After considering all the steps involved in building plants and generating power, researchers from the International Atomic Energy Agency (IAEA) have calculated that nuclear power lowers emissions 4–150 times below fossil fuel combustion. IAEA scientists estimate that nuclear power helps us avoid emitting 600 million metric tons of carbon each year, equivalent to 8% of global greenhouse gas

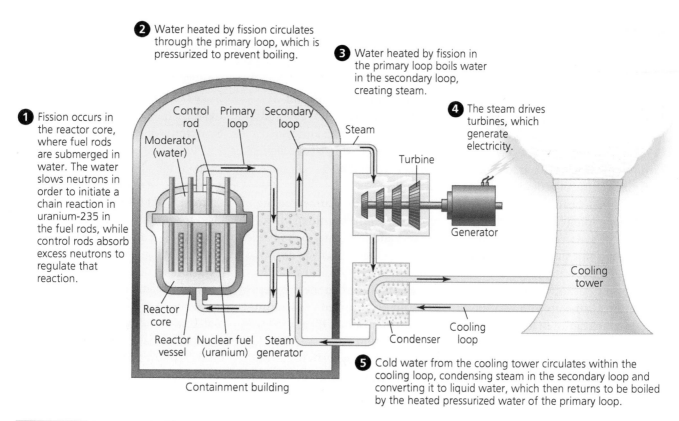

2 Water heated by fission circulates through the primary loop, which is pressurized to prevent boiling.

3 Water heated by fission in the primary loop boils water in the secondary loop, creating steam.

1 Fission occurs in the reactor core, where fuel rods are submerged in water. The water slows neutrons in order to initiate a chain reaction in uranium-235 in the fuel rods, while control rods absorb excess neutrons to regulate that reaction.

4 The steam drives turbines, which generate electricity.

5 Cold water from the cooling tower circulates within the cooling loop, condensing steam in the secondary loop and converting it to liquid water, which then returns to be boiled by the heated pressurized water of the primary loop.

Control rod · Primary loop · Secondary loop · Steam · Moderator (water) · Turbine · Generator · Cooling tower · Reactor core · Reactor vessel · Nuclear fuel (uranium) · Steam generator · Condenser · Cooling loop · Containment building

FIGURE 14.17 In a pressurized light water reactor, the most common type of nuclear reactor, uranium fuel rods are placed in water, which slows neutrons so that fission can occur (1). Control rods that can be moved into and out of the reactor core absorb excess neutrons to regulate the chain reaction. Water heated by fission circulates through the primary loop (2) and warms water in the secondary loop, which turns to steam (3). Steam drives turbines, which generate electricity (4). The steam is then cooled by water from the cooling tower and returns to the containment building (5), to be heated again by heat from the primary loop. Containment buildings, with their meter-thick concrete and steel walls, are constructed to prevent leaks of radioactivity due to accidents or natural catastrophes such as earthquakes.

emissions. Moreover, for residents living downwind from power plants, scientists calculate that nuclear power poses far fewer chronic health risks from pollution than does fossil fuel combustion.

Nuclear power has additional environmental advantages over fossil fuels, coal in particular. Because uranium generates far more power than coal by weight or volume, less of it needs to be mined, so uranium mining causes less damage to landscapes and generates less solid waste than coal mining. Moreover, in the course of normal operation, nuclear power plants are safer for workers than coal-fired plants.

Nuclear power poses small risks of large accidents

Nuclear power also has drawbacks. One is that the waste it produces is radioactive and must be disposed of safely. The second main drawback is that if an accident occurs at

a power plant, or if a plant is sabotaged, the consequences can potentially be catastrophic.

The nuclear industry's first major accident took place at the **Three Mile Island** plant in Pennsylvania in 1979. Through a combination of mechanical failure and human error, coolant water drained from the reactor vessel, temperatures rose inside the reactor core, and metal surrounding the uranium fuel rods began to melt, releasing radiation. This process is termed a *meltdown*, and at Three Mile Island it proceeded through half of one reactor core. Area residents stood ready to be evacuated as the nation held its breath, but fortunately most radiation remained trapped inside the containment building. The accident was brought under control, the damaged reactor was shut down, and multibillion-dollar cleanup efforts stretched on for years. Three Mile Island is best regarded as a near-miss; the emergency could have been far worse had the meltdown proceeded through the entire stock of uranium fuel, or had the containment building not trapped the radiation.

The Science behind the Story

Health Impacts of Chernobyl

In the wake of the nuclear power plant accident at Chernobyl in 1986, medical scientists from around the world rushed to study how the release of radiation might affect human health.

Determining long-term health impacts of a discrete event is difficult, so it is not surprising that the hundreds of researchers trying to pin down Chernobyl's impacts sometimes came up with very different conclusions. In an effort to reach some consensus, researchers at the Nuclear Energy Agency (NEA) of the Organization for

Economic Cooperation and Development (OECD) reviewed studies through 2002 and issued a report summarizing what scientists had learned in the 16 years since the accident.

Doctors had documented the most severe effects among plant workers and firefighters who battled to contain the incident in its initial hours and days. Medical staff treated and recorded the progress of 237 patients who had been admitted to area hospitals diagnosed with acute radiation sickness (ARS). Radiation destroys cells in the body, and if the destruction outpaces the

body's abilities to repair the damage, the person will soon die. Symptoms of ARS include vomiting, fever, diarrhea, thermal burns, mucous membrane damage, and weakening of the immune system. In total, 28 (11.8%) of these people died from acute effects soon after the accident, and those who died had had the greatest estimated exposure to radiation.

IAEA scientists in 1990 studied residents of areas highly contaminated with radioactive cesium and compared their health with people of the same ages living in uncontaminated settlements nearby.

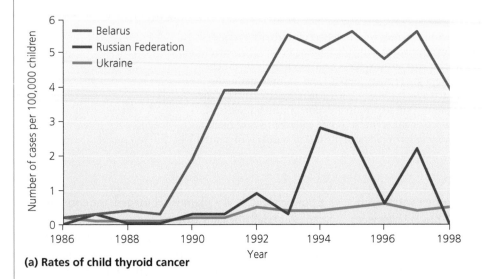

(a) Rates of child thyroid cancer

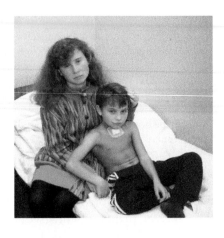

(b) Cancer patient with mother after surgery

The incidence of thyroid cancer (a) jumped in Belarus, Ukraine, and southwestern Russia starting 4 years after the Chernobyl accident released high levels of radioactive iodine isotopes. Many babies and young children (b) at the time of the accident developed thyroid cancer in later years. Most have undergone treatment and survived. Data from Nuclear Energy Agency, OECD, 2002.

Chernobyl saw the worst accident yet

In 1986 an explosion at the **Chernobyl** plant in Ukraine (part of the Soviet Union at the time) caused the most severe nuclear power plant accident the world has seen. Engineers had turned off safety systems to conduct tests,

and human error, combined with unsafe reactor design, led to explosions that destroyed the reactor and sent clouds of radioactive debris billowing into the atmosphere. For 10 days radiation escaped from the plant while emergency crews risked their lives putting out fires. Most residents of the surrounding countryside remained at

Medical exams of 1,356 people showed no significant differences between the two groups or health abnormalities attributable to radiation exposure. However, the study was criticized for the quality of its data, its small sample size, and potential conflict of interest (the IAEA is charged with promoting the nuclear industry). Moreover, the study was conducted only 4 years after the accident, before many cancers would be expected to appear.

Nonetheless, studies by the World Health Organization and others have come to similar conclusions. Overall, the NEA summary concluded, there is little evidence for long-term physical health effects resulting from Chernobyl (although psychological and social effects among residents displaced from their homes have been substantial). If cancer rates have risen among exposed populations, they have risen so little as to be statistically indistinguishable from normal variation in background levels of cancer.

The one exception is thyroid cancer, for which numerous studies have documented a real and perceptible increase among Chernobyl-area residents, particularly children (who have large and active thyroid glands). The thyroid gland (located in the neck) is where the human body concentrates iodine, and one of the most common radioactive isotopes released early in the disaster was iodine-131 (^{131}I).

Realizing that thyroid cancer induced by radioisotopes of iodine might be a problem, medical workers took measurements of iodine activity from the thyroid glands of hundreds of thousands of people—60,000 in Russia, 150,000 in Ukraine, and several hundred thousand in Belarus—in the months immediately following the accident. They also measured food contamination and had people fill out questionnaires on their food consumption. These data showed that drinking cows' milk was the main route of exposure to ^{131}I for most people, although fresh vegetables also contributed.

As doctors had feared, in the years following the accident rates of thyroid cancer began rising among children in regions of highest exposure (see the figure). The yearly number of thyroid cancer cases in the 1990s, particularly in Belarus, far exceeded numbers from years before Chernobyl. Multiple studies found linear dose-response relationships in data from Ukraine and Belarus. Fortunately, treatment of thyroid cancer has a high success rate, and as of 2002 only 3 of the 1,036 children cited in our figure had died of thyroid cancer. By comparing the Chernobyl-region data to background rates elsewhere, researchers calculated that Ukraine would eventually suffer 300 thyroid cancer cases more than normal and that the nearby region of Russia (with a population of 4.3 million) would suffer 349 extra cases, a 3–6% increase above the normal rate.

Critics pointed out that any targeted search tends to turn up more of whatever medical problem is being looked for. But the magnitude of the increase in childhood thyroid cancer was large enough that most experts judge it to be real. The rise in thyroid cancer, the NEA concluded, "should be attributed to the Chernobyl accident until proven otherwise."

Thyroid cancer also appears to have risen in adults. Adult cases in Belarus in the 12 years before the accident totaled 1,392, but in the 12 years after Chernobyl totaled 5,449. In the most contaminated regions of Russia, thyroid cancer incidence rose to 11 per 100,000 women and 1.7 per 100,000 men, compared to normal rates of 4 and 1.1 for Russia as a whole. And although rates of childhood cancer may now be falling, rates for adults are still rising. As new cancer cases accumulate in the future, continued research will be needed to measure the full scope of health effects from Chernobyl.

home for these 10 days, exposed to radiation, before the Soviet government belatedly began evacuating more than 100,000 people. In the months and years afterwards, workers erected a gigantic concrete sarcophagus around the demolished reactor, scrubbed buildings and roads, and removed irradiated materials (Figure 14.18). However, the landscape for at least 30 km (19 mi) around the plant remains contaminated today, and an international team plans to build a larger sarcophagus around the original one, which is deteriorating.

(a) The Chernobyl sarcophagus

(b) Technicians measuring radiation

FIGURE 14.18 The world's worst nuclear power plant accident unfolded in 1986 at Chernobyl, in present-day Ukraine (then part of the Soviet Union). As part of the extensive cleanup operation, the destroyed reactor was encased in a massive concrete sarcophagus (**a**) to contain further radiation leakage. Technicians scoured the landscape surrounding the plant (**b**), measuring radiation levels, removing soil, and scrubbing roads and buildings.

The accident at Chernobyl killed 31 people directly and sickened or caused cancer in many more (see "The Science behind the Story," above). Atmospheric currents carried radioactive fallout across much of the Northern Hemisphere, particularly Ukraine, Belarus, and parts of Russia and Europe.

Nuclear waste disposal remains a problem

Even if nuclear power generation could be made completely safe, we would still be left with the conundrum of what to do with spent fuel rods and other radioactive waste, which will continue emitting radiation for thousands of years. Currently, such waste is held in temporary storage at nuclear power plants across the world. Spent fuel rods are sunken in pools of cooling water or encased in thick casks of steel, lead, and concrete to minimize escape of radiation.

In total, U.S. power plants are storing over 49,000 metric tons of radioactive waste, enough to fill a football field to the depth of 3.3 m (10 ft). This waste is held at 125 sites spread across 39 states (Figure 14.19). The U.S. Department of Energy (DOE) estimates that over 161 million U.S. citizens live within 125 km (75 mi) of temporarily stored waste, and a 2005 National Academy of Sciences report judged that most of these sites were vulnerable to terrorist attacks.

Because storing waste at many dispersed sites creates a large number of potential hazards, nuclear waste managers have long wanted to send all waste to a central repository that can be heavily guarded. In the United States, the search homed in on Yucca Mountain, a remote site in the desert of southern Nevada, 160 km (100 mi) from Las Vegas. If given final approval, Yucca Mountain is expected to begin receiving waste from nuclear plants and military installations in 2010. Waste would be stored in a network of tunnels 300 m (1,000 ft) underground, yet 300 m (1,000 ft) above the water table (Figure 14.20). Scientists and policymakers chose Yucca Mountain because they determined that it is remote and unpopulated, has minimal chance of earthquakes, receives little rain that could contaminate groundwater with radioactivity, has a deep water table atop an isolated aquifer, and is on federal land that can be protected from sabotage. However, some scientists, antinuclear activists, and concerned Nevadans have challenged these conclusions.

Waste would need to be transported to Yucca Mountain from the 125 current storage areas and on a regular basis from all current and future nuclear plants and military installations. Because this would involve many thousands of shipments by rail and truck across hundreds of public highways through almost every state of the union, many people worry that the risk of accident or sabotage is unacceptably high.

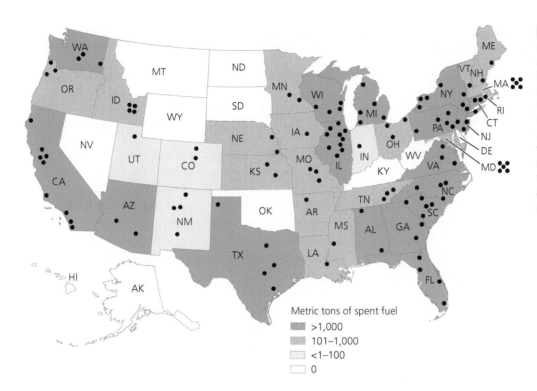

FIGURE 14.19 Nuclear waste from civilian reactors is currently stored at 125 sites in 39 states across the United States. In this map, dots indicate each storage site, and the four shades of color indicate the total amount of waste stored in each state. Data from the Office of Civilian Radioactive Waste Management, U.S. Department of Energy; and from the Nuclear Energy Institute, Washington, D.C.

Metric tons of spent fuel

- >1,000
- 101–1,000
- <1–100
- 0

Weighing the Issues:
How to Store Waste?

Which do you think is a better option—to transport nuclear waste cross-country to a single repository or to store it permanently at numerous power plants and military bases scattered across the nation? Would your opinion be affected if you lived near the repository site? Near a power plant? On a highway route along which waste was transported?

Multiple dilemmas have slowed nuclear power's growth

Dogged by concerns over waste disposal, safety, and expensive cost overruns, nuclear power's growth has slowed. Since the late 1980s, nuclear power worldwide has grown by 2.5% per year, about the same rate as electricity generation overall. Public anxiety in the wake of Chernobyl made utilities less willing to invest in new plants. So did the enormous expense of building, maintaining, operating, and ensuring the

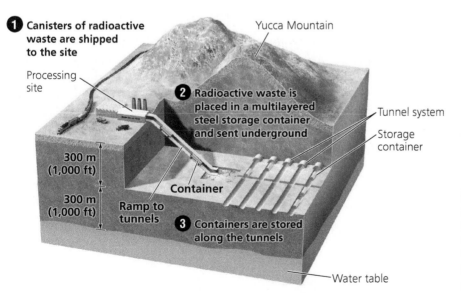

❶ Canisters of radioactive waste are shipped to the site

Yucca Mountain

Processing site

❷ Radioactive waste is placed in a multilayered steel storage container and sent underground

Tunnel system

Storage container

300 m (1,000 ft)

300 m (1,000 ft)

Container

Ramp to tunnels

❸ Containers are stored along the tunnels

Water table

FIGURE 14.20 Yucca Mountain, in a remote part of Nevada, awaits final approval as the central repository site for all the nuclear waste in the United States. Waste would be buried in a network of tunnels deep underground yet still high above the water table.

safety of nuclear facilities. Almost every nuclear plant has turned out to be more expensive than expected. In addition, plants have aged more quickly than expected because of problems that were underestimated, such as corrosion in coolant pipes. The plants that have been shut down—well over 100 around the world to date—have served on average less than half their expected lifetimes. Moreover, shutting down, or decommissioning, a plant can sometimes be more expensive than the original construction. As a result of these economic issues, electricity from nuclear power today remains more expensive than electricity from coal and other sources. Governments are still subsidizing nuclear power to keep consumer costs down, but many private investors lost interest long ago.

Nonetheless, nuclear power remains one of the few currently viable alternatives to fossil fuels with which we can generate large amounts of electricity in short order. This is why both the Bush administration and an increasing number of environmental advocates propose expanding U.S. nuclear capacity using a new generation of reactors designed to be safer and less expensive.

With slow growth predicted for nuclear power, fossil fuels in limited supply, an oil production peak looming, and climate change worsening, where will our growing human population turn for clean and sustainable energy? People increasingly are turning to renewable sources of energy: energy sources that cannot be depleted by our use.

Conclusion

Over the past 200 years, fossil fuels have helped us build complex industrialized societies capable of exploring (and exploiting) all parts of the world, and even venturing beyond our planet. Today, however, we are approaching a turning point in history: The availability of fossil fuels will begin to decline, just as we are becoming increasingly aware of the negative impacts of their use. Nuclear power showed promise to be a pollution-free and highly efficient alternative form of energy, but high costs and public fears over safety in the wake of accidents at Chernobyl and Three Mile Island stalled its growth.

We can respond to this new challenge in creative ways, particularly by encouraging energy conservation and developing renewable energy sources. Or we can continue our current dependence on fossil fuels and wait until they near depletion before we try to develop new technologies and ways of life. The path we choose will have far-reaching consequences for our environment and our civilization.

TESTING YOUR COMPREHENSION

1. Why are fossil fuels our most prevalent source of energy today? Why are they considered nonrenewable sources of energy?

2. How are fossil fuels formed? Why are they often concentrated in localized deposits?

3. Describe how coal is used to generate electricity.

4. How do we create petroleum-based products? Look around you, and at what you are wearing and carrying with you, and provide examples of several such products you use in your everyday life.

5. Explain why many scientists and oil experts are predicting that global oil production will soon begin to decline. What could be the social and economic consequences of such a decline?

6. Describe at least two major impacts of fossil fuel emissions. Describe at least one major impact of fossil fuel reliance for national economies or governments. Compare some of the contrasting views regarding the environmental impacts of drilling for oil in ANWR.

7. Describe two main approaches to energy conservation, and give a specific example of each. Name one barrier or disincentive to energy conservation.

8. Describe how nuclear fission works. How do nuclear plant engineers control fission and prevent a runaway chain reaction?

9. In terms of greenhouse gas emissions, how does nuclear power compare to coal, oil, and natural gas?

10. In what ways did the incident at Three Mile Island differ from that at Chernobyl? What consequences resulted from each of these incidents?

SEEKING SOLUTIONS

1. Imagine we were living in the 1950s and the United States were facing an oil shortage. Do you think the nation would be debating whether to drill in ANWR? Why do you think so many people today are concerned about wildlife and about wilderness preservation? Now fast forward to the 2020s. Do you think the nation will still be debating whether to drill in ANWR? Why or why not?

2. In February 2006, noted petroleum geologist Kenneth Deffeyes analyzed oil production data and calculated that the world had reached its peak of oil production on December 16, 2005. Let's suppose he is correct. What do you think our policymakers, businesses, and consumers should do in response? Now let's suppose that instead, the oil peak will not come until the year 2020. How do you think our society should react in response to this information?

3. If the United States and other developed countries relinquished dependence on foreign oil and on fossil fuels in general, do you think that their economies would benefit or suffer? Imagine that oil became 50% less available than it is today and that prices rose four times as high as today's. What sorts of incentives would these events create for the development of alternative

energy sources and for investments in conservation and efficiency?

4. Nuclear power has by now been widely used for over three decades, and the world has experienced only one major accident (Chernobyl) responsible for any significant number of deaths. Would you call this a good safety record? Do you think we should maintain, decrease, or increase our reliance on nuclear power? Explain the reasons for your answer.

5. Imagine that you are the head of the national department of energy in a country that has just experienced a minor accident at one of its nuclear plants. A partial meltdown released radiation, but the radiation was fully contained inside the containment building, and there were no health impacts on area residents. However, citizens are terrified, and the media is playing up the dangers of nuclear power. Your country relies on its 10 nuclear plants for 25% of its energy and 50% of its electricity needs. It has no fossil fuel deposits and recently began a promising but still-young program to develop renewable energy options. What will you tell the public at your next press conference, and what policy steps will you recommend taking to assure a safe and reliable national energy supply?

CALCULATING ECOLOGICAL FOOTPRINTS

Wackernagel and Rees calculated the energy component of our ecological footprint by estimating the amount of ecologically productive land required to absorb the carbon released from fossil fuel combustion. For the average American, this translates into 2.9 ha of their 5.1-ha ecological footprint. Another way to think about our footprint, however, is to estimate how much land would be needed to grow biomass with an energy content equal to that of the fossil fuel we burn. Assume that you are an aver-

age American who burns 287 gigajoules of fossil fuels per year and that average terrestrial net primary productivity can be expressed as 160 megajoules/ha/year. Calculate how many hectares of land it would take to supply our fuel use by present-day photosynthetic production. A gigajoule is 10^9 joules; a megajoule is 10^6 joules.

	Hectares of land for fuel production
You	1,794
Your class	
Your state	
United States	

Data from Wackernagel, M., and W. Rees. 1996. *Our ecological footprint: Reducing human impact on the Earth.* Gabriola Island, British Columbia: New Society Publishers.

1. Compare the energy component of your ecological footprint calculated in this way with the 2.9 ha calculated using the method of Wackernagel and Rees. Explain how and why results from the two methods differ.

2. Earth's total land area is approximately 1.5×10^{10} ha. Compare this to the hectares of land for fuel production from the table.

3. How large a human population could Earth support at the level of consumption of the average American, if all of Earth's land were devoted to fuel production? Do you consider this realistic? Provide two reasons why or why not.

Take It Further

Go to www.aw-bc.com/withgott, where you'll find:

▶ Suggested answers to end-of-chapter questions

▶ Quizzes, animations, and flashcards to help you study

▶ *Research Navigator*™ database of credible and reliable sources to assist you with your research projects

▶ **GRAPHit!** tutorials to help you interpret graphs

▶ **INVESTIGATEit!** current news articles that link the topics that you study to case studies from your region to around the world